LOCAL

Delicious Ways to Save the Planet

For Alan

Local Harvest

Delicious Ways to Save the Planet

by
Kate de Selincourt

LAWRENCE & WISHART
LONDON

Lawrence & Wishart Limited
99A Wallis Road
London E9 5LN

First published 1997

British Library Cataloguing in Publication Data
A catalogue record for this book is available from
the British Library.

ISBN 0 85315 853 3

Photoset in North Wales by
Derek Doyle & Associates, Mold, Flintshire.
Printed and bound in Great Britain by
Redwood Books, Trowbridge, Wiltshire.

CONTENTS

ACKNOWLEDGEMENTS

The idea for this book came from Matt Dunwell of Ragman's Lane Farm and Helena Norberg-Hodge of ISEC; Matt because he was beginning to sell locally from his own farm, and wanted to start up a debate on the subject, and Helena because of her long-standing belief in the power of a localised economy and, in particular, the virtues of direct connection between a community and its food production. I am extremely grateful to them both. Thanks are also due to Mandy Pullen who did some of the initial work on the subject, and convinced me of what an important topic this is.

A huge number of people have been enormously helpful to me. I particularly want to thank all those people who gave up so much time to talk to me or show me round their farms, introduce me to their consumer groups, and so forth – and even greater thanks to those whose comments I have not found room for – it doesn't mean they weren't equally useful.

Much of the information about consumer groups and local marketing of food in Japan, the USA, and France is based on overseas research by Harriet Festing of the Department of Food Industry Management, Wye College, University of London: she in turn would like to thank the Ernest Cook Trust, the Daiwa Anglo-Japanese Foundation, the JJ Barker Fund, the Bath and West of England Society, the Studley College Trust, the Canterbury Farmers' Club, the Kent Agricultural Society, Professor David Hughes and Sally Festing.

I owe many of the insights into the effects of food production for export in Third World countries to Naila Marharaj, who edited the Special Focus on the food trade for *Panoscope Magazine* in April 1995.

I also want to thank all the people who sent me ideas and information, made suggestions about the text, read and refereed various sections, and offered other forms of help, advice and moral support; in particular Charles Peers, Eric Booth, Lawrence Dungworth, Cathy Read, Peter Thomas, Lisa Smith, Nina Woodrow, Kelly Haggart, Moyna and Jean de Selincourt, Jan Deane, Tara Garnett, Suzi Leather, Tim Lang, Margaret Clarke, Jules Pretty, Heather Hunt, Nina Taylor and her partners in the Perry Court Scheme, Julie Alderson, Julie Lawson and Alison Khan at ISEC and all the staff at Lawrence and Wishart – and many others too.

Lastly I want to thank my partner Alan for his amazing and consistent support – support of every kind – without which this wouldn't have been possible.

FOREWORD

Helena Norberg-Hodge

This book offers the reader an exciting opportunity: to save the world by eating fresh, delicious food. It shows how simple steps towards closer links between farmers and consumers are helping to rebuild community, enhance human health, and restore ecological balance.

An international movement is taking off, bringing consumers back in touch with the producers of their food. British consumers are part of this movement, finding new pleasures and new friends from more direct ways of buying food. This book shares the discovery that buying locally-produced food, where possible direct from the producer, enables everyone to get hold of the best food that there is: tasty and nourishing and at affordable prices. This in itself is a good enough reason to look for local food. How satisfying, then, to know that by taking a step which is so good for us and our families, we are also making a very real contribution to preserving diversity and distinctiveness, protecting jobs and the environment and rural livelihoods – not only in Britain, but in the developing countries as well.

We live in a world where New Zealand butter sold in British shops is cheaper than local butter, Spanish markets sell Danish butter and Danish stores sell butter produced in France. The food we eat has often travelled farther than many people do in a lifetime; the average pound of food in America travels 1,200 miles before it reaches the kitchen table. Ever-busier motorways criss-cross the countryside as more and more giant trucks carrying almost-indistinguishable products travel the length and breadth of the country – or even the continent – until every shop in every town displays the same range of goods; no town sells its own distinctive products any more. Yet generally speaking, the further something has travelled, the more it has been processed, the less delicious and the less nourishing it will be.

FACTORY FIELDS, FACTORY SHOPS

This absurd situation is a result of national and international policies that encourage, and subsidise, ever-more intensive and industrial agriculture, food processing and food retailing.

The model of agricultural efficiency is a 'monoculture' – acres and acres with just one crop sown, sprayed and harvested by massive machines and employing a minimum of human labour. Intensive farming is subsidised with guaranteed prices for crops and stock which promote intensive monocropping for long distance transport, whatever the ecological and social costs. Acreage payments ensure that large agribusinesses earn stupendous sums, enabling them to buy up smaller holdings and swell ever-larger. Government- and industry-funded research and advice is geared to mechanisation, high yields and intensive chemical use.

The model of efficiency in the food industry is one massive factory churning out a product in a package which can be transported the breadth of the continent, to be consumed in every home. The dream of the industrial retailers is a hypermarket with staff replaced entirely by automatic bar-code readers and robotic shelf-fillers, where people come from miles around to do all their shopping. National and international processing and retailing operations are subsidised by publicly funded superhighways, constantly 'upgraded' to accommodate large lorries, thus handing the commercial advantage to businesses that move massive volumes. National media networks allow the largest, most profitable food companies to sell the least nourishing foods by forcing 'brand awareness' down the throats of the nation, while smaller, more local producers and retailers stand mutely by.

The result is a loss of diversity, the loss of locally distinctive food, landscape and culture – and the loss of the environmental benefits of integrated agriculture.

Industrial, monocultural production and distribution is far more resource-intensive and more polluting than diversified small-scale production. When animals, grains and vegetables are combined on the same farm, they all help each other: the grain and vegetables feed both humans and animals, the straw is bedding for animals and converts poisonous slurry into valuable fertiliser. There is no need for external input as there is with monocrops. Large-scale monoculture is far less efficient and destroys the land and pollutes the water around it. Thousands of cattle on one side of the country, for example, produce mountains of polluting slurry and waste, while on the other side, equally large amounts of chemical fertilisers have to be imported. In the south of Spain recently, even lemons were responsible for contaminating soil and water over a large area, when farmers were forced to dump huge quantities because of a sudden collapse in the market.

The effects of industrial food production are all too obvious in the rural landscape: the destruction of hedgerows as smaller farms are amalgamated into sprawling industrial plains, and the once vibrant hills – home to a great diversity of animals, plants and trees – laid bare to accommodate vast flocks of sheep. And the urban and suburban landscape has suffered just as much: city centres declining and abandoned; narrow streets, crooked buildings and the precious greenbelt fields at the town edge, vanishing beneath ring-roads, superstores and car-parks.

Households not only pay for this devastation through the taxes used for agricultural subsidies, transport networks and the like. We pay directly as well. We *buy* the unnecessary packaging, then *pay again* for the local council to take it away and bury it. We pay for soil erosion and greenhouse gas emissions as insurance premia go up. We pay to have pesticides which were dumped onto the ground removed from our drinking water. We pay when our house values fall as the roads outside grow busier and noisier; we pay the health bill for low quality food. And we pay with loss of joy.

We don't only pay now – the bill will extend for into the future – the future is, in effect, subsidising the present unsustainable system. It is not only environmental damage which extends into the future. Health problems from bad nutrition begin in the womb and are passed down through the generations.

To understand why our countryside – and indeed our diet – is being destroyed we have to look beyond agriculture and beyond our national boundaries, to the global economy. International trade based on the notion of 'comparative advantage' that is, intense specialisation, is the dogma of the age.

A Global Monoculture

Governments around the world, without exception, are promoting more global trade in the blind belief that their ailing economies will be boosted by throwing themselves open to economic globalisation. The goal of 'free' trade – of all the treaties, agreements and 'single markets' – is to amalgamate every local, regional and national economy into a single world system.

All around the world the hidden subsidies promote industrialisation to fit in with the demands of the 'global marketplace'. Vast sums of taxpayers' money have been spent, for example, on research into biotechnology with the aim of allowing food to be transported even greater distances, survive even greater doses of pesticides, and ultimately to be produced without the troublesome need for farmers. Scientists look forward to the day when tomato ketchup will be synthesised in huge vats and then piped into cities, thus avoiding the 'inefficient' use of labour and land in planting and growing tomatoes. Internationally, taxpayers' money, including our money in the form of aid, is used to build up a large-scale industrial infrastructure – irrigation schemes, roads, freight terminals, power stations, credit arrangements and tax-free 'enterprise' zones – which favours industrialisation and globalisation. For all of this our tax money is being used virtually without our knowledge or consent.

All over the world, it is the big, global enterprises which are best placed to profit from such subsidies and policies. Often transnational corporations do best of all: companies like Del Monte, which owns plantations all over the world, companies like McDonalds, which owns fast-food outlets all over the world, and companies like Cargill, which sells the crop varieties which the other transnationals want to buy. And do they make money! Only 4 cents of every food dollar in the US goes to the farmer, while 96 cents goes to the middleman.

The impact of export-led economics is particularly evident in developing countries, where the impact is more recent and the process is frighteningly fast. Industrial, export-oriented production allows goods produced on a large scale to be transported long distances and sold at artificially low prices – in many cases lower than goods produced locally. In Ladakh, on the Tibetan plateau, the Indian government is bringing in subsidised food from India's breadbasket, the Punjab. Ladakh's local economy – which has provided enough food for its people for 2000 years – is now being invaded by produce from industrial farms located on the other side of the Himalayas. The food arriving in lorries by the tonne is cheaper in the local bazaar than food grown five minutes' walk away. In Mongolia, a country which has survived on local milk products for thousands of years, and which today has 25 million milk-producing animals, one finds mainly German butter in the shops.

Under these conditions, most small farmers find that it is no longer worthwhile to continue farming.

A HARVEST OF MISERY

The end result of all this long-distance transport of subsidised goods is that local economies are being steadily dismantled and the fabric of local communities is being eroded. Thousands and millions of rural people, their livelihoods destroyed, flood into the burgeoning urban slums where they must hope to find a job. Urbanisation is, indeed, equated with 'development', and seen as the future for all nations, with predictions that 90 per cent of the world's population will be living in cities by the year 2015. Yet in the rapidly burgeoning megalopolises jobs are few and far between, and wages, working conditions and security are in free-fall as governments compete to offer an ever more 'attractive' environment for foreign TNCs to set up shop. A growing middle class in some developing countries is entering the consumer culture on the back of this economic 'progress'. But they are in the minority. For the majority, the end result of these changes is a fragmented society suffering growing levels of crime and violence, AIDs and child neglect, drug abuse, homelessness and despair.

In the West the urban poor are experiencing similar stresses. And just as rural society in the developing world is disintegrating, so it is in the West. Social fragmentation in the British countryside may be quieter than in the cities, but it is every bit as painful. The divide between the rich and the poor small farmer echoes the economic apartheid in the developing world. Small farmers, often rooted in the land for generations, struggling financially and isolated socially, are demonised by the media and the ignorant urban majority. The BSE crisis, which grew straight out of the intensive farming system, means that many are being broken under the strain. Farming has one of the highest suicide rates of all British occupations.

The many negative impacts listed here are all too real. But because they don't appear in the national balance sheet, the GDP, they are ignored by economists. Economic theory claims that this system brings gains for everyone. Some regions enjoy comparative advantages over others in given areas of production, so to economists it makes sense to specialise in monocultures for trade – be it manioc grown in Thailand to feed European cattle, or cheap labour in China producing plastic carrier bags for British supermarkets. Everyone's GDP goes up, everyone supposedly gains. But when distantly produced goods are heavily subsidised, often in hidden ways, we cannot really talk about comparative advantage, or for that matter free markets. We should instead be talking about the unfair advantage that industrial producers and huge corporations enjoy at our expense.

Clearly, changes at the policy level are necessary. In the past, organisations promoting sustainable farming, environmental protection or better food have tended to campaign on single issues. But it is increasingly clear that they need to look more broadly at economic policies which are artificially lowering the prices of industrially produced foods by shifting the costs of production onto the community.

If groups campaigning for sustainable farming and better food do not take 'hidden subsidies' into account, they risk falling into the trap of arguing that consumers should pay more for their food in order to compensate farmers adequately. This approach marginalises the poor and opens campaigners to charges of élitism. In fact, if the resources spent on hidden subsidies were diverted into developing decent agriculture and decent retailing, society would produce better food at no extra cost at all. This is a fantastic opportunity to argue for change.

Recognising the global consequences of the economic system also gives organisations campaigning for better food, sustainable agriculture and landscape and wildlife issues in European countries common cause with those campaigning for social justice and decent human development internationally. These diverse bodies are just beginning to join hands to demand a different view of economic priorities. One vital step is to pressure governments to renegotiate the trade treaties. New treaties could ensure that the hidden subsidies and unfair advantage now given to large-scale producers and marketers would be gradually reduced, and thus that balance would be regained between long-distance trade and local, regional, and national production.

THE POWERFUL CONSUMER

Meanwhile, despite an almost complete lack of support from government or industry, producers and consumers are taking the food economy into their own hands and making tomorrow's solutions happen today. Throughout the world, particularly in industrialised countries, increasing numbers of people are recognising the importance of supporting their local economy. Farmers' markets are appearing in many cities, particularly in North America, and shops are stocking locally-produced goods. More and more people are joining a variety of community supported agriculture (CSA) schemes which bring farmers and consumers into closer contact. This movement is sweeping the world, from Switzerland, where it first started 25 years ago, to Japan where many thousands of people are involved. In America, where all but 2 per cent of the population has already been pulled off the land, the number of CSAs has mushroomed from two in 1986 to 200 in 1992, and it is closer to 600 today. Significantly, in a country where small farmers dependent on markets beyond their reach continue to go bankrupt at an alarming rate every year, not a single CSA in America has failed for economic reasons.

This book describes the emergence of the movement linking farmers and consumers in Britain. Here, so-called 'box schemes' are particularly successful and widespread. The idea is to eliminate the middlemen in the food business. Members of various communities have forged direct relationships with farmers, ordering fresh produce directly from the farm, which is brought to the community in boxes once a week. The farmers receive better remuneration for their work, while the consumers enjoy fresh produce and a more conscious awareness of the origins of their food. The local economy benefits from closer consumer-producer links. Big business would like us to believe that diversifying and localising food production leads to inefficiency, job loss and economic hardship. The reality is quite the opposite: jobs are created within the community and the prosperity of small agricultural businesses is secured.

Environmentally, as well as nutritionally, the benefits of closer links between farmers and consumers are enormous. Local food systems promote biodiversity as well as production based on regional conditions. Unlike commercial food distributors who demand large supplies of one crop, local markets by their very nature create consumer demand for a wide range of products that are valued for their taste and nutritional content, rather than their ability to withstand the rigours of long-distance transport or conform to supermarket standards. The cucumbers need not be perfectly straight, nor the apples perfectly round. Direct communication between producers and consumers creates a responsive economic system, one shaped by the needs of society rather than the needs of big business. When consumers rather than corporations control the market, the economic pressures often benefit rather than harm the environment: for example, farmers move increasingly towards organic methods in response to their customers' concerns about chemical pesticides and fertilisers. The absence of packaging means a significant reduction in the huge amount of non-reusable, non-biodegradable waste that is daily thrown into dumps all over the world. Meanwhile, cutting down transport distance means a reduction in the use of fossil fuels, less pollution and lowered amounts of greenhouse gases released to the atmosphere.

Bringing producers and consumers closer together has an amazing number of positive implications, but perhaps the most significant of all is the rebuilding of community. Close connections between people lead to an understanding of their dependence on one another. In community shops, people know each other and talk to one another. Nearby farmers who sell to local shops, knowing the people who will be buying their produce, are far less likely to put toxic chemicals on their crops. Conversely, those who know the farmer who grows their food are more apt to lend a helping hand in difficult times. This is exactly what happened in Kentucky, when a CSA group rushed out to help a farmer with the harvest while his neighbours, who were selling to distant agribusinesses, lost their crops to an early frost.

The stronger sense of community that stems from closer producer-consumer links in turn has important psychological benefits. Research in the West makes it clear that the rise in crime, violence, depression, divorce, and even physical ill-health, is closely linked to the breakdown of community and the loss of social support. Depression is now rated by the World Health Organisation as the world's largest health problem in terms of working days lost, costing the world more than any other illness. Conversely, people who have a sense of connection to their place on the earth and to others around them – in other words people who are rooted in community – enjoy a stronger sense of self-esteem and healthier identities.

In a world where many children know how to use a computer, but don't know how to boil an egg, where pre-packaged TV dinners are hastily cooked in microwaves, a world in which so many don't even know where their food comes from, more and more people are beginning to say no to the dominant culture. They are developing a closer relationship to food and farming, and gaining the immense satisfaction that comes from eating delicious food with family and friends as well as helping a local farmer. Their lives are richer.

We have the power to change things. The destructive, global system can only exist as long as we are prepared to accept produce of any quality and of any origin. We can reject it. This book describes a win-win formula for solving a whole range of social and environmental problems, from climate change to rising unemployment and community breakdown. We can honestly say that eating fresh, delicious food is one of the most effective ways of saving the world!

INTRODUCTION

In a world where environmentalists and social campaigners are forever complaining about how terrible everything is – and as often as not warning that it is rapidly getting worse – it is a rare pleasure to be able to present an argument which shows that it is possible to contribute towards environmental protection and a fairer deal for many by doing something which is also enjoyable and personally advantageous.

This came as a surprise to me as much as to anyone. I have to confess that I was initially attracted to write this book because I fitted so well into the 'gloom and doom' category myself. I believed buying local food was the correct thing to do in order to combat the evils of supermarkets, intensive farming, economic globalisation and the rest, but I had little idea what local food tasted like. To my delight I found that people think it's delicious, and when I tried it, I could only agree! As I listened to the many satisfied customers I interviewed in my research, I learned that people were getting a great deal of pleasure from doing the 'right' thing – indeed, that pleasure was frequently their main motivation for changing their eating habits. I thought we shopped and ate pretty well at home before but we really eat superbly now. And believe me it's affordable: taking time to write this book meant that my income went down dramatically – not that I regret it!

One of the other discoveries I made was that many farmers, so often cast as the villains of 'bad food' practices, in fact often receive an extremely unfair press. This is an insight for which I also owe a great deal to my cousin Charles Peers, himself a farmer, who has been battering away at my prejudices for many years. Farmers truly find themselves between a rock and a hard place, and BSE is making matters worse for all but the richest. They can certainly be grumpy and awkward people at times, but farmers need us and we need them, so we need to try to work together.

This is an inclusive book; there should be something in it for more or less everyone. It does not exclude meat-eaters, or car-drivers, people on a tight budget, or 'working' (that is, working twice over) parents – or even people who go to the supermarket! In fact, it is for anyone who wants good food and good health, who would prefer less, rather than more, environmental and social destruction. And it isn't hard work!

There is one technical point which needs explaining, and that is the use of the term 'organic'. When I say 'organic' in conversation, what I mean is food produced in an environmentally-friendly way: crops grown without chemical fertilisers and pesticides, and animals reared without routine medication and under humane, non-factory conditions. This is the sense in which the word is used in the book, though I do sometimes alternate with 'sustainable', 'environmentally friendly' or similar terms.

However, when you buy food described as organic the meaning is slightly more specific. By law, the only foods which can be marketed as 'organic', are those which have been produced on a holding, and sold by a business which holds organic symbols: certificates issued by one of the approved organic registration bodies (see resources at the end). These certificates guarantee that the 'symbol holder' follows a published set of rules determining what is and is not allowable practice, and, further, that the business has been scrutinised and passed by an inspector from the symbol-awarding body. There are a number of growers (including some in this book) who follow the principles of vegetable growing agreed by the organic registration bodies, but because they do not hold a symbol, they cannot legally describe their vegetables as organic – or even 'unsprayed' or 'ecologically grown'! However, their customers can, and do, describe them as such to each other.

I have followed the conversational, rather than the official, usage of the word because it seemed too cumbersome and artificial to do anything else. Generally, I have used the term 'symbol organic' when I mean from a producer who holds a symbol. I hope it is fairly clear in the text what I mean at each point and that I haven't caused too much confusion.

The 'how to do it' section at the end gives practical hints on how to find sources of good, local food and how to contact producers in your area, tips on how to spot good, local produce in your local shops and markets (including a chart of seasonal fruit and vegetables), and how to set about getting hold of local, directly-bought produce if it isn't available.

If you are interested in what you read, as well as getting hold of as much local produce as possible, I do strongly recommend looking at the bibliography and resources section at the back. Many of the books and reports make excellent reading, and the periodicals and membership organisations will give readers and members a chance to become actively involved in campaigns, conferences and even direct action (even if that means with a fork and wheelbarrow!). For the technologically-equipped I also suggest a few websites.

This book has been tremendous fun to research and write – I hope you enjoy reading it, and, even more important, enjoy some good food as a result!

Kate de Selincourt
October 1996

International Society for Ecology and Culture

The International Society for Ecology and Culture (ISEC) is a globally active grassroots organisation promoting environmental sustainability and community regeneration. Founded in 1975, ISEC runs a range of practical and educational programmes, collaborating with governmental and non-governmental organisations in both the North and South. ISEC has worked extensively in Ladakh, ot 'Little Tibet', founding several indigenous NGOs, and establishing a comprehensive ecological development model, now being implemented by the regional government. ISEC's educational materials include books, films, plays, position papers and even comic books. *Ancient Futures: Learning from Ladakh*, by ISEC's Director Helena Norberg-Hodge, and an award-winning film of the same title produced by programmes Director John Page have been translated into more than twenty-five different languages.

A major focus of ISEC's work is on agriculture, as well as the need to revitalise local economies and maintain cultural diversity. In 1991, ISEC set up the Local Food Links project in the UK, starting with the publication of the booklet *Linking Farmers and Consumers*. This scheme, now being implemented by the Soil Association, has connected 40,000 families from all over the country with their local food producers. In 1984, Ms Norberg-Hodge and the Ladakh Ecological Development Group shared the Right Livelihood Award, or 'Alternative Nobel Prize'.

1
THE BEST FOOD IN THE WORLD

Every Thursday evening summer, autumn and winter, a succession of visitors comes round the back of Helen Williams' house in Bristol and up the path to her brightly-lit kitchen. They hurry towards a pile of boxes and peep inside: 'What's Mandy got for us this week?' 'Oh yes, squashes, brilliant!' In the boxes are carrots, potatoes and beetroot still damp with the earth of Mandy Pullen's Gloucestershire market garden; tiny yellow squashes, lush green spinach, sweet red and orange tomatoes and crunchy salad leaves – all picked that same day.

The vegetables on Mandy's one-acre plot are all grown for individual customers like these. Once a week she drives into Bristol and delivers boxes to Helen's house and a dozen or so friends, neighbours and word-of-mouth acquaintances come to collect and pay for a box or bag, and to catch up with the news about family and school, health and holidays. They may buy some eggs or extra potatoes, or put in an order for meat from the same farm – Ragman's Lane – to be delivered the next week along with the vegetables, while their children hunt for frogs in Helen's pond or play with Mandy's baby as his mother drinks a well-earned cup of tea. Mandy drops a few more boxes off in central Bristol, and makes another delivery to the villages around the farm.

The main attraction of the scheme, Helen says, is the quality of the food: vegetables grown with care and picked only hours earlier; and the meat, not so much humanely raised as completely spoiled, as farmer Jan Davies is sometimes teased. 'The quality of the vegetables is superb, you can't beat it, you just couldn't get what she does anywhere else. And the meat is wonderful: I wouldn't want to buy any other meat.'

But it is not only the quality of the food which draws people. Helen and other Ragman's Lane customers are regular visitors to this small

mixed farm, an hour from Bristol in the Gloucestershire countryside.
'I really like being so close to the place our food comes from, feeling
part of it, feeling that we are supporting a small farm which is farming
in a good way without chemicals. My daughter is even more involved
than we are. She knows all about how to feed the pigs, and sometimes
goes to stay there to help at weekends.' The farm has open days for
customers: in summer there is a barbeque, a farm walk – and people
can even swim in the lake.

All the vegetables, eggs and meat produced at Ragman's Lane are
sold locally: by delivery, from the small farm shop and through a local
butcher. Jan Davies and Matt Dunwell who rear the meat, and Mandy
Pullen who grows the vegetables, farm to ecological principles, though
neither operation is registered with an organic symbol. As they sell
direct to customers they feel no need for the additional bureaucracy
and occasional restrictions that registration would bring. They prefer
to discuss farming methods direct with their customers. And because
their produce is sold direct, prices remain competitive (the area around
the farm is not a wealthy one and people will not pay fancy prices)
though not rock-bottom. What keeps people coming back for more is
the knowledge that the food has been produced ecologically and
extremely humanely, the pleasure of personal contact with the farmers
– and the taste.

As Jan Davies explains: 'All the animals are chosen for flavour. With
direct customers, meat has to taste good if we want them to come back!
The breeds are also chosen to do well on a low-input system, to be
healthy and not need a lot of looking after or medical attention. For
example, we use Aberdeen Angus cattle, which are known as one of
the best breeds for beef. They calve easily and do well on pasture and
silage. The Gloucester old spot/Berkshire cross pigs we use fatten well
outdoors on barley and peas, without needing high protein meal like
soya or fish meal.' The pigs run in family groups outdoors with all
modern conveniences, including mud wallows for keeping off the
summer heat. The bacon has a distinctive sweet flavour: it sells out
very fast.

Jan's approach means the animals do not need routine medication
and the farm does not have to rely on vast quantities of imported
fodder. Selling direct brings the producer higher prices than selling
into the market, which means that Jan is able to stock at a low density
and still make a return on what is considered a marginally small (70
acre) holding. And fewer animals means more time to give attention to

each beast as well. It is the smallness of the farm that makes it possible to produce such high quality food. But it is the fact that they sell direct to customers that makes it possible for such a small holding to survive.

Mandy Pullen devotes similar care to the vegetables and fruit she grows on the one-acre field she rents at Ragman's Lane. She grows well over 100 different varieties – probably more like 150 – chosen for flavour, yield and, well, variety: 'I like to have at least 20 different kinds of leaves to put in salad bags through the year, and I grow 10 different potato varieties; I don't want my customers to have the same old potatoes week after week.'

She grows several different tomatoes, including powerful and massive Marmande beefs, and the exquisite orange 'Sungold', which can be eaten off the vine like sweets. Her pumpkin patch is a spectacle of green, orange, and yellow, striped, spotted and warty, sizes ranging from tiny yellow patty-pans the size of golf-balls, to a pumpkin a child could climb into.

Using muck from the farm and compost from her heap, black plastic or straw mulches, weeding and early detection for pests, her vegetables are produced entirely without chemicals. With detailed daily attention paid to soil moisture (enough but not too much), temperature and ventilation in the polytunnels and so on, the plants stay healthy and any potential problems can be spotted straight away. Organic food in the past had a reputation for looking a bit tired and spotted: not so Mandy's. The produce in her boxes is obviously bursting with health and is delivered on the day it is harvested.

Food like this is food at its best. It is grown carefully and is very fresh, which makes it taste delicious. Freshness and flavour mean high nutritional value, while growing with care means fewer or no chemicals, and no cruelty. Buying locally means avoiding long, polluting journeys in huge lorries, and using minimal packaging. And buying direct from the producer means cutting out middlemen and waste – so the price is right. Wouldn't it be wonderful if we could *all* get hold of food like this: food which was not only delicious, but was healthy too; food at a reasonable price which had nonetheless been raised and transported in an environmentally-friendly and humane way. Wonderful, yes, but surely too much to ask?

Not so. Most of us in Britain can buy at least some food which is delicious, healthy, environment- and welfare-friendly, and still fairly priced. The secret is that it isn't on sale in big stores – it is produced locally by small growers, and you often buy it from them direct.

There are farmers, growers and bakers all over the country who really care about the quality of what they produce and who care about how they sell it. Such producers are almost all small, as personal attention to detail – loving care and no corners cut – is essential to consistently high quality. Small producers find it very hard to sell into the mainstream, particularly supermarkets, for reasons we will look at more closely in the later chapters. Organic producers, who use no chemicals for fertiliser or pest control, often find it especially hard to produce in large volumes. But this doesn't mean that good, local food is impossible to find.

There are all kinds of ways to buy carefully produced, high quality food. There are farms like Ragman's Lane which will sell you a joint or a steak from their freezer, or will let you know when they are slaughtering a lamb so you can buy a quarter or a half; little brick dairies where you can watch the cheeses being made before buying one to take home; pick-your-own farms where you select the reddest raspberries or tiny melting mange-tout peas; bakeries wafting the scent of baking bread even as the last partygoers stumble home. There are formal delivery services where you phone an order and the round comes past your door, or you can join a vegetable box scheme and have fresh, often organic vegetables delivered to your street. Even your local market might offer honey from local hives, apples from local orchards, pies from WI members' kitchens. And ask at the greengrocer's: they may well tell you which farm the carrots and celery came from, how they were grown. The butcher's shop might well have some local rabbit, or free-range duck. And the farm you pass advertising free-range eggs: stop and look. If you can see the hens scratching, then nothing will beat the flavour of their eggs.

Many careful producers prefer to sell through their own shops so that they know their produce won't disappear into an anonymous stream. If you want the produce from a small holding and you want it fresh, the best way will probably be to buy it directly from the producer, or from someone who knows the producer personally. Direct buying and especially buying by regular order, cuts down the costs to the producer so much that the price may well be the same as – or cheaper than – the price in the supermarket so the pleasure need not be an exclusive one. And what a pleasure it is. For, most of all, people buy food direct for enjoyment: for the pleasure of eating wonderful food, confident that it is the best for the health of themselves, their families, and the planet. They enjoy meeting the growers, visiting the farms and dairies, linking up with friends and neighbours to support good agriculture.

People are rediscovering the value of direct communication with those who are doing something extremely important for us: nourishing our bodies. Exchanging information is a two-way process but what kind of a conversation can you have with a supermarket shelf? People find that when they have more information, they aren't passive any more. They find they have more say in their lives.

The less joyful consequences of mainstream food production and retailing are set out in this book. There is a lot wrong with the food industry: cruelty to animals; degradation of food; pollution of soil, water and food; roadbuilding and congestion; soil erosion and the loss of wildflowers and birds, hedgerows and forests. And many people are fed up with the lack of personal service, lack of information, lack of any say in how food is produced.

It seems so hard to get it right: even trying to avoid one of these 'undesirables' seems to be a tremendous effort. What does 'traditionally reared' really mean? Do I really want this organic cabbage when it looks rather yellow and costs three times as much as an ordinary one? Yet funnily enough, by buying local food direct you can avoid most or all of these 'undesirables', all at once, as this book shows. So many of the worrying problems being related to food are problems brought about by scale: mass production, huge machinery, mass distribution, massive stores on the ring road covering the ancient meadows. Warehouses, factories, machine harvesters, lorries: these are the 'customers' who demand huge fields, chemical sprays, sheds containing 60,000 chickens, courgettes packed into plastic boxes. You don't need these things – but then neither do the growers.

If growers are growing for you, not for the machines and warehouses, they can concentrate on growing good food and miss out on most of the damage. And you get better food and wonderful value. It really works.

2

OUT OF THE BAD FOOD TRAP

Buying delicious, wholesome, locally produced food sounds attractive to almost everyone. And in many parts of the world, eating like this is the norm. When a Greek family sits down to a lunch of baked-this-morning bread, local ewe's milk cheese, organic olive oil and knobbly, tasty, sun-ripened organic tomatoes they are not eating out of anyone's good food guide. They are eating ordinary food.

But although many of us wish we ate as well as this, we do not. It is hard to imaging anyone seeking out our ordinary food in any delicatessen. In fact, many of us are rather ashamed of what we eat. Most of the time, most of us are eating food which has come from who knows where, produced who knows how. It is not local, whole, fresh, and full of the flavour of natural ingredients. We do not eat the abundant, nourishing produce of British fields and gardens simply prepared (by ourselves) with minimum fuss and maximum flavour. Instead, we consume more and more processed food, ready-cooked meals, take-away or restaurant meals. Sandwiches, burgers, canned soup, spaghetti sauces, pre-chopped salads – it is now estimated that at least 80 per cent of the food bought in Britain has been processed in some way; one-third of meals are pre-prepared. And we hardly ever know who produced it.

This chapter looks at some of the reasons why we let this happen, some of the forces pushing us to eat badly, some of the factors which make it harder to see the wonderful food right under our noses: it suggests changes in attitude which might bring us closer to eating good, wholesome food, every day.

IT SAYS DELICIOUS ON THE BOX ...

Processing can save time and trouble for the consumer: shop-bought pies, mashed potato flakes, custard powder or indeed carton custard, biscuits, packet soups, pre-sliced beans, baked beans, frozen cheesecake, ready-to-microwave vegetable lasagne are all quicker to serve than the same dishes from basic ingredients. There is also a lot to be gained for the manufacturers and retailers. Processed food costs the consumer more than they would spend on buying the basic ingredients, so it is a way to get people to spend more money on the same quantity of food. And if the food industry wants to go on making bigger and bigger profits it has to get us to spend more on food without eating more: after all, there is only so much most of us can eat!

Processed food production suits manufacturers in other ways: it enables cheap, unhealthy basic ingredients (oils, fats and starch) to be disguised and sold at high prices. It also allows food to be transported and stored more easily, reducing spoiling, increasing economies of scale, and allowing manufacturers to expand their empires nationally and internationally. Tins, sachets, packets can stay in the warehouse and on the shelf for days, weeks or even months: no chiller cabinets, no worries, maximum flexibility.

Unfortunately, although processed food is both convenient and profitable, it does have shortcomings. The first of these is taste. On the whole, a factory-processed product is unlikely to be as good as the home-made equivalent. Although taste and flavour are individual matters, some things are just indisputably delicious. The smell and taste of freshly-baked pies and bread, for instance, are pretty universally liked, and pull people into kitchens and shops – they are even supposed to help you sell your house. On the other hand, not many people would go out of their way for the chance to eat a Pot Noodle (a product that seems to me to be almost without flavour, if not virtually inedible).

Processed foods tend to be bland, flavoured with sugar and artificial sweeteners, salt and monosodium glutamate. Whether 'sweet' or 'savoury' the same flavourings are simply used in differing proportions: crisps, soup and even tinned meat dishes sometimes contain artificial sweeteners. Processed meat is often particularly nasty. Take 'dinosaur' turkey roll, made from the scraps of flesh left on turkey skeletons after the meat had been removed, with water, wheat flour, starch, salt, dextrose, di-tri-polyphosphates, flavourings, spices, stabiliser, lactose, sodium caseinate, antioxidants, spice and herb extracts added. It tastes salty, reminiscent of other processed meats, but it doesn't taste of animal. Even cats refuse it.

And sometimes one wonders what manufacturers mean when they describe a ready meal as being 'long life': as the old joke runs, if you eat them you won't live longer, it will just seem like it. Any recipe described as 'vegetable' seems permeated with the same metallic tomato and old boiled carrot flavour. Mince is grey and granular. Pasta is toothless, potatoes rubbery and stale. Food just doesn't work like this.

Upmarket versions aren't necessarily better. Some favourites can be found in the select delicatessen realm (tinned Spanish octopus in spicy sauce), or the creamy comforting nursery-style foods so successfully marketed by Marks and Spencer. But when *Taste* magazine sampled some of the rather expensive convenience foods available in supermarkets the results were often indifferent. For example, mussels in garlic butter were described as 'small and chewy', their sauce spoiled by a 'stale' garlic flavour.

Food processed in a factory, some days or weeks ago, is bound to taste different from something freshly prepared. Among other things, lower quality ingredients can be used. Many products containing vegetable fat, hydrogenated vegetable oil, vegetable suet – which sound healthy enough – turn out to be full of 'trans' fatty acids, substances rarely found in nature and as bad for the heart as animal fat. Elaborate chemical cocktails are used to mimic simple natural foods. As Andrew Whitely of The Village Bakery put it on BBC Radio 4's *Food Programme*: 'It's not so much I can't believe it's not butter, as I refuse to believe it's food.'

In the US it is indeed possible to buy food which is not only not food, it is effectively negative food: it actually removes nutrients from the body. According to reports from the Food Commission, the 'wonder ingredient', Olestra, a fat which is designed to be totally indigestible and therefore calorie-free, is used in processed food like crisps or biscuits and passes through the digestive tract untouched – although it manages to 'wash out' up to 60 per cent of important A, D and E vitamins, the ones found in carrots, tomatoes and spinach. The presence of this lubricant in the intestines tends to cause wind, bloating and diarrhoea – a diarrhoea which leaves a telltale oily film on the water in the lavatory bowl. And because the body literally cannot get a grip on Olestra, an oily yellow residue, stained with the oil-soluble vitamins leached from the body, has been known to seep out unstoppably into the consumer's underclothing. Olestra had not been approved for sale in Europe in mid-1996.

Since high temperatures, pressures and industrial stirring processes may change or destroy flavours, and since cheap, bulky ingredients such as vegetable starch (flour) and vegetable oils and fats have very little flavour to begin with, flavours are added in instead. Synthetic flavours are infinitely cheaper than the real thing. A US advert for an artificial tomato flavour recommended for soups, sauces, dips, salad dressings and convenience foods, proudly proclaimed: 'One pound replaces the flavour and aroma of 1,200 to 1,600 pounds of tomato juice at a cost of $5'. Colours are destroyed and artificially replaced in much the same way, while thickeners and emulsifiers (soaps) are added to improve the texture of a processed food. Emulsifiers, for instance, can disguise the greasy 'mouth feel' of a high-fat product like a meat pie.

Food processing enables manufacturers to replace recognisable ingredients with cheap fillers such as starch, fat and minced gristle. Deregulation of the food industry in recent years has certainly 'stimulated innovation' as the government claimed that it would, when ingredient restrictions were removed from processed meat products in 1984. According to Sheffield public analyst Dr Peter Clare, a Sainsbury's Chicken Kiev – 'shaped and filled chicken breast meat coated with breadcrumbs' – was made largely from reconstituted, mashed chicken skin with fragments of muscle meat. This is a common practice, with pig rind ground up and added to tinned ham, and water and cellulose (an indigestible starch) bulking out 'scampi fries'. As Lincolnshire's trading standards officer Peter Heafield pointed out to the *Observer* newspaper: 'Food technology is so advanced that they can make a product look like something else entirely.'[1]

Preservatives, including anti-oxidants, stop the food going off, deteriorating, losing its colour and flavour, and to help maintain what vitamin content there is. In the words of the Ministry of Agriculture, Fisheries and Food: 'Preservatives help keep food safe for longer. This is useful to us as well as to shopowners and food companies. We need not shop so often or use food so quickly ... Preservatives can also reduce wastage of food in shops and at home [and] foods can be safely imported, stay available out of season, and be stocked in variety.' Any flavour you like as long as it's stale.

The food industry, of course, maintains that all the additives they use are tested and safe. It is hard to be completely convinced of this when, as with pesticides, every so often another 'safe' additive is quietly withdrawn from use. Tartrazine was staunchly defended as 'safe' in its day; saccharin is supposedly safe in the UK, but in the US

1. *Observer*, 21 July 1996, p12.

saccharine-containing products carry a warning that the sweetener has caused bladder tumours in lab animals.

In the US, the 1988 *Report on Nutrition and Health* estimated that as many as 10,000 cancer deaths a year could be caused by chemical additives in food. Awareness of the possible dangers of additives has led manufacturers to remove them from some products, or to employ different processing and packaging techniques, sometimes opting for a shorter shelf-life instead. But additives are still widely used. The label 'no preservatives' means that the product will still contain artificial colouring and flavouring; 'no artificial colouring or flavouring' suggests that there will be preservatives in there.

VALUE-ADDED, VALUE TAKEN AWAY

Processed food has nourishment taken away, even when it doesn't have anything artificial added. Just as chopping, mixing and cooking alter flavour and texture, so they alter nutritional content too: all are chemical properties of the food, after all. Processing foods can be the final blow to oxygen-sensitive nutrients. Cutting up green beans or courgettes into little strips and storing them on a brightly-lit shelf is a sure way to destroy vitamins – and, of course, to part the shopper from a bit more money. Cooking is another. Boiling peas for just five minutes can destroy up to 40 per cent of their vitamin B and C content, but industrial processing is particularly harsh. Freshly cooked and mashed potatoes lose around one third of their vitamin C; potatoes converted to dried potato flakes then reconstituted lose three-quarters.

Proteins may be altered too, suffering chemical changes which leave our digestive enzymes unable to break them down and absorb them. This was shown up rather tellingly when the American Office for Civil Defense decided to test the content of 'survival biscuits' designed to have a high content of amino acids in order to nourish people stuck in a nuclear bunker. Sadly, one of the essential amino acids did not even survive the baking process, never mind the holocaust. Lysine levels in the cooked biscuits were only one third of the level calculated from the recipe.

Of course, cooking at home destroys some nutrients as well. But at home you can ensure food is cooked gently and for a short time, and eaten immediately afterwards. Processed foods are not only cooked at high temperatures, they are then stored for days, weeks or even months – then cooked again when you heat them up at home. Our senses tell us that such food is no longer crisp, fresh, alive-tasting. Aren't our bodies missing out on something too if most of our food is in this state?

Frozen products are among the most popular forms of processed food. They generally have no chemical preservatives – though of course frozen ready meals have flavourings and texturings, and all frozen foods contain whatever pesticide residues there may be in or on the ingredients. Also, because vegetables may be frozen within hours or even (at least for peas) minutes of harvesting, frozen veg can contain a relatively high proportion of nutrients. And vitamins and other nutrients are thought to survive freezing better than they survive cooking. All of which makes freezing the most attractive of the options for preservation – indeed many growers freeze produce for their own consumption later in the year.

However, few foods survive the process completely unscathed. Freezing produces ice crystals which burst the cells that give living tissue its structure. Once the food defrosts, the cell walls collapse, which is why a frozen carrot is not exactly crunchy. With meat the texture is less altered, but cell structure may still be damaged. Research has shown as a consequence that soluble nutrients are more likely to be lost in any subsequent cooking. Even during thawing nutrients are lost: niacin, thiamine, vitamin B6, vitamin B12 and riboflavin have been found to seep out in the watery red juice that drips from defrosting meat. Enthusiasts for biodynamic farming and for raw food point out too that foods frozen then thawed are dead, and no longer contain the invigorating vital energy of the fresh original.

BUT I HAVEN'T GOT TIME

When someone you don't know has cooked your food for you, you don't know where the ingredients came from, how fresh they were, or whether pesticides were washed off before cooking. Manufacturers are never going to be as concerned that you and your family eat good healthy food as you are yourself. They are motivated primarily to make a profit.

Processed food is more expensive, less delicious, less healthy and less nutritious than food bought whole and cooked more simply at home. So why do so many of us who want to feed ourselves and our families in the best possible way, and don't have money to burn, buy more and more processed food every year? One of the most obvious answers is time. We say 'I'd love to buy/prepare/cook proper food at home but there just isn't time'.

The food companies know this: 'People are standing in front of the toaster saying faster! faster!' Joel Weiner, the marketing executive of Kraft General Foods, has been quoted as saying. Even the manufacturers sometimes admit convenience foods are not particularly delicious: 'Food today is more of a maintenance function than a pleasurable experience,' says Richard Nelson, director of market research at Campbell Soups. These views were echoed by a London market stallholder: 'People here don't live to eat, they don't take an interest in food the way they do in Spain or Italy. They eat because you die if you don't'.

Thirty or even twenty years ago, we were told that technology was going to create a 'leisure society', that by the end of the century (now, that is) we would all be spending half our time being incredibly creative with clay, dinghy sailing with our children, or playing the piano at concert standard. It hasn't happened. The 1980s and 1990s have ushered in an era where almost everybody is suffering an acute shortage of time. People in work are working long and/or unsocial hours with little leisure time, while insecurity presses them to work ever-longer hours. People out of work have no money, no choice, and on top of that they have no hope.

For parents with a job outside the home, perhaps the shortage of time is felt most acutely. Unicef reports that in the western world the time parents and children spend together has dropped by 40 per cent in a single generation. Understandably, many parents try to devote what little time they have at home exclusively to 'quality time' with their children focusing directly on the child's world of toys and stories and school. Far better, they are bound to feel, to read a story and play with the animal dolls or toy trains, and quickly heat up some spaghetti monsters in sugary tomato sauce, than to abandon the child in front of the TV and make the sauce with fresh tomatoes.

But childcare expert Penelope Leach argues persuasively that 'quality time' might actually have greater value if it is not spent in fairyland but with the child in the kitchen. In her book *Children First*, she argues that children benefit from sharing an adult activity, where the child learns by example what it is to be an adult, and feels included in the adult world. Cooking – like gardening, cleaning, helping to sort the washing – can be enjoyed if you are young enough. 'Play and education are indeed crucial to the development and self-fulfilment of

Chris, Ivan and Jessie cooking.

individuals,' she writes, 'but it is towards adulthood that children develop and into adult society that they must eventually be integrated. Children accomplish that by using parents or parent figures as models.' In other words, children who never 'watch, help and emulate' their parents cooking, will be less likely to expect to cook for themselves when they grow up. Whereas children who help to prepare a meal for the family feel – because they are – important and valued.

Food writer Julie Alderson agrees that children suffer from being segregated. 'Children spend their days behind desks from five to 18 with a pencil in their hand being prepared for a life behind desks. That's not what young bodies were made for. They are made to run around – children should be learning to feed themselves, to grow things, so they can look after themselves as adults. And at home we spend our time with our children in a phoney Disney world as well. I say No! Refuse this lifestyle, refuse these deadly jobs, refuse the deadly food!'

CHILDREN EATING

Betsy Dickson and her husband buy organic vegetables direct from nearby Ayrshire Organic Growers, and their bulk wholefoods from another co-op, and not surprisingly, feel good quality, organic food is as important for their children as it is for them.

Barry works full-time. Betsy puts in about 25 hours a week outside the home, so with housework too, her hands are fairly full, but she believes it is worth making the effort to cook for their two children: 'It's a choice I've made. It isn't always easy, feeding children can be difficult, but I think its worth it. Food is fundamental. There is not much point in having a wonderful career and lots of money in the bank if you aren't healthy, after all.

'And though of course the children do like burgers and other junk food, they like our good food too. I sometimes make bread and when my seven-year-old tasted my loaf yesterday he declared it was 'the best'. At least they have tasted good food. Hopefully, it is giving them a good foundation.

'Even if I had to work full-time I think I would still try, though there would be more compromises; I don't think food is a part of the quality of life which is worth sacrificing. If I don't eat well I just don't function so well, and when we've been away, the children are glad to get back to our food as well.'

Betsy Dickson added that her four-year-old, who is the more enthusiastic eater of the two, often joins in and helps her to prepare meals. He is by no means an unusual child. Rosie Davis of the Grange cookery school found her daughter wanted to follow in her mother's footsteps as soon as she could talk: 'My daughter loves to cook, and one of her first phrases was 'I do it on my *yown*.'

CAN WE DO IT ANY MORE?

Children also miss out on the chance to watch and learn from parents or other relatives' cooking if their parents don't cook because they have not learned how to do so, or because they have no confidence, or because they have so little money that they have to buy the same food every week to be certain everyone will eat it. The poorest families face the worst difficulties, and the problems of eating well on a low income are looked at more closely in chapter eight. But right across the income range, buying processed foods and not cooking feeds into a cycle of 'don't use it, and you'll lose it'. Many cookery teachers and writers agree that knowledge about basic cooking – storing and cooking vegetables, preparing and cooking meat, making pastry, sauces, simple puddings – is being lost day by day.

Even adults who consider that they can cook and throw dinner parties to prove it, may still have a lot to learn. We all need a grasp of the basic techniques which enable everyday food to be delicious – 'tasting strongly of itself' – without the need for elaborate sauces, spices and expense, and without taking up too much precious time. Cooking simple food well can be a revelation, as Rosie Davies has shown many of her students at The Grange cookery school in Bath. And yet few of us have ever been taught how.

'People sometimes don't even know basic things like the importance of putting green vegetables into boiling water so they can cook quickly and keep their flavour. It is staggering. People ought to know these things but there is amazing ignorance. We spend a lot of time on the courses gently breaking habits of a lifetime to replace them with techniques which we have found to work. And people are amazed and surprised at the way these things do work: cabbage for instance – learning to cook it so it isn't the horrible experience I had at boarding school.'

Cooking has never been that well taught in schools – I remember flabby boiled fish, rubber scrambled egg, and never a hint of garlic –

and it has seldom been taught to boys. Remarkably for such a fundamental life skill, cooking is absent from the National Curriculum; schools no longer teach cookery or home economics, but 'food technology'. Some praise this approach for being modern and relevant to employment, with its projects to design a cook-chill meal for an old-age home or a high-energy biscuit for an athlete. But these projects tend to be at the expense of developing the basic cooking skills which will leave students confident about feeding themselves, meaning that the next generation of adults and parents may be even less competent in the kitchen than we are.

Grace Mulligan, a former home economics teacher, told a *Food Programme* debate that people were being cut off from the information they could use to look after themselves: 'Home economics teachers all over this country are weeping because they are not allowed to teach the basic skills that they used to do.' June Scarborough of the National Association of Teachers of Home Economics and Technology agrees: 'There are so many obstacles to cooking, especially in lower income households. Mums are still starving themselves in order to feed their children. Nothing's moved in 100 years as far as I'm concerned. We know about this and we don't care. True home economics should help these people to feed their families.'

When cookery does feature in schools now, the processed 'n' packaged approach has sometimes crept in, to the horror of cookery teacher Rosie Davies. 'My daughter goes to an all-girls school because she said she wanted to learn to cook, but they are teaching them to open packets. My daughter comes home and says 'It was gross, Mummy!' They're teaching them to use sauce mixes to produce dishes. I would rather they just taught them to make fudge and scones. Why start them off thinking cooking is about opening packets?'

There are, fortunately, examples of inspiring excellence in schools' cookery teaching, as June Scarborough can attest. And 'Get Cooking' clubs, begun by the National Food Alliance, have sprung up in schools, guide packs, youth clubs and are strongly popular. But how sad that these are still available only to a small minority of future adults, when each one of us has to eat.

FEAR OF SHOPPING

Confidence and knowledge count even before you enter the kitchen. In a popular TV show Raymond Blanc advises on basic as well as sophisticated cooking techniques; he has also advised viewers how to shop. In an engaging sequence he visited a French and an English market, smelling and examining produce to the accompaniment of interested debate with French stallholders – and to some rather unfriendly suggestions about leaving the produce alone from the British one.

Blanc was demonstrating that good cooking has to include good shopping. Indeed in France, farm outlets can be 'as exclusive as restaurants', says food retailing researcher Harriet Festing. A writer in *Taste* magazine warned that we have become 'apathetic shoppers, seduced by supermarket convenience ... no longer used to pondering, selecting and rejecting fish, meat and vegetables or discussing with our suppliers what we intend doing with them. Or is it partly laziness and partly fear of the sometimes surly supplier?'

One London greengrocer told the BBC's *Food Programme* that some customers seemed quite unaware of the fact that vegetables change through the seasons. 'You see people buying fruit and veg, and they obviously haven't a clue about what they are buying. Older customers won't buy food out of season, but younger people think everything should be here all the time, and that there is something wrong with me if I ain't got it.'

INSTANT HELPLESSNESS

The decline of cooking is certainly profitable to the food industry and retailers. If we don't believe we can cook, then we are at once at the mercy of what the food industry chooses to offer us – and what it chooses to charge.

Australian writer Cherry Ripe argues this point very powerfully in her book *Goodbye Culinary Cringe*. 'Not being able to cook renders people powerless. It severely restricts the choices they can make in their diets.' She reports the extraordinary statistic that in the average American household, only one meal per month is cooked 'from scratch'. 'There are now whole households where no one knows how to cook ... If you cannot cook, you surrender your food choices to someone else to cook for you, which increasingly these days is the food industry. You also surrender your nutrition, and that of your family, to commercial concerns. 'Let's face it; the first priority of a commercial operator is not your health; it's making money.'

The commercial interest involved in replacing home cooking with the consumption of processed foods was clearly set out in the US journal *Food Engineering* in a much repeated quote from 1971: 'Shy away from price-oriented commodity items [that is, basic foodstuffs] and look to highly manufactured products in the decade ahead. The more additive addicted foods created, the higher will be the profit margin'. In other words it is in the economic interests of multinationals to discourage people from being able to cook.

Ripe cites the packets on boil-in-the-bag meals which proclaim 'perfect results every time': 'The subliminal message is that you wouldn't or couldn't get perfect results cooking it yourself every time'. Similarly, the very existence of powdered mashed potato, cauliflower cheese in a microwave-to-table dish, pancake and scone mixes that are little more than packets of flour, rice in a plastic bag, and the way these are marketed, suggests to people that the dishes must be too difficult to make from scratch. Sadly, the message seems to be getting through: how else, in a poor area like Hackney in east London, would Marks and Spencer be able to sell baked potatoes with cheese as a ready-to-heat snack, at an astonishing £1.65 for just one indifferent-tasting potato. One survey of young adults found that 80 per cent had never cooked a potato. There are no instructions on a potato, comments Cherry Ripe. The fact that there are high-flying legal executives who 'don't know how to' make salad dressing because 'Sainsbury's do it so well' suggests that Ripe is right: we have been persuaded we can't do it.

Julie Alderson agrees that we are being deskilled. 'We are losing the fundamental skills of living. It is fundamental to living to know how to feed yourself. It's a tragedy of the industrial lifestyle and industrial culture that we cannot,' she says. 'All the producers at the TV company where I work live off cook-chill and meals out: they are eating sub-standard food even though they are on good salaries, then all of them suffer from bladder infections, colds and so on, all the time. The industrial lifestyle, with people kept going on caffeine and sugar instead of stopping for a proper meal, really means we go out and kill ourselves so someone else can get rich.'

THE POWER OF ADVERTISING

Those families who are not taken in by the existence of tinned macaroni cheese and feel more than equal to the task of boiling macaroni and grating cheese into a white sauce, may face another problem: the children won't eat it. In the ultimate industrial take-over, advertising and branding have conditioned children into preferring – or believing they prefer – the commercial product. In fact, in blind tastings people (of all ages) frequently pick out a different product from the highly-advertised brand (Heinz beans, Coca-Cola) they insist is their 'favourite'. However, the point is that we – or our children – *are* convinced, and clamour for and buy the products that the ads have persuaded us we like.

The consumer society encourages us all to believe we have gained when we buy rather than do something. This belief combined with time pressures and the lack of confidence, discourages us from looking after ourselves. An enormous part of the economy depends on persuading people that they don't want to do things for themselves, that they would prefer to buy it ready done. You could say we are being infantilised. Some cynics go so far as to suggest that processed food, generally softer and sweeter than home-made equivalents, resembles baby food: even meat in its most popular processed form, the hamburger, is effectively ready-chewed!

The main route through which we are persuaded that happiness is ready-packaged there for us to buy and consume, is that universal message, the advert. The Food Commission surveyed food advertising on children's TV, and found that the ten most highly advertised brands were: burgers (two), cereals (three, two of them highly sweetened) pizza, sugary fruit drink, sweets, and chocolate. In another survey 74 per cent of the adverts shown during children's viewing time were for sweetened cereals, sweets, crisps and other salty, fatty snacks, fast food, sweetened drinks and ice cream.

One very highly-advertised product is the Pop-Tart: in this author's opinion a stale-tasting and quite nauseating flavoured, coloured, stabilised and emulsified biscuit with sticky jam inside, which, as if it were not sweet enough, is then iced, and sold wrapped in a foil envelope. For some bizarre reason, it is designed to be toasted until the jam is hot, then must be allowed to cool before you eat it so the jam doesn't burn you. This confection is apparently beyond the skills and sophistication of any British baker – so it is imported ready-assembled from the USA.

Not surprisingly, 74 per cent of the parents interviewed by MORI for the Food Commission felt that food advertisements do not encourage children to eat a healthy balanced diet but rather to spend pocket money on food their parents disapprove of. Parents admit they are influenced by advertising; indeed, eating habits closely mirror advertising habits, rather than what parents would *like* their children to eat. Parents said, in a survey carried out for the National Food Alliance, that children frequently pestered them into buying products they would not otherwise have bought, and that this pressure was greatly influenced by TV advertising.

Adverts do not just appear on TV. Sporting events and even educational materials are often sponsored by sweet and confectionery firms, and some of these firms also provide 'educational' resources to schools (usually too financially hard-pressed to refuse them) and even sponsor 'educational' sites on the Internet. Schools have even been invited to consider selling advertising space on their walls – for example for sports shoes (a big drain on many family budgets) and for soft drinks – too often a sugary food-substitute for children – in return for significant sums of money.

On adult TV the food advertising bias is marginally less unhealthy, but still features chocolate, breakfast cereals, frozen and processed foods and canned drinks, with the healthiest choices, fresh fruit and vegetables, almost invisible except for occasional promotions by countries exporting produce to the UK. Is it coincidence, then, that the national diet is officially regarded as too high in fat and sugar and too low in fresh fruit and vegetables? Or is this just the food we prefer?

Certainly, some nutritionists believe that once children have acquired the taste for a diet high in intensely sweet flavours (commonly achieved by combining sugar *and* artificial sweetener) high in fat, and low in texture, it is harder to interest them in more nutritious foods. Never, however, underestimate the power of advertising. As is demonstrated in tests with blind tastings, children are extremely susceptible to well-designed adverts. When Canadian researchers showed young children adverts for sweet processed foods the children chose more of these foods, whereas after viewing 'public service announcements' stressing nutrition, they opted for more nutritious snacks. The researchers also found that children who had seen commercials for fruit said that fruit was a 'favourite snack' more often than children who had only seen ads for sweets. In fact, just banning sweet ads in itself increased children's fruit intake. It seems clear that it would be worth advertising healthy foods to children – and, hopefully, to adults too.

Western society's very proper reverence for knowledge and freedom is shamelessly exploited by food companies wishing to dominate our shopping baskets. 'Freedom of information!', they cry. 'We are just informing shoppers, it is up to them to make their choice.' But of course this 'information' is not free at all – it is very expensive. To advertise commercially you need a product with a high enough profit margin that an increase in sales will cover the cost of the advert and leave you with profit in hand afterwards. Fruit and vegetable producers simply aren't in a position to do that.

Yet, extraordinarily, when a tiny bit of healthy information does seep through, the same interests who dominate the airwaves with chocolate ads complain of 'food fascism' or claim the advice is 'unfounded in science'. In August 1994, the government Committee on Medical Aspects of Food (COMA), published a practical sample menu illustrating exactly what they meant by a healthy diet, in concrete terms (numbers of biscuits, helpings of beans, and so forth). Immediately the food industry mustered its forces and large feature articles appeared in the national papers wilfully misrepresenting the advice and claiming the 'nanny state' was telling us how big our potatoes were supposed to be and how many sweets we were allowed. It was in fact helping people understand what two ounces of starch or 200 calories of sugar looked like.

United Biscuits fell back on the oldest excuse in the book: that there was 'no scientific evidence' for the desirability of cutting sugar intake. This is not a little contentious – there is considerably less evidence for the desirability of increasing it, at any rate – but the idea was to confuse and distract. As COMA chair Professor Michael Marmot commented: 'it was hard to hear industry's arguments above the deafening din of grinding axes'.

COMPANIES IN WHITEHALL

As Professor Marmot and his colleagues discovered, the industrial food processing and retailing industries have a powerful voice. And they don't just have to shout from the newspapers: they can whisper in the ear of ministers as well, via their suspiciously close links with government and other official bodies who set policy and take decisions about food and agriculture.

The Food Commission uncovered the fact that, in 1995, five of MAFF's senior civil servants were also on the boards of food companies. Firms with this kind of direct line into national food and agriculture policy include: RHM (processed foods), Cadbury, Dalgety (industrially-milled animal feeds, industrial-scale grain merchants), Coca Cola UK, and Golden Wonder. Meanwhile, Joanna Blythman reported in the *Guardian* newspaper, the chairman of the government's Food Advisory Committee in 1994, Professor D Georgala, was a (paid) 'consultant' or 'advisor' to Marks and Spencer, Unilever, Dalgety and Northern Foods, while his colleagues on the committee also held posts for Tesco, Sainsbury and United Biscuits.

Similarly, the Pesticides Trust reports that, on the Pesticides Forum set up by the government to address 'concerns' over pesticide use, representation is 'mainly' of larger-farm groups and the agrochemical industry. Press releases reporting Forum proceedings publicised 'integrated crop management' but there was no mention of more radical approaches to reducing pesticide use.

These bodies have the power to decide what it is fit and appropriate for us to eat: conspiracy theorists and ordinary cynics alike suggest it is hardly surprising that the promotion of a highly-processed, high-profit, unhealthy diet is so much more prominent than the healthier alternatives.

COOKING TO IMPRESS

On the one hand, we are eating more and more processed, degraded food, and yet increasingly we see fancy restaurants springing up, lusciously illustrated food pages in the weekend papers, dried wild mushrooms and bamboo steamers adorning the shelves of the smarter kind of kitchen – all of which seems to point to a greater interest in good food. But this is food as fashionable leisure pursuit, and not as daily routine. 'Good' food is seen as something for special occasions, the rest of the time many of us feed ourselves rubbish. Even the good, honest, ordinary foods which one might identify as British, have been 'ghettoised', excluded from the family dinner-table: hand-made cheeses, well-cured bacon, delicious yellow pole beans, Staffordshire oatcakes, Kerr's Pink potatoes, organic lamb, smoked eel – these sound like something from a delicatessen or, even worse, a restaurant.

Writer and broadcaster Derek Cooper rails against the 'niche marketing' of high-quality food. '*Why* must they insist on referring to really excellent producers of, say, cheese or bacon as producers of speciality cheese or speciality bacon. It's not speciality. It just happens to be bloody good, whereas the other 98 per cent is pumped full of polyphosphates and is awful.'

Middle-class interest in 'good food' was greatly stirred up – almost evangelically – by Elizabeth David. As Jane Grigson pointed out in her book *Good Things*: 'Since the publication of Elizabeth David's *Mediterranean Cooking* in 1950, we have opened our kitchens, not always wisely, to a host of influences.' As Grigson hints, the choice and range of cuisines and recipes can sometimes seem too rich, too varied and abundant. With so many dazzling choices – with food magazines featuring 50 recipes a month, bookshops promoting recipe books featuring 40 or 50 different nations or regions – how will any of us actually get to know, understand and perfect any one dish?

Fashion plays a huge role in what is eaten at 'foodie' tables. Magazines ask food experts to pick out 'the most exciting food today' (Indonesian? Philippine? Bolivian?) as though tilling the land and nourishing the body were rather akin to deciding on hemlines or shoulderpads. To columnist Keith Botsford, this 'Cook's Tour cooking' is regrettable. In an article in the *Independent* he notes that Italians 'love the food they know' and Italian cooking is one of the most satisfying and healthy diets in the world. 'In a sense ... regularity – which implies a degree of monotony – is reassuring and desirable. The stomach knows what the mind does not: that what it anticipates, expects and appreciates is probably more satisfying than the hodge-podge eating to which many of us have become prey; today, Tex-Mex; tomorrow, cabbage with paprika Hungarian style; then a bit of Thai; a bash of Brazil, a Portuguese soup and whatever might be the next bit of exotica.' Variety may be the spice of life, which may have been Don Juan's excuse, but marriages can be stable and instructive, Botsford concludes.

Fiona Burrell of Leith's Cookery School in London also suspects that we might sometimes be trying too hard. 'People think they have got to turn out an amazing meal, their friends will expect it. Actually they would do better to stick to simple really well-prepared food that is good and fresh, and it will have enough flavour in itself '. For instance, a *Good Housekeeping* 'Recipes to Freeze' supplement advises readers to 'cook these dishes in advance and freeze them so they can be whipped out at the last moment, so you'll be able to amaze your family and friends'. The recipes include complicated dishes like saffron chicken with spinach stuffing and beef and smoked mussel pie, which are certainly impressive but are unlikely to improve with freezing. Yet good free range chicken or organic beef wouldn't need saffron sauce or spinach stuffing to make them delicious. What a shame that people are to be impressed, rather than nourished.

BREAKING BREAD

When meals are no longer shared occasions, but either quick refuelling stops or displays of status and prowess, more is lost than vitamins and flavour. Food is fundamental, and the way a society eats is a fundamental part of the way it looks after itself. Eating together has a tremendous significance, a sign of a social group, a sign of respect and acceptance of your fellows: feeding people is a sign you value them, to be fed is to feel valued, cared-for and loved. As author Margaret Visser puts it: 'Every time we eat together we express the togetherness of society'. Every time we eat apart, on the other hand, we are expressing a lack of care.

This may sound over-dramatised, but one young man in California felt this lack of care only too keenly. Writing in *Yo!* magazine, Ron Fox described his changed experiences of eating:[2]

'Every night, around 6.30, all of us – me, my father's girlfriend, her two daughters, and my sister – sit down to dinner together. Last night we had pork chops, mashed potatoes, cabbage and greens. We all trade off cooking different nights. If someone can't be there, we always save him some food. We look out for each other like that.

'Maybe this doesn't sound like such a big deal, but it's something I've never experienced before. In [my old family home] the family motto was 'do for yourself'. My motto was "eat what you can, when you can". I used to eat alone all the time, and so did everyone else. I ate a lot of fast food ... My parents were young and struggling. When they got home they were either so tired they'd go right to bed, or else they'd want to go out and party. If they did eat at home, they'd eat by themselves in the bedroom ...

'For a long time I just pretended to myself that I didn't care whether I ate alone. Now I know how good it feels to sit down every night and share a meal with my family. It means we're taking care of each other.'

The experience of eating together is denied British children too, at home and at school. In June 1994 a letter to the *Guardian* newspaper described schools in which children 'wait in line still wearing coats and carrying bags ... in a grotty hall waiting to buy an assortment of nutritionally poor snack foods. Many of the younger children are

2. Cited in *In Context*, no. 37, Winter 1993–94.

frightened to ask for a selection of foods because they cannot add up the prices fast enough. They wander off to eat, standing in the playground or perched at a table in the hall without cutlery, water jugs or plates.'

For adults too, eating has to be squeezed in to the slots in the schedule. How many people 'go out for lunch' from their workplaces any more (unless there is a meeting to be had, of course)? A sandwich at the desk or a frantic dash around the shops seems to be the norm. The typical British worker's lunchbreak has shrivelled to 32 minutes, with 14 per cent working through lunch. That's how much trouble we are prepared to take over feeding ourselves.

As Suzi Leather and Tim Lobstein, authors of a National Food Alliance document on food and low income point out, in order to eat well, all of us, including people on the lowest incomes, not only need the correct nutrients, we also need the right social setting. We need to buy, prepare and eat our food with confidence and in a way which strengthens our social connections – and it needs to be enjoyable. 'The food we eat, the way we eat it, is a big part of what it is to be human,' Leather points out.

BUT WHAT ABOUT WOMEN'S LIBERATION?

With good ingredients, cooking need not be elaborate. Cooking fresh meals from wholesome ingredients and sitting down to eat them together brings gastronomic, nutritional and other wider benefits. But it still takes longer than heating up ready meals in the microwave. Where is this time to be found?

Some families are able to shift their priorities in order to spend less time, say, on earning money and more on cooking. Cathy Read is a journalist, married to a hospital doctor, with three children. She is ambitious, successful and extremely busy, but a spell living near the terrific farmers' markets of San Francisco, and her research for a book on the prevention of breast cancer, convinced her that the family must put more effort into eating healthily, and that really good, healthy food was simply much nicer than rubbish. Cathy collects a weekly 'bag' of organic vegetables from a local wholefood shop where she does much of her other food shopping. 'I have prioritised good food and healthy eating – you could say eating healthily is the biggest challenge in my life! – I haven't got it quite right yet. It means I accept

I will earn less, but I have decided it is important.'

Like many women, Cathy Read has found she is the one mainly responsible for feeding the family. Her husband Rob's hours are long and inflexible. Many of the activities – cooking, shopping, childcare – which are highlighted here as being at the heart of physical and social health, are 'traditional' female preserves. Isn't calling for more cooking, childcare, washing up, calling for a reversal of what women have achieved in the way of liberation in recent decades? Does this mean then 'a woman's place is in the home', while 'working mothers are bad mothers'? Is this an argument that 'selfish career women' are neglecting their children because they care only for themselves? Emphatically not.

There is certainly no eternal 'tradition' of men being separated from home, family care, and the production of food, nor of women spending their days *exclusively* concerned with the care of husbands, children and other dependent relatives, and doing so more or less without adult company. Before the industrial revolution the work which provided food and income was home-based for most people; all that only has changed in the past few centuries. Now, though, because of the way work is organised, the reality is that women at home with small children may be lonely and bored; homes are isolated and the men will try to get out during the day – to work, to the betting shop, wherever – leaving women to cope alone. This isolation is one reason why people tend not to relish a lifetime of 'housework': if you are going to have to do boring work all day, you might at least have some adult company.

But there are far more pressing reasons why women are keen to get out of the home. Firstly, many households are now completely dependent on women's earnings. This may be the case whether or not there is a man in the household, and whether his earnings are high, low or none. In many areas, it is much easier for women to get work than it is for men: of the 3.5 million new jobs which appeared in Britain between 1970 and 1995, 3.2 million were jobs taken by women.

There has been a tendency to blame the family time famine on ambitious career women who want to 'have it all', but this is grossly unfair on most women who work outside the home. Ambition and job satisfaction – the forces supposedly motivating stereotype 'career women' – do not rate very highly in most mothers' reasons for going out to earn money; women are too realistic to expect that to be possible. Patricia Hewitt's studies for the Institute for Public Policy

Research (published in 1993) show that women overwhelmingly prefer part-time work which fits in with school hours, and know perfectly well that the best they can hope for from these types of jobs is a bit of money to eke out the family income, and a bit of companionship.

Even when the family does not need the money, home-based carers have no economic independence, and a low self-esteem, as their contribution is not economically recognised. 'Only a housewife' you hear many women say of themselves: only providing nourishment, love, care, hygiene and support without which children would die and adults would despair. How many men – or women – who earn money in jobs outside the home, are doing something so important? Economic recognition seems to be the only recognition which counts in a society which measures everything in cash terms. Nor have men valued the contribution *they* could make in the domestic sphere. Women are putting in the hours for their families. Most mothers live, work and compromise for their families, one way or another, all the hours they are awake; many men could do more.

There is no doubt that the way the national and global economy is moving is making proper caring harder for everyone. The drive towards 'flexibility' and 'global competitiveness' has led to a combination of low hourly wages and high insecurity which keeps people in work working longer hours than ever. A terrifying eight out of ten Britons never go home on time, a 1996 survey by the charity Parents at Work discovered; a complementary survey found that two-thirds of workers believed their careers would suffer if they left for home on time every day. Perhaps surprisingly, blue-collar workers were most likely to feel obliged to stay after their paid hours. This is a crazy, barbaric situation. Britain is probably the worst example in Europe of such practices, and it is taking a huge toll in direct, stress-related illness for workers, and indirect health problems and other negative consequences for families and society. In 1996, the TUC declared that stress-related illness was now Britain's Number One occupational health hazard.

As a society, and to a varying extent as individuals, we do have a choice to lay more priority on 'living well' in terms of doing, rather than consuming. Part of the solution is undoubtedly political. But there is also some leeway for altering individual priorities and making different choices. For some (mostly middle-class) individuals and families, it has been possible to make a conscious choice to opt out of the hectic spiral of competitive hours and escalating consumption. This used to be called 'dropping out'; the latest US-inspired description is 'downshifting'. Some of the very young, seeing so little prospect of joy in the world of work, are opting never to enter. For others, without some capital or other security, especially when there are children or other dependants, opting out of the competitive system completely is difficult or impossible, but it is still possible to take the time to prepare and eat good food.

If anyone does have more time to offer at present, it is men. Men have more time free of paid employment or housework than women do. In 1985, men in full-time work did 35 minutes work a day in the home – up from an inexcusable 11 minutes in 1961! – while women with full-time jobs did three times as much at home: one hour and 40 minutes: a full day a week more than the men. Women working part-time spent another hour-and-a half each day working at home, while men working part-time did a measly quarter-of-an-hour more than their full-time brothers. Even unemployed men managed only an hour a day working at home. Such detailed figures are not available for the 1990s, but it seems likely that the balance between the sexes remains much the same, with men having more time free from either paid work or housework than women.

Ambitious career men frequently put their jobs and hobbies before caring for their families, and this may be another reason why ludicrous working hours are not challenged. Men polled in 1995 said they preferred playing sport or pursuing a hobby to spending time with their children; half of these fathers spend less than five minutes with their children on the average weekday.

The time it takes to chop an onion, fry some mince and boil up some pasta rather than microwave a ready meal, is quite possibly being wasted by someone sitting on the sofa watching a football match, or boozing in the golf club bar. He could be cooking – or he could be putting away the washing so she can cook. There are a lot of fathers, brothers, husbands and sons who could be contributing a great deal more than they do. At present, for every extra hour a married woman spends outside the house each week, her husband contributes only a few extra minutes of housework. No wonder so may women buy convenience foods. The men are lucky to get dinner at all. Surely they can do a bit better?

NEW HABITS

The quality squeeze and the time squeeze make it more difficult for many of us to eat as well as we would like to. But these problems are not insuperable. As the 'greedy eighties' finally fade into the past, there is more and more concern about quality of life, quality of parenting, the role of fathers, the dangers of insecure, long-hours employment. Things may not yet have improved, but at least, as a society, we are beginning to think about it.

Meanwhile, at the practical level, individual households *can* increase the priority they place on good food: and with highly rewarding results. Simply by noticing when we are being conned into thinking we couldn't do something well ourselves, when in fact we can, we will regain some independence. Meanwhile, supplies of good, local food are booming, and the more we buy, the more there'll be. What is more, the more we buy, the more we will enjoy cooking and eating good food – at least, this is the experience of many people interviewed later in this book. They have found a good, fresh source of local ingredients and have noticed, to their delight, that new improved cooking and eating habits come as a natural consequence. The food is so good, so tempting, so interesting, that cooking it and enjoying it seem to come naturally.

3

WHY LOCAL IS BEST

Nothing beats wonderful tasting food, which is an incentive to cook and eat well. The customers of Ragman's Lane farm, mentioned at the beginning of chapter one, and the people buying from all the many outlets mentioned later in this book, have all discovered that the secret of good food is not fancy recipes or fancy prices, but simply well-produced food, bought direct from someone they know does their job well. Food gets no better than this – and by golly, it does you good too.

Top food writer, the late Jane Grigson, celebrated and loved the humblest foods. She wrote that, 'one of the greatest luxuries you can have is simple food of the best quality'. When ingredients are at their best, well-grown, and fresh, it takes nothing elaborate for anyone to make them delicious.

VEGETABLES AND FRESHNESS

Freshness is a very important measure of the quality of most foods, but when it comes to vegetables this is really crucial. For vegetables to be fresh, really deliciously fresh, they need to have been picked very recently indeed. To achieve this freshness chefs who take vegetables seriously often grow their own, as does Patricia Hegarty at Hope End in Herefordshire. 'The ideal is picked this afternoon. The quality of really fresh food just speaks for itself. We just don't use tinned or frozen, particularly vegetables. It's not just for the flavour, freshness affects the texture as well, the colour, everything really.'

If you want to get produce which was harvested less than 24 hours ago it has to come by a pretty direct route. It might be straight from the farm: from a good farm shop, a direct delivery, for instance through a box scheme, by picking it yourself, or buying from a local greengrocer who collects daily from local growers. Unfortunately, the way mass market retailers operate means that most people are buying produce that has been stored and probably transported across considerable distances before reaching the shelves.

Sweet vegetables probably suffer most during transportation because the sugars which give them their sweet flavour are found only in the living plant. At the moment of harvest the metabolism alters and the sugars begin to be converted into tasteless starches. Although chilling does slow deterioration, it does not arrest it completely. Chilling alters the balance of those processes that do continue, which can spoil some foods, especially tropical foods which cannot deal with low temperatures. Keeping vegetables in a chilled container or display, or in the fridge at home, may be doing the flavour no favours.

As the flavour deteriorates during transport and storage, so does the nutritional value. Time spent during transport allows vitamins to break down and this is worsened by handling. Plant or animal tissues inevitably become damaged, if only a little, every time a crop, crate or container is moved, jostled and put down. Oxygen will penetrate more quickly into damaged tissues and ageing speeds up.

Vitamin C is particularly likely to be destroyed as fruit and vegetables travel from field to kitchen because it reacts with the oxygen in the air. Vitamins A, B and E are also destroyed by rough handling, bright lights or exposure to air. In a study carried out in North America, cabbage and brussels sprouts bought out-of-season (which means they had been stored for a long time, shipped a long way, or both) had no detectable vitamin C content whatsoever. These foods when fresh are very rich in this essential nutrient.

Vitamins A, C and E are probably the nutrients in fresh fruits and vegetables which give them their protective power against cancer and heart disease. Both these diseases are caused by 'wear and tear' to our cells. Heart disease starts with an injury in the lining of an artery; cancer, with an unrepaired change to the DNA pattern which contains the instructions for cell and tissue growth. Vitamins A C and E are all good metabolic cleaners, neutralising substances which might otherwise damage cells, in particular, the dangerous 'free radicals'. Free radicals are produced by oxidation: cooking and burning. They are present in cigarette smoke, air pollution, burnt food, and they are likely to react with, and damage, any tissue they meet unless they are neutralised first.

The retailers of imported food don't deny that it will have deteriorated. Sainsbury's customer service department accepted that: 'because of the long time spent in transit, it is very probable that there would be some loss of vitamins and minerals in imported produce compared to home-grown.'

Another gastronomic handicap faced by imported produce is that it cannot be picked at the perfect moment for eating since it is not going to be eaten for several weeks and sometimes has to travel several thousand miles first. Fruit that has ripened to perfection in the sun can be eaten in the area it grew in, but it doesn't travel. Many fruits: peaches, avocados, kiwi fruit, pears – and let's not forget tomatoes – are frequently imported from far away, and frequently tasteless. Asparagus from Peru bought in October, packed into a plastic box then shipped half-alive across the Atlantic simply does not have that tender, melting, slightly rude flavour which makes the first asparagus in May so exciting. It looks like asparagus, but it has lost its power to seduce.

Mike Farr, manager of one of the UK's main importers of sweetcorn, Kingcob, freely admits that corn imported from France, Greece and Florida to extend the British season year-round, couldn't possibly be so delicious as home-grown. 'Well of course it's not so good. Sweetcorn is best if you have it straight off the plant. It can't be as good after all that time in a container.' Imported sweetcorn is, moreover, anything up to three times the price of local cobs.

HAVE ADDITIVES, WILL TRAVEL

The closer to home your food has been grown or raised the fresher it can be, and that is only the start of the advantages. Food that has not had to undertake a long journey is less likely to have been sprayed with 'post-harvest' treatments against mould, and needs less processing and packaging.

The further food has to travel, and the longer it has to wait, the more chance that potatoes will sprout, carrots shrivel, oranges and grains go mouldy. Crops which have to stand the test of time are very often sprayed with fungicide to stop fungi and bacteria getting their teeth into them before we do. This is so common on produce to be shipped it is almost the norm. Over 90 per cent of the Californian citrus crop is fumigated after the harvest.

In 1988 the UK Ministry of Agriculture's Residues Subgroup published a report on residues of post-harvest treatment. The report warned that cereals, leafy vegetables and root crops were also frequently treated with post-harvest pesticides by 'fairly crude' 'bucket and shovel' techniques which meant there was no real control of quantities applied, and that residue levels would be unpredictable, some very much higher than others.

LOOKS CAN BE DECEIVING

There is nothing quite so beautiful as a fresh vegetable, plump, shiny and glowing with health – unless it is a not-so-fresh vegetable, plump, shiny and glowing with fungicide-contaminated wax. Wax is designed very much like face cream, to keep the water in, preventing that shrivelled, wrinkly look that gives away the vegetable's age and traumatic life story and at the same time, imparting an artificial glow of health to seduce the customer. As wax is designed to be waterproof it does not come off when you rinse fruit and veg before use.

The wax in itself may not be so harmful, except that it conceals the age and true state of un-freshness of the produce. It may also be of animal (usually insect) origin and thus unwanted by vegetarians. But the wax is an excellent medium for fat-soluble fungicides, which do pose a serious health hazard. According to David Steinman's US book *Diet for a Poisoned Planet*, waxes are 'frequently laced with carcinogens and neurotoxins' including Benomyl, Dicloran and several others.

Obviously wax is most hazardous in produce whose peel is eaten, or used in cooking: apples, lemons, nectarines, peaches, cucumbers, peppers, parsnips and aubergines are likely candidates. All of the smooth-skinned members of this list look perfectly shiny without any wax when they are fresh.

An alternative method of preserving food is irradiation. Though not yet widespread in Britain, one company in southern England has a plant for irradiating spices and other flavourings. Irradiation works in place of a post-harvest pesticide, to kill off pathogens which might damage the stored produce. However, it does not prevent ageing, vitamins are liable to be lost and flavour may well deteriorate. There may also be actual dangers. For instance, irradiated potatoes exposed to light still produce the toxic chemical solanin, as ordinary ones do, but do not turn a warning green colour to tell the consumer that the potato is poisonous. Similarly, with the normal 'rotting ' and 'moulding' micro-organisms killed off, other more insidious organisms may start to multiply in the food: they may be *more* dangerous then the usual moulds, but *less* conspicuous.

FOOD FROM NEARBY WILL BE
FOOD IN SEASON

Once a year, on one of those light, bright evenings in early summer, Tony and Libby Hall have a small ritual. 'We sit down to a meal of the first English asparagus and new potatoes with lots of butter, then English strawberries eaten with sugar. We look forward to it every year, because it is just so delicious. It's a feeling of amazing extravagance. You feel as if you could be in the Savoy.' The Halls are in fact eating at home in a modest terraced house in a rather run-down part of east London, but even on their low income this seasonal delight is as delicious and exciting at it would be anywhere.

The marking of the turn of the seasons by the arrival of a new treat in the kitchen is one of the joys shared by the members of the Perry Court vegetable scheme in Kent. These households club together to grow a field of vegetables, paying the wages of a gardener over the summer and sharing some of the gardening and all of the harvesting among themselves. Week by week they see the bounty in their overflowing boxes alter as the season shifts: this will be the last of the sweetcorn because frost is expected, but very soon the parsnips will be ready for lifting.

Anyone sourcing their food locally will become more sharply aware of the seasons: the welcoming and savouring of new treats in their proper time. All the seasons bring their delights: spring with its melting lamb and sharp pink rhubarb; summer with its succulent soft fruits, buttery spinach, sweet young peas and tender broad beans, new potatoes, then juicy sweetcorn and flavour-packed garden tomatoes. As the year turns around, summer fruits give way to the plums and apples of the orchards; autumn brings darker flavours: the richness of nuts and mushrooms and the earthier sweetness of chestnuts and parsnips. Winter brings big warming roasts and stews; crisp biting cabbages, chicories and sprouts; satisfying and colourful roots that store the summer's plenty.

There are positive health benefits to eating in season too. Plants growing in their season will grow strongly, so will need fewer sprays and none of the protection and artificial heat required to bring us tomatoes in December and lettuces in February. Seasonal changes in the diet may well provide some extra nutrient that we need at that time or, at the very least, ensure we don't stick completely in a rut. Just as it is gastronomically exciting and satisfying to taste the first asparagus in

May and the first chestnuts in September, perhaps our physiology is getting a bonus too. Certainly many people believe so: roots full of comforting sugars and carbohydrates in the winter; cleansing, cooling greens in summer. Macrobiotic theory says that food from nearby and in season will help balance heat and coolness ('yin' and 'yang') round the year.

WELL-GROWN

The way in which food is produced is crucial to its quality: gastronomic and nutritional. And different food production techniques have very different environmental and ethical impacts too. Buying direct from the producers themselves may be the only way to get hold of some well-grown foods – many of the best producers are too small to supply national chains. At the same time, going direct enables you to assure yourself that the production standards are, indeed, first rate.

Perhaps the most widely-appreciated example of the importance of production methods is the difference between free-range chicken and the broiler variety. Most people readily agree that free range chicken tastes of chicken, while the other sort tastes rather more like cardboard.

Intensive, inhuman animal husbandry produces indifferent meat. Stress alters body chemistry, as anyone who has suffered from stress knows. Parisian restaurateurs say they do not use crate-reared veal because 'the happier the calf, the better the meat'; similarly, a goose farmer in Worcestershire told author Henrietta Greene that to achieve her 'magnificent meaty birds with moist, deeply resonant flesh', the birds have to be grown at a steady speed and not allowed to become frightened or frustrated. The best producers will select an abattoir to ensure that slaughter takes place with minimum fear and stress; with poultry, the birds can be slaughtered on the farm, reducing stress to the absolute minimum.

Slower growth is also important for a richer flavour in meat (as it probably is for vegetables). The flesh of an animal bred and then fed for maximum weight gain in minimum time has a lower concentration of the elements which add flavour, and a higher proportion of those which are simply bulk. Hanging is the other major factor. Hanging allows the natural micro-organisms present in the meat to act on the muscle tissue, developing and enriching the flavour. For the best flavour meat should hang for two or three weeks (depending on the meat). For a high-volume retailer such as a supermarket, three weeks' worth of stock hanging at any one time represents a very large amount of space, and therefore a large expense, so this stage is generally pruned down to just a few days, nothing like enough for the best flavour.

Other factors which contribute to good flavour include a breed chosen for hardiness and flavour rather than fast fattening potential; a wide range of natural foodstuffs; slaughter on the farm or close to home in a small abattoir with minimum stress. None of these conditions fits a system geared to a high, continuous volume of meat to be sold for cheapness rather than quality. Cheap meat in high-volume, national distribution operations has to be fattened fast, killed young (after a long journey to a factory abattoir) and hung for the minimum time.

Vegetables too taste different depending on how they have been grown. Vegetables raised carefully on a small scale, using soil-building and natural fertility, are very different from those grown in 10-acre greenhouses or 100-acre fields, under the spray boom of a tractor. Potatoes seem somehow more potatoey, carrots more carroty when they are organically raised. This may simply be because the produce is less pumped up with fertilisers, which add mainly water. According to the Henry Doubleday Research Association non-organically grown vegetables may contain as much as 20 per cent more water than organic equivalents. It may also be because slower growth and a wider range of nutrients in the soil make for a more rich and complex mix of compounds in an organically grown plant.

According to the Consumers' Association, 'several studies have shown higher levels of calcium, iron, protein, vitamin C and potassium in organic food.' According to the *Food Magazine*, Swedish research in the 1970s also showed that rabbits and hens lived longer and were more fertile when fed organic rations. Worryingly, an international report by the United Nations concludes that diets composed mainly from conventionally-grown, high-yielding crops such as modern varieties of wheat, rice and maize are dangerously deficient in iron, zinc, vitamin A and other micronutrients.[1]

Even more suspect are vegetables grown hydroponically, that is, on mineral wool soaked in artificial fertiliser. The plant can only take up what plant scientists have deemed necessary: nothing else is available. So if the plant scientist has missed something – well, it won't be there,

1. *New Scientist*, 30 March 1996.

even if the peppers and lettuces appear big, green and shiny. And it is not just a matter of putting in the necessary nutrients. A plant root is a living system working symbiotically with soil bacteria which help the plant to take up nutrients; these bacteria are deliberately removed from artificial systems.

And of course ecologically-grown food has no poisons sprayed onto it. Pest and disease control is perfectly possible without poisons – but it needs skill and attention: much likelier if the vegetables are being grown on a small scale. Mandy Pullen's delicious vegetables, mentioned in chapter one, are raised on just one acre so everything gets regular attention. While many large-scale growers use sprays in greenhouses in winter, Mandy comments: 'I don't need to use fungicides on lettuces and so forth in the tunnel. I keep a close eye and control soil moisture, and this keeps down any fungus infections.' This kind of attention is much likelier, of course, on a small holding.

There is no question that organic veg and meat have better flavour. A tasting organised by the *Daily Express* found that organic vegetables were generally liked better than non-organic equivalents, with the most lavish praise reserved for organic produce. The organic grapefruit had 'much, much more flavour', and as for chicken 'the difference is incredible' another taster commented that he 'thought the non-organic chicken was tuna fish'.

Industrial veg are built for endurance. They cannot afford to melt in the mouth, as they would have collapsed in the crate first. Writing in the *Independent* newspaper, Joanna Blythman described Dutch glasshouse peppers: 'Try grilling a kebab with Dutch peppers and they are likely to be hard long after the meat is cooked. They are planted in chemical substrates ... that merely support the roots as synthetically produced liquid nutrients, water and fungicides are pumped into them. Deprived of sun, of the natural struggle to grow, [you end up with] a flavourless and thoroughly artificial creature.'

KNOW YOUR GROWER

When vegetables are grown on a massive scale for mass transport and mass retailing, the delight of good flavour too often fails to count in the equation. Even if you buy a delicious, tender, aromatic pepper one week in the supermarket, when you return the next week you have no way of knowing how to select more produce from the same farm. On the other hand, if you know who grew or raised something especially delicious, you can go back and get more. If the grower knows you know, they have a huge incentive to attract you back by growing food which tastes wonderful.

As organic vegetable grower David Wenman told author Judy Steele, the best way for him to be assured of sales of his wide range of carefully-produced vegetables is not by sending them to an anonymous wholesaler or supermarket, but by building up a good name, a recognisable identity for his produce 'and you have to do that by selling locally'. Similarly, organic meat producers Louise Unwin and her husband sell direct to customers around their Suffolk farm, and direct to London customers though market stalls, including one at the Spitalfields farmers' market. Customers can admire pictures of their animals enjoying the sunshine as they queue for a whole range of organic meats: steaks, chops, mince, sausages, liver and bacon. The quality is superlative and the customers know it: lamb joints often sell out by mid-morning, and chicken has to be ordered in advance! The Unwins wouldn't get this kind of response – or these prices – selling into the main stream. They are looking especially for the kind of customers who are looking especially for them.

DIVERSITY: NEGLECTED TREASURES

If you were to visit the celebration of Apple Day at the Brogdale Fruit Collection, you would be able to get a real taste of what biological diversity can mean. In a vast packing shed a spectacular array greets the eye: row upon row of trestle tables, neatly set out with bowls of gold, green, orange, crimson or russet-brown fruit – apples of every colour, size and fragrance; apples dating back to the time of the Romans, apples loved in the seventeenth century, apples competitively prized by gardeners of country houses, apples discussed and appreciated at Victorian apple parties, which were as enthusiastic as any modern-day wine-tasting. On the chilly concrete standing, you can join the punters filling plastic bags with 'pick and mix' selections, labelling each precious fruit with its own curious, romantic name. Or you can queue to join a trailer ride through the multicoloured abundance of the surrounding orchards.

The breed or variety of animal or plant chosen by growers makes a tremendous difference to flavour, texture and other qualities. Cox's apples are unfailingly popular, despite the fact they often cost a bit more, because of their aromatic, sweet flavour. Cox's won't travel and

Harvesting cider apples in an old orchard, Gloucestershire

store like some of the blander varieties imported from Chile and New Zealand, so we can't have them all year round. Strictly speaking, this might make them unsuitable for mass retailers such as supermarkets, which like to supply the same goods every week of the year. But they wouldn't dare not to stock such a favourite. Other treasures have vanished, though. The Peasgood Nonsuch, raised and grown in Lincolnshire and suited to the chilly eastern climate, was an 'enormous golden fruit, perfect for baking', and was awarded a first-class certificate by the Royal Horticultural Society in 1872. But it is a soft apple and doesn't travel far. The economics of food retailing mean that even consumers in Lincolnshire are now deprived of this treat.

Tomatoes have suffered notoriously as a result of the demands for mass-produced, long-distance, uniform crops. Many probably just get left on the side of the plate, so tasteless are they. Consumers have grumbled so much, that tomatoes with taste are once again available – but priced and packaged like an exotic luxury, as though eating food with a flavour was some kind of privilege.

There is the same potential for real flavour in all our vegetables and fruits. Perhaps one reason that we don't eat as many vegetables as we should is that the ones widely available are so tasteless. Jeremy Cherfas, who founded UK Heritage Seeds, says that in the journal for commercial horticulture, *The Grower*, he sees new vegetable seed varieties advertised for yield, uniformity, synchronised ripening, ease of mechanical harvesting, transportability and storability – 'but flavour doesn't enter the calculation ... Sometimes for fruit, but for vegetables I've never once seen it mentioned. And in the process of breeding for all these other qualities, flavour has been lost along the way.' He adds that the EU nearly banned the Bramley apple because it's a large and lumpy apple and it refuses to be uniform in size.

Varieties which may have a better flavour tend not to be chosen by commercial growers because of their 'shortcomings'. Modern varieties are bred for yield, uniformity, evenness of ripening, resistance to machine harvesting, long journeys and long storage without blemishing. Industrial processors and retailers will demand a vast, predictable, uniform supply of just one or two varieties. Uniformity is not only demanded by most retailers, it is even enforced by European regulations, despite the fact that it has almost no value to the consumer. Less common, local varieties bred for quite different priorities can find no place in this market. When people grow their own food, variety is much richer.

The machines which make Kellogg's Cornflakes can only accept three varieties of maize. Over 50,000 varieties of maize have been recorded over the years, particular varieties suited to particular kinds of farm and particular kinds of farmer. But if the farmers want to sell to Kellogg's, too bad, they have virtually no choice at all, Kellogg's being such a dominant customer, farmers generally cannot afford to ignore them.

A further, massive blow to variety is dealt by the regulatory authorities. For a seed variety to be sold legally in the EU, for example, it must usually be registered on a national list. And to get onto the list seeds must meet extremely rigid standards of uniformity. Interesting, useful, adaptable varieties which contain a range of sub-types and are not completely uniform are not permitted.

Registration is extremely expensive. Once upon a time gardeners or local farm groups could proudly register their own new varieties. In the UK they cannot now do this unless, as well as passing the uniformity exam, they can also afford the fee of around £7,000. Such a sum is just a token for a multinational seed firm producing and selling a variety in thousands of tonnes, but it has ruled out thousands of varieties produced by small, local seed firms. Many smaller firms have gone out of business, or stopped paying to register their less profitable varieties, which means that these are lost forever. Smaller seed companies have also been swallowed up by the big conglomerates at an alarming rate, all over the world. Once again, this leads to the deletion of all but the biggest-selling varieties. And once a variety has gone, it has gone: that is extinction.

There is no doubt that we are the losers in this tragedy. We lose choice, we lose flavour, and we may well be losing vitamins too. Some of our traditional apples, not necessarily the ones bred for shelf life and cold storage, have six times more vitamin C than a golden delicious. 'You could say that industrial varieties have been bred not so much to stop decay, but to stop decay from showing. They look fresh, but they aren't, really,' Cherfas says.

STRENGTH IN DIVERSITY

Farmers and the environment are losing, as well. Seeds bred to give high yields under high chemical inputs *get* high chemical inputs. They may not perform well at all under more ecological farming techniques. The varieties adapted to a craft-scale, organic-style mixed farming approach are the ones we have been losing.

Lost are varieties developed in a particular region and adapted to local growing conditions: soil, climate, and even the ideal timing to fit in with other local crops. Varieties bred at one huge research station hundreds of miles away in another part of the country, or even the world, cannot do this. 'We used to have the Ormskirk cabbage and the Altrincham carrot – those were specialities which grew best around Ormskirk and Altrincham. Why should Lancashire and Cheshire gardeners have to grow carrots and cabbages that grow indifferently all over the world?' Cherfas asks.

Currently, varieties are bred to give record yields if they are given the optimum combination of water, fertiliser and pesticides. If sustainable agriculture means relying on natural fertility rather than resource-hungry inputs, then different qualities will become important. For example, the Maris Widgeon strain of wheat very readily takes up nitrogen from a healthy, well-manured soil and grows strongly without artificial fertiliser, but the mainstream industrial wheats will not perform so well, even in a good rich soil, without being spoon-fed nitrate from a bag. Maris Widgeon is perfect for organic farmers but it is very hard to get hold of.

Modern, so-called 'high-yield' varieties are poorly adapted to being grown sustainably. They are often susceptible to pests and yield poorly without their favourite chemical pick-me-ups. But as Cherfas points out, the legislation which has killed the old varieties also makes it impossible to breed new ones to meet our new concerns and new eating habits. For example, many of us have acquired a taste for foods which can't, currently, be grown well here. 'It is impossible for a small breeder to develop new commercial varieties just for local or specialised use,' says Cherfas. 'I mean, I think I could develop a chick pea which grew well in Britain in about six or seven years. But it wouldn't be worth my while.'

It is not because breeding is difficult, but because big companies want to hold on to the market, that small breeders have been discouraged. 'There is a lot of mystique about plant breeding but in fact selection and stabilisation of new lines is just exactly what farmers and gardeners have always done, until recently when they have been actively discouraged from doing it and have been disempowered.'

It is no coincidence that agriculture contains the word 'culture'. Local eating habits and local varieties represent local heritage. Farm crop seeds and garden seeds have been handed from grandmother to granddaughter, father to son, for centuries. But now, as Renée Velvé of

GRAIN, a leading international genetic resources campaigning body points out, all of us, gardeners and farmers, are being told that seed saving is better done by 'experts'. 'When you take seeds away from local farmers and gardeners and their production systems, you are severing something very deep,' Velvé writes in her book *Saving the Seed*. Generations have built up an intimate relationship with the plant and animal varieties they cultivate in their family and in their region, understanding and appreciating them. Seed companies take over the seeds, but they don't replace that relationship.

Gardening magazines warn us we won't do it properly, that the varieties will deteriorate. Seed multinationals want to deter farmers from selling seeds by imposing stiff royalty charges. The National Farmers' Union has agreed with the seed industry that farmers who save seed from one crop for the next year's sowing will now pay a royalty to the original breeder of something like 35 per cent of that paid by growers multiplying up seed for resale: what used to be a farmer's right is now a privilege which he or she must pay for. Furthermore, many 'high-response' seeds are F1 hybrids, whose genetic make-up means that if you save the seed it will not breed true, so you have to go back each season and buy fresh seed, which certainly contributes to their popularity with seed companies.

It is not just varieties, but whole species that are extinguished by the 'modernisation' of agriculture. Velvé reports research in France which shows that 100 years ago, people in Provence grew and ate 250 plant species, whereas now it is only 60.

In many European countries small organisations like Cherfas' are struggling to save seed variety, depending on local farmers and gardeners for the treasures they find. For instance, in Austria, Nancy Arrowsmith has worked with elderly women growers who have encouraged her to conserve the remaining varieties – 95 per cent of the varieties grown in Austria are now imported by foreign companies. She set up an organisation, Arch Noah, which works by swapping seeds for growers to multiply and conserve: at stands at local markets, at sympathetic wholefood stores or by post. Arrowsmith particularly worried about the risk that the agricultural 'development' promised in eastern Europe will wipe out the diversity that still remains there, as it already has done in the west of the continent. Time is running out. Dorset grower Mike Michaud, who grows as many unusual varieties on his holding as he can, has visited the Czech Republic and says, 'already they're growing Dutch hybrids'.

Michaud has tried to find regional vegetables in Britain, but 'there aren't really any left'.

In 1994, about 30 years after the introduction of the first restrictions on seed selling, there at last appeared to be signs of softening within the EC. The British and French seed registration authorities proposed a 'Heritage list' whereby seed varieties which had been registered in the past could be re-registered at a reduced fee. However, as Cherfas pointed out, this plan made no allowance for new varieties being developed for small scale gardening and growing. In the event the proposal was not adopted by the EU but there remained interest in stopping the genetic landslide, and alternative proposals are expected to surface.

It is not just sentimentality to want to keep these varieties going, as the European Parliament may at last have recognised. Today's funny garden variety may be tomorrow's saviour from blight, plague or drought. Some of the old varieties being elbowed off the shelves by the big 'performers' have valuable properties: a waxy surface that shrugs off mould-inviting raindrops, a different sugar in the sap which the aphids don't find so sweet. These kinds of properties are essential to breed into crops to ward of disease and the more we want to cut down on pesticide use, the more valuable they become. Alan Gear of the Henry Doubleday Research Association (which runs the organic gardening centre at Ryton Gardens) has warned that, 'The history of agriculture is littered with epidemics of disease and outbreaks of pest; in almost every case salvation was found in either an old variety or a wild relative of the crop.'

The other great asset is, simply, variety itself. Many fields are planted with seeds so highly bred that they are almost clones. Genetically identical individuals have genetically identical susceptibilities to pests and diseases. It happened, famously, with the nineteenth-century potato famine caused by blight which knocked out the two varieties of potato on which virtually every Irish family depended. A potato variety with different genes had to be found to breed new blight-resistant varieties. In the 1990s, blight has started to reappear, hitting many of the closely-related commercial potato varieties once again.

Eighty per cent of Dutch potato fields are planted to just one single variety, Bintje. The Netherlands has set itself a target of reducing sprays by 50 per cent. According to Jeremy Cherfas, Scottish potato researchers have estimated that if the Dutch changed their main potato variety to one which was not quite so vulnerable to blight, that alone could reduce the entire national fungicide tonnage by 50 per cent. A farm raising 100 different plant and animal varieties is much safer from plagues than one raising two or three varieties, while actively promoting the preservation of genetic diversity at the same time.

The same agro-industrial machine that has effectively reduced the choice of thousands of maize varieties to just three dominant players, has seen national and local animal breeds replaced by factory animals. Like industrial crops, industrial animals are bred to grow extremely rapidly when offered large quantities of artificial feed. At their most grotesque, these animals are built to suffer: dairy cows bred with such large udders that they cannot walk properly; male turkeys with such large breasts that they cannot mate, and must be 'milked' of semen so that females can be artificially inseminated; chickens bred to be slaughtered at six weeks and four pounds in weight, which if allowed to run around outside till they are older and heavier, will fall over as their feet are congenitally unable to support them.

Meanwhile, fine hardy animals characteristic of their region, which may well produce tastier meat, have been sidelined, some lost altogether. The Gloucester old spot pig was adapted to growing fat on the copious windfalls of Gloucestershire's orchards – just ready to be killed for the winter. Raised this way its bacon, though fatty, is delicious. The Herdwick sheep is a characteristic sight on the Lakeland fells. It is bred to endure an extraordinarily tough life, and to thrive on the fragrant mixtures of herbs, bilberries and heathers which clothe the high slopes. This forage gives the meat a flavour all its own, quite different from that of the soft, south-country cousins who fatten on boring sown pasture, artificially greened with nitrates.

Like the Gloucester old spot pork, there are breeds of beef – the well-known Aberdeen Angus but also the rarer Galloway and Devon, Lincoln and Sussex reds – which yield fatter meat than the gigantic continental Charolais, but how much tastier those are.

Genetic diversity has been used again and again to rescue intensive agriculture from the latest strain of rust, blight, spot or sawfly. But this diversity is an even more vital foundation to a sustainable, eater-friendly agricultural future. The modern breeds of plant and animal are designed to respond to industrial fertilisers and feedstuffs. But they also depend on them, and often cannot cope with a more 'natural' life. We need to ensure that those breeders who are still keeping the varieties suitable for 'sustainable' agriculture going, stay in business – and to do that they need customers.

Growers who aim to grow sustainably and, in particular, those who grow for direct customers (vegetables, fruit or meat), are much keener to make the most of the diversity of varieties they can find: they want to offer their customers good flavours and a variety of them, to prolong the cropping season, and to insure their crop supply against disasters. In the introduction we read about the many varieties grown at Ragman's Lane: their approach to selecting hardy, well-adapted, flavoursome varieties is common. These varieties are essential to our future. By buying from growers who use them, we are safeguarding them for everyone.

4

THE ENVIRONMENTAL COST

Eating and shopping the way we do is bad for us – and it is destroying the country, leaving it demolished, denuded, poisoned. As the majority of the population has lost involvement in food production and distribution, so a huge 'efficient' machine has taken over, and it is doing a lot of damage, while supplying us with second-rate food.

FOOD MILES

The land on which Heathrow Airport was built was once Heath Row, one of London's most productive market garden areas. Now, many of those gardens have gone under tarmac and the planes that roar in, reeking of kerosene, are carrying fresh vegetables and fruit.

Imported vegetables are only the most conspicuous facet of an enormous trade; within the UK itself, all kinds of food rushes hither and thither. The cheapness to big companies of using road transport intensively leads to some absurdities. The Sustainable Agriculture, Food and Environment Alliance (SAFE) reports that bananas imported into Southampton by Geest are sent by road all the way to Lancashire to be ripened before returning again by road to a Somerset warehouse from which they are then distributed across Britain, Southampton and Lancashire included. Pigs reared and slaughtered in Suffolk for Marks and Spencer have been driven to Barnstaple in north Devon for final butchering and packing, before being distributed to stores all over the country.

Food, drink and tobacco only form one-tenth of the British economy but account for a quarter of freight transport, and the distances covered are rising fast. Government figures reveal that in the 15 years to 1994, the distance travelled by food and drink on UK roads increased by 50 per cent.

Supermarkets are particularly large 'consumers' of road space because they tend to have all their supplies delivered to large regional distribution centres from where they make another journey, sometimes to a store very near the original source of the food. Sometimes only one distribution centre serves the whole country: as a rule, there will be no more than two or three regional depots through which all produce must pass between source and retail outlet. As the SAFE Alliance warns in its 'Food Miles' report, Sunday trading has made things worse, with half-empty vehicles bringing top-ups of the most perishable items. The largest UK supermarkets are all members of the Freight Transport Association, a group which lobbies the government to build roads.

And, of course, supermarkets sell a lot of processed food. Food processing and transportation go together like sliced bread and palm oil margarine. Processed foods are easier to transport: killed and packaged, they won't suffer further damage en route. Equally, processed food generates lots of demand for transport. The same brands of packet soup or biscuit, sweetened breakfast cereal or fruit yoghurt, made in one big factory, are to be found in stores the length and breadth of the country. Lorries on their way to Kent with biscuits made in Lancashire pass lorries on their way to Lancashire with very slightly different biscuits made in Kent. Ingredients arrive at the factory from all over the world – wherever the price is lowest this week – then fan out all around the country, if not the continent.

This kind of nationwide distribution is expensive to the country in terms of congestion, roadbuilding and pollution. But it suits the manufacturers and supermarkets, who pay none of these costs, and are able to use centralised systems to distribute widely, and to control exactly what is sold in every single one of their branches. Modern economic theory insists that a factory or retail chain ought to be looking to sell from Salzburg to Swansea if it really wants to show economies of scale. The profits are made by retailers, food processors, hauliers, construction companies and oil companies. Farmers still receive a very low price for the food on which this huge industry is built.

It is hard to see how consumers benefit, as the kind of foods which we eat at the far end of this journey are seldom either healthy or delicious. We are told we are getting choice, but wouldn't it be better to have one truly wholesome and delicious variety of frozen cheesecake, rather than seven insipid ones? We are also told that competition keeps down prices. As we are beginning to see though, even when the prices at the checkout are low we pay in other ways.

Many of us have already paid with our health and some with their lives. As well as the deaths and injuries suffered in road accidents, disability and death are caused by traffic pollution. During the London smog of December 1991, the death rate in London rose by 1 per cent: 160 extra deaths, mainly among people suffering from lung and heart disease. Much of the pollution was from motor traffic. Diesel engines alone are estimated to contribute to 10,000 deaths a year in Britain. Diesel particles get deep into the lungs and seem to increase the death rate from many different conditions, including heart disease and infections.

There are now very few places in the whole of southern England where it is possible to get right out of earshot of traffic noise. Ironically, many city homes are quieter, protected from the main through routes by other buildings, than homes in the open countryside. As the country roads running past people's doors have grown wider, straighter, busier and faster, so people's quality of life is insidiously worn away. The main routes through towns are the worst, though. How depressing is the sight of a tiny, filthy front garden or doorstep right next to a busy road, the net curtains inside as grimy as net curtains used to be in the darkest days of the industrial revolution.

Roads – and large superstores – have also made their contribution to the aesthetic erosion of the countryside. Twyford Down near Winchester in Hampshire, Dartmoor in Devon, the woods and water meadows around Newbury – these are a few famous beauty spots and 'protected' habitats scarred or erased by motorways or trunk roads, but there are countless others.

Roads bring development in their wake. Bypasses, ring roads and motorways skirt round towns like Newmarket or Ledbury or Tewkesbury through open country; it costs less to build a road through open fields. But then the buildings rush to fill out the town up to the ring road, and the new trading sheds take their positions next to the roundabouts. Orange glare from sodium lamps replace the stars of the night sky.

It's not only humans that dislike the lights, pollution and noise: birds in particular are sensitive to noise and for this reason some species, like nightingales, are believed to avoid areas up to one mile from major roads and motorways. Oxfordshire members of the British Trust for Ornithology counted far fewer nightingales on the unique pastoral landscape of Otmoor after the M40 extension opened nearby. Other habitats are simply being wiped out. SSSI status is supposed to confer protection on a site, but in 1995 the EU was obliged to introduce a new, even more highly-protected classification, because SSSIs were disappearing so fast under tarmac, out-of-town shopping centres and the rest. And, of course, most fields, hedges, ponds and streams have no formal protection.

In 1994 the government did ease off on its roadbuilding programme, mainly because it was desperately strapped for cash; doubtless the public controversy over roads made roadbuilding easier to cut than budgets for schools and hospitals. At the end of that year the Royal Commission on Environmental Pollution called for the government to go much further and to create a positive, integrated, sustainable transport policy. However, the aggressive revival of the Newbury bypass in 1995, on the day the then roads minister left office, indicates that there is a way to go before the Royal Commission's recommendations are taken on board.

Similar attitudes prevail at the European level. Goods transport in the EU is forecast to rise by about 90 per cent by the year 2010. Food transport in particular is soaring, with more tonnes of food being transported, and each tonne making longer and longer average journeys, which are expected to more than double over the next 20 years.

To accommodate this, the EU is sponsoring a network of new and 'upgraded' roads throughout the continent. In Britain these will link east coast ports, major British cities and the west coast ports for Ireland. Building began covertly in some places in the guise of enormous three-lane dual carriageway 'bypasses' which the DoT finally admitted were so big because they were part of new trunk routes. In 1996, the EU formalised a plan to support an entire new network, the Trans European Road Network, involving over 50,000 km of new roads all over Europe, 12,000 km of them motorways. The EU has also decided that even heavier lorries should be able to penetrate right through the single market (more freight for less driver time, making long-distance transport even more convenient); in order to accommodate these increased loads Britain is supposed to be spending £2.2 billion on bridge strengthening by 1999.

The House of Commons' Select Committee on Agriculture has pointed out that a network of fast roads across Europe 'makes the domestic market relatively easy to penetrate from abroad'. This new EU road network, which British taxpayers are paying for, also should make export from this country easier, but since we import more than we export it seems likely that overseas producers exporting food into

Britain will benefit most.

VEGETABLES THROUGH THE STRATOSPHERE

No discussion of food miles is complete without a look at the very special role of supermarkets in promoting the international jet-setting life of today's vegetable.

Air freighting is an incredibly energy-intensive way of transporting heavy cargo such as vegetables. Air freighted imports to Britain are soaring: the volume went up 15 per cent in just one year, 1993 – 1994. Mile for mile, air freighting uses nearly 40 times more fuel than shipping. Air traffic is the world's fastest-growing source of carbon dioxide, the greenhouse gas, and aeroplanes burn their fuel in the upper atmosphere where it can do most damage, including to the ozone layer. Any they fail to burn is dumped into the air near the airport – that is, over the homes, schools and workplaces of our major cities.

Worse still, much of the air-freighted produce is crops which can be grown at home – peas and beans, in particular, or fresh flowers – imported out of their European season. Long-haul operators are deliberately seeking out traders in African and Asian countries to export horticultural produce back to Europe, thus increasing the profitability of their flights. If the operators can cut prices of holiday travel and of freight, the trade seems likely to boom, further escalating the pollution damage to the earth's atmosphere. Both tourism and luxury horticulture also have social and environmental effects in the countries we trade with, and they are by no means an unmixed blessing to the poorest and most vulnerable people there, as is discussed in chapter seven.

Attempts to curb the growth in transport-related emissions have been drowned out in the clamour for 'modernisation' and 'growth'. Food is likely to be a particular culprit for years to come, warns transport expert Chris Bowers: 'The EU has policies for reducing transport-related emissions over the next 15 years. I don't believe they will make their targets because they never do; and, in particular, I think much food transport is likely to be exempted from any restrictions (such as being required to go by rail) because it is perishable and so can be classed as "urgent".' Yet so much of this 'urgent' produce – milk, cheese, soft fruit and vegetables – could be grown much nearer to home.

Food bought from a local producer will travel perhaps one-thousandth of the food miles of an imported item, or of an item made up from many ingredients trucked in from all over the continent, or of an item that has travelled somewhere in Britain to be packed, somewhere else to be warehoused, and somewhere else again to be sold. Vegetables delivered direct from a grower, eggs from a farm, local meat in the local butcher, might only travel five, ten or 50 miles from the farm to your table. Hardly anything in a supermarket has done less than 100 miles, most has done much, much more.

PROCESSED, PACKAGED

Processed food does not just require energy to carry the ingredients to and fro, it also uses energy in its manufacture. A large proportion of the food we buy has been chopped, minced, stirred, cooked, extruded, shaped and sometimes dried. In total, food processing can use 10 times more fuel than was used to grow the ingredients in the first place, says the SAFE Alliance. Even basic foods such as a parsnip or potato are washed before they are sold nowadays, using a machine rather than a pair of hands. Chilled and frozen foods need energy to run the refrigerators and special lorries to transport them.

And all processed food has to be packaged, often in not one but two or even three layers: plastic sachet, tray, cling-wrap, foil lid, plus sachets of sauce or 'sprinkles' compartments, cardboard sleeves or cartons. If you don't have the wit to buy some ready-made burgers, some soft buns and a jar of relish, Safeway will sell you two buns and a two-burger portion of relish in its own separate little jar, with two chilled burgers in their own thick plastic sleeve, in a further dent-proof, warehouse-man-proof moulded plastic box. So if you've got some friends coming for a barbeque you might end up buying 32 separate packages whereas in fact you only need, say, four. Supermarkets in particular use high quantities of packaging.

Packaging consumes natural resources: wood, aluminium, iron, glass, oil. These are usually extracted in socially and environmentally unfriendly ways, including open-cast mining or clear felling of natural forest. Non-reusable packaging also generates large quantities of waste. Plastic in particular is virtually indestructible when dumped or buried; frequently toxic when burned. And, as we all know, a plastic bottle labelled 'recyclable' is just a joke. Who does anything with such containers other than put them in the bin? Most supermarkets have made gestures towards environmental concerns by installing paper and glass re-cycling bins. But they are not prepared to participate in the far more environmentally friendly option of return-and-reuse schemes, though with glass bottles and jars, it would be perfectly straightforward to do so, and people would be happy to co-operate. A Friends of the Earth survey in 1991 showed 84 per cent of the population were willing to use returnable bottles. On average, washing and refilling glass containers requires about one-quarter of the energy it takes to manufacture a new bottle. Recycling, on the other hand, uses almost as much energy as making containers from the raw materials: after all, the broken glass still has to be melted and re-moulded.

Paper and glass recycling are huge-scale, highly-capitalised, centralised industries and the materials may be transported hundreds of miles, even between countries: i.e., more lorries, more smelters. Return-reuse systems, by contrast, favour local businesses with loyal customers, and need only hot soapy water.

Reusable containers do need to be sturdy, but on a short journey the extra energy used to carry a heavier glass bottle hardly counts: it is much less than the energy used to make a new bottle for each trip. Nationwide distribution erodes this advantage. International food distribution undermines the logic of re-usable containers further still, making resource-intensive throw-away packaging even more attractive to manufacturers and retailers. At home, almost all milk bottles are the same shape and size so even if the bottle does not go back to the same dairy, other dairies can use them just the same. Similarly, most British bottled beers come in the same shape and size of bottle, so even if you insist on drinking a Yorkshire beer in Dorset, a West Country brewery could use that bottle next time round. German mineral water companies use a standard bottle in this same way. Alas, as Friends of the Earth laments, German beer imported to the UK, or French mineral water imported to Germany, disrupts this system.

Food and drink packaging accounts for about two-thirds of all packaging manufactured, making up a fair proportion of the household rubbish removed every week by the council's bin men; 90 per cent of domestic waste is dumped in holes in the ground.

Waste disposal is a huge headache for local authorities – and a huge money-spinner for disposal companies. In 1993, Castle Cement proposed to convert a massive spent chalk quarry at the foot of the Chiltern escarpment into a landfill site. In a designated area of outstanding natural beauty, adjoining a National Trust chalk downland site of special scientific interest, this 150-acre site would be clearly visible – and smellable – from the Ridgeway long-distance path. Over 200 lorries per day could be bringing rubbish rumbling along the narrow Hertfordshire lanes to the site, with considerably more coming in by rail. If the plan is approved, Castle Cement stands to make millions of pounds from the site, much of which would be paid to them by local authorities – from the local council tax, in other words.

Spirited opposition from local residents and councils concerned about the prospect of the traffic, the plastic bags, seagulls and rats, an evil smell and a hideous blot on their lovely landscape, has given Castle Cement a fight: all the relevant local authorities are opposed to the plan which went to public enquiry in 1995. But several people mentioned in the course of the campaign that 'we all have a responsibility to cut down our rubbish, unless we want this site and others to face similar threats'. The community is now looking at the idea of a community composting scheme, and demanding skips for recycling.

In cities there are no empty holes to fill. Waste must either be trucked out of the city to rural landfills, or incinerated. The massive chimney of the incineration plant at Edmonton, north London, is visible for miles around. This is just one of scores of suspected dioxin emitters in Britain. Any packaging materials containing chlorine – PVC film, for example – produces small quantities of dioxins when burned. Dioxins are some of the most toxic substances known. They cause cancer and attack the immune and reproductive systems, and are linked with male and female fertility problems. Sulphur compounds, heavy metals, carcinogenic hydrocarbons all come wafting out of the chimneys, according to the *Ecologist* magazine; even those plants equipped with 'state of the art' exhaust purifying systems tend to leave them switched off as they make the incinerator too expensive to run.

The idea that we are 'recycling' the waste by generating electricity has got a great deal more to do with public relations than with environmental logic. 'Incineration with energy recovery is a very attractive option as a contributor to sustainable development'. Attractive to whom? Why, to the Director of the British Plastics Federation, Ron Jones, that's who. And, as the *Ecologist* also reports, a writer in the BP house magazine even described discarded yoghurt pots as a 'renewable' energy source, presumably believing them to grow on trees (when of course, they come from oil wells). The energy recovered from burning a yoghurt pot in a waste incinerator nowhere near covers the resources and energy cost of making a new yoghurt pot. If it did, people would pay to take away the rubbish in our bins. In fact, the electricity generated from burning domestic rubbish doesn't even cover the cash cost of running the incinerator.

The 'green con' is practised on consumers again and again. When we are told something is 'greener' we are attracted to buy or support it. Sadly, just a little investigation into the reality behind many of these slogans, reveals business (almost) as usual, with a little green make-up. Chapter five will explore the way food retailers engage in similar tricks.

Truly green solutions tend to be simpler, rather than more elaborate and technological, ways of doing things. The obvious way of avoiding food miles, and the attendant packaging and waste problem, is to buy food from nearby. This is something that anyone can do. It enables every consumer to participate in 'direct action' without necessarily being young, bold and agile enough to climb trees at Newbury or scale an incinerator chimney with a Greenpeace banner; and local shopping brings its own pleasures and rewards.

THE POISONED DESERT

As the food manufacturers, retailers and distributors criss-cross the country with lorries, so the same industry is eroding and poisoning the fields which remain between the new highways. Pressures on farmers, which I look at in more detail in chapter six, have forced them to squeeze higher and higher yields from their fields, and everything that is not 'productive' has to go. As farmers use larger and larger machines, so turning them at field ends becomes more and more of a nuisance. The machines sneak ever closer to the hedges, as anyone following a footpath supposedly along the grassy strip between crop and hedge will have discovered. Everywhere, winding overhung streams, their banks full of waterside flowers, willows and alders with birds in the boughs and otters and voles burrowing in the roots, have been 'canalised'; the vegetation raked out, the meanders straightened, the bed excavated, as the farmer hurries to rush the water away from his land and downstream. Flower rich meadows and summer hay fields are happy enough to be waterlogged in winter; fields of winter wheat or oilseed rape are not. So, if the support price is right, away with the landscape.

Whole landscape features are sometimes ploughed away. On the scarp of the Lambourne downs, above the Vale of the White Horse, the chalk forms beautiful folds, almost like a heavy fabric. In one hilltop field, three or four of these graceful folds have been decapitated, remaining only as whiter ghosts showing against the grey soil of the field. Such drastic impoverishment of the landscape causes very real pain to those who love a particular area, and even distresses those who have never visited it, but hear what has happened. There are serious biological and economic implications as well.

Soil is completely essential to life. It is the source of all our food (apart from fish). It is the factory where spent organic matter is reprocessed so that new life can grow from it. But we aren't taking care of it. In East Anglia in 1992, residents observed that the soil in the fields was being picked up in the wind, then raining down on their homes, gardens and roads in wet weather. Oliver Arditi, who lives in Suffolk, noticed that the soil in nearby fields was no longer soil at all, but sand. 'I could see no evidence that it contained any humus [organic matter] whatsoever.' Farming in the area had relied for so long on chemical fertilisers, without restoring any of the natural matter, that there appeared to be no natural fertility left at all. Arditi's impression is backed up by the figures: much of the soil in Norfolk and Suffolk contains less than 1.5 per cent organic matter. Most soils in England and Wales have four times this much.

Soil without humus not only loses fertility, it loses its structure. As every gardening book tells you, organic matter helps stick sandy soils together, and keeps clay porous. Arditi believes that the land could not support agriculture for many more years at such a rate of destruction. In flat areas, degraded soil blows away; if there is any kind of a slope, it will wash away too. Hedgerows may be the only defence against this erosion, yet of course many of these have been removed. Estimates of soil losses in arable (crop) land range from two to 40 tonnes per hectare per year. No more than one tonne per hectare can be made each year to replace it. It has to be made up with chemicals.

In a rare reference to soil erosion in the mainstream farming press, readers of *Crops* magazine in 1994 were told: 'A field in the South Downs holds the dubious record for measured annual erosion losses of 200 tonnes per hectare per year.' This is happening all over the world: the Worldwatch Institute in Washington has estimated that so much topsoil is lost from the world's fields and plantations every year that you could fill a freight train with it, stretching to the moon, and back, five times.

British householders are already paying for this destruction. Autumn ploughing of steep sloping land, the vanished hedgerows and the weaker structure of the soils, means that instead of soaking into the ground and recharging the underground water supplies, heavy winter rain pours off the fields, carrying the topsoil with it. This increased run-off has contributed to some of the devastating winter floods suffered in recent years: one flood of muddy water from recently-sown land was estimated to have caused £1 million worth of damage to a village in south-east England. And as Wales and the West Midlands struggled under the torrential rains of December 1994, with flooded roads and houses and fields underwater, millions of tons of good red Welsh Borders topsoil was carried away for ever, down the Severn Estuary and into the sea, staining the waves a disturbing muddy brown.

According to agricultural scientists Jules Pretty and Rupert Howes, the floods in Chichester the year before, which cost households, local authorities and insurance companies millions of pounds, could be attributed as much to winter ploughing and hedgerow removal as to the heavy rains. After the floodwaters receded, the downhill corners of field after field showed the telltale dregs of silt – the residue of the soil after the lighter organic matter, our organic topsoil heritage, had been carried away in the waters.

And because the rain is not soaking into the underground water stores, in the summer, streams and rivers are drying up. In recent summers some rivers in southern England have completely disappeared, with devastating loss of wildlife, and loss of delight to anyone who wanted to fish for minnows, paddle, picnic or just pause and enjoy.

A huge range of habitats and landscapes have succumbed to agricultural intensification, as well as to 'suburbanisation' and roadbuilding. We have lost woodlands, hedgerows, rough 'unimproved' pasture, salt marshes, wetlands, flower-rich meadows, heaths, old orchards and chalk grassland full of flowers, insects and birds that depend on that particular ecological niche and are wiped out by intensive monocultures. In their place we now have big monotonous fields and scrappy, motheaten hedgerows; huge aluminium and concrete sheds; hard concrete driveways to carry the weight of machines without them sinking into the mud. The landscape of intensive farming is bleak and boring.

The 'traditional' countryside – its appearance and its wildlife – is also a product of farming, but scale and appropriateness are all important. The changes wrought by the muscle power of men and animals can be assimilated by the eye, colonised by nature; they are on the same sort of scale as a tree, a river, a hedgerow. Many of our favourite landscapes are associated with a particular kind of farming: the patchwork of fields in the West Country, the dry stone walls of the Cotswolds and Pennines, the dreamy willows and lush pastures of Oxfordshire, Cheshire, and the southern marshes and levels. The Cornish cherry orchards in bloom looked so stunning that boat trips used to take people from Plymouth to admire them – and carried them back again at harvest time to have cherry pie picnics. But bring in a machine with 200 times the strength of a man, and the other landscape features can be dwarfed or eradicated in an afternoon.

The British countryside has been farmed for so long that many species are in fact dependent on particular kinds of agricultural management. Chalk downland needs regular grazing by sheep to keep down hawthorn scrub and allow the tiny, exquisite orchids, thymes, harebells and cinquefoils to flourish and, in turn, feed the grassland butterflies. Wild bees flourish in old orchards. Many of our prettiest wildflowers like cornfields: cornflower, corn cockle, corn marigold, as well as the pheasants eye, the poppy, and many others. Many of these are now almost extinct. Until recently, agriculture changed slowly enough for nature to adapt. But now the changes wrought by machines and chemicals are too fast – and too directly geared to destroying nature in the shape of shape of wild insects and wild plants considered 'pests' – for nature to keep up.

The dramatic fall in the population of one of the birds most emblematic of a summer day – the skylark – is thought to be connected with intensified cultivation practices. Butterflies are found in much larger numbers on farms where insecticides and herbicides are not used and so are insect-eating birds. Traditional 'extensive' farming techniques (non-intensive, based on natural and locally-produced fertility, rather than chemicals and imported feeds) help wild birds to breed. For example, waders like lapwings and snipe nest in rough grassland during the summer. If that grassland is pumped up with fertilizer and mown early for silage, the nests will be destroyed. If, however, it is grazed by cattle kept outdoors, as for example in the traditional rearing of Scottish beef, the land supports fewer cattle, but they will be of much finer quality, and according to *Birds* magazine, the birds breed successfully.

Chemical and mechanical agriculture have eradicated variety in so many different ways. Once, a mixture of crops and animals all met their particular needs and contributed their particular services – composts, soil clearance, weed suppression – to the farm 'ecosystem'. As these services have been replaced by machines or bags of chemicals, there has been a great simplification of the agricultural scene, and a reduction in the 'niches' for wildlife. Chemicals have removed the immediate need for crop rotations, as spent goodness from the soil can be temporarily 'topped up' by applications of soluble fertiliser. Chemical fertilisers enable a profitable weight of crop to be taken off a field year after year, while the soil structure gradually breaks down to the sand Oliver Arditi described in Suffolk. Mechanisation has also allowed huge areas of the same crop to be sown, fertilised or harvested in a short time, once again removing the need to vary the crops and therefore spread out the workload.

CHEMICALS

In place of balance and variety, we have unstable soils, monotonous landscapes, and poisons. Nitrate is the main ingredient in artificial fertiliser; nitrate is also a concentrated ingredient in the slurry runoff (that oily-looking brown liquid) which seeps from intensive animal sheds. So many animals in one place leads to a massive waste disposal problem. There was a perfectly serious proposal from the Netherlands that the animal manure piling up in the intensive cattle and pig units there should be exported to India – expending yet more fossil fuels. As it is, slurry is one of the most common causes of river and groundwater pollution in Europe. It might be an organic waste, but it is so concentrated it will devastate an ecosystem at once. The slurry also gives off methane, a gas which has a powerful 'greenhouse effect' potential, worse than carbon dioxide.

In streams and rivers, nitrate from slurry or arable fertiliser makes algae grow like wildfire, cutting off the light, consuming all the oxygen in the water and choking the balanced life of a previously clear river, making it murky, slimy and near-dead. Rivers become the foul-water drains of the agricultural factory.

Nitrate pollution in rivers and groundwater also contaminates the domestic water supply. At its worst, nitrate pollution can cause dangerous blue baby syndrome, in which nitrate molecules substitute for oxygen in the baby's blood, effectively suffocating it. At lower concentrations it may be linked to cancer in the digestive tract. Nitrate pollution is costing the water companies £148 million in capital expenditure, and the water companies believe that pollution levels in water will rise unless expenditure on clean-up apparatus is expanded further. Friends of the Earth has angrily pointed out that although action has been taken to limit the amount of nitrate applied to the land where drinking water is drawn, there has been no action to reduce nitrate use where ground or river water is already so badly contaminated with nitrate that it cannot be used for drinking – in other words, sections of our water reserves have simply been written off.

If chemical fertilisers are poisonous, how much more so the pesticides and herbicides which have been designed to kill animals and plants (that is, pests and weeds). Cereals, the biggest arable crop in Britain, are sprayed six or seven times per year on average, as is sugar beet; potatoes are sprayed even more often, at eight or nine times a year. And sheep and cattle are also treated with pesticides against insect infections. Anyone who makes a cup of tea with water from the tap is likely to be exposed to these chemicals. Insecticides sprayed on plant crops are washed through the soil into the groundwater and rivers. Pesticide contamination is the commonest reason for drinking water to fall below the required standard in Britain. For instance, in 1993 Anglian water supplied 1.8 million of its customers with water in breach of pesticide limits, even more people than the 1.2 million who received water contaminated with nitrate. In 1994 the water regulator OFWAT reported that one in four samples of drinking water in England and Wales failed to meet the standards set for pesticide levels.

Remarkably, pesticides can also get into rainwater: it is not clear whether this is because of aerial spraying in windy weather, or evaporation of these volatile organic compounds, but a particularly toxic shower was recorded by the Ministry of Agriculture in Oxfordshire in 1992, with 5.5µg/litre of the insecticide lindane: 55 times the level permitted for drinking water.

The most common water contaminants are herbicides, chemical weedkillers, which harm aquatic life and in some cases are suspected of contributing to cancer and other diseases in humans. These weedkillers come from municipal spraying of weeds on footpaths, and from farms, where they are the most commonly applied pesticides on most arable crops. One of the commonest agricultural herbicides, atrazine, appears to last months or years in groundwater.

Some of the most controversial pesticides are the insecticides: the organophosphate and organochlorine insecticides are amongst the most toxic. Lindane, or gamma-HCH, is an organochlorine and it appears to be associated with breast cancer, possibly by altering the hormonal metabolism in women's bodies. Lindane use in this country has doubled in the 1990s: 114 tonnes are sprayed each year on vegetables, arable crops, orchard fruit; one-third of it goes onto sugar beet. Produced in vast quantities to satisfy the nation's sweet tooth and the demands of its confectionery and food-processing industries, sugar beet has been suffering increasing pest attacks in recent years, particularly from leatherjackets. Sugar beet is often grown in tremendous acreages, especially in the hedgeless acres of eastern England. Under such conditions, a pest can really take over and demolish the harvest.

Though the lindane may be washed out of the sugar, it turns up in the beet pulp, which is then fed to milking cattle. This may be the route by which lindane finds its way into milk: in 1996, almost 50 per cent of milk samples in a Ministry of Agriculture survey were contaminated with lindane, with four in every hundred being above the maximum residue limit set by the government. Research in Finland has found that the bodies of women with breast cancer have higher levels of a lindane derivative than women who are well. Similar results were found from looking at the bodies of women with breast cancer in eastern England. Sadly, such women are easy to find: the Women's Environment Network reports that Lincolnshire women have a 40 per cent higher rate of breast cancer than those in other parts of Britain.

Insecticides are also used in large quantities in animal husbandry. As with crop sprays, these chemicals end up on the land and in the water; 20 million gallons of highly toxic sheep dip solution is disposed of each year: no-one quite knows where, but in one survey in Scotland, 5 per cent went straight into streams, another 50 per cent into soakaways from which the solution could 'soak away' into the groundwater – how else is the farmer to get rid of it? In fact, the Soil Association reports, the Ministry of Agriculture actually recommends that the used dip is spread on the land 'because there did not seem to be a viable alternative'. Although the ministry forced farmers in many areas to use these chemicals until 1992, no safe means of disposal was provided. The Scottish survey found significant damage to populations of invertebrates and crustaceans (caddis flies, dragonflies, water shrimps and daphnia, mussels and snails) downstream of almost all the dips they inspected. These creatures are the food of fish such as trout (which we might want to eat in turn) and birds like the dipper. Whole webs of nature are thus affected.

Organochlorine compounds seem to be linked to reproductive disorders, too – also because of their 'hormone-mimicking' effect. (This effect is shared by other industrial chemicals, including those used in the plastics industry, which find their way into food via packaging, and also contaminate the water supply.) Contamination of water by a variety of pesticides, including the herbicide atrazine and the insecticides lindane and dieldrin, have been linked to genital deformities in wildlife in the US. In a book called *Our Stolen Future*, US scientists argue that although chemicals, including pesticides, are tested for their chances of killing or of causing cancer, other more insidious effects are ignored. Theo Colborn and her co-authors warn that pesticides are among many chemicals which affect the sexual development of fetuses – including human fetuses – in the womb, permanently compromising their future fertility. DDT injected into young male chickens, for example, castrates them, so they look and act like hens. DDT was banned in some countries when it was found to concentrate in the bodies of birds of prey and interfere with their eggs, making the shell so thin that the parent birds crushed their young even as they incubated the eggs.

Now we have the scary situation where traces of pesticides such as dieldrin, lindane and DDE (a metabolite of DDT) are routinely found in women's breast milk over the world, as the Pesticides Trust reports. This doesn't mean we shouldn't breastfeed – not least because the ingredients of 'formula': cow's milk, tap water, soya beans, are contaminated too – but it does show just how saturated our environment has become.

DDT can still be found in fish in the North Sea, and wood pigeons in the British countryside, years after it was banned in Europe. Either it is still being used illegally or it is extremely persistent – or both. In her book, *Preventing Breast Cancer*, Cathy Read reports that in Long Island, in the US (an area with very high rates of breast cancer), heavy spraying of potato fields against nematode worms in the 1950s has contaminated water supplies to this day. More recently, herons have been poisoned by the aldrin-contaminated eels they caught in the river Avon in Warwickshire, which led to the banning of aldrin in 1989. Lindane, however, is still in use, approved by the ministry for use on a number of crops including grass (to be eaten by cattle and sheep), cereals, oilseed rape (for cooking oil, margarine and processed foods), cabbages, brussels sprouts, apples, pears, tomatoes, cucumbers, strawberries and, of course, sugar beet.

Equally frightening are the organophosphate compounds (OPs). These were based on nerve gas and are extremely toxic to the nervous system. They are used to kill insect pests both on plant crops and those, like warble fly, which affect sheep and cattle. For many years, the government's Ministry of Agriculture enforced by law the routine treatment of cattle and sheep with either organochlorine pesticides or OPs, to prevent scab and flystrike in sheep, and warble fly in cattle.

Gradually, many of the farmers and farm workers who had handled these toxic chemicals began to realise their health was being harmed. OPs are nerve poisons, and research by the Institute of Occupational Medicine has shown that farmers who have been exposed to OPs have slower mental functioning and nervous responses than workers with similar backgrounds not exposed to these chemicals (the only farmers tested for the study were those *not* suffering from obvious mental or neurological disorders!) OPs are now considered by some scientists to be behind serious depressive and fatigue illnesses suffered by many in the farming industry. Horrifyingly, there are especially high levels of suicide among farmers in sheep-farming areas of Britain, and among the population of the intensive vegetable-growing areas of southern Spain: both forms of agriculture that have a high dependence on OP pesticides. These are the same insecticides sprayed on troops during the Gulf War and thought to have contributed to the frightening symptoms of 'Gulf War Syndrome'.

Belatedly, strict rules about protective clothing and special training for the use of OPs have been introduced, and the legal obligation to use them in animal farming removed. But the chemicals are still on sale, and still widely used. In 1995, the Ministry of Agriculture warned consumers that their tests had revealed 'unexpectedly high' levels of OP residues in carrots, in some cases enough to exceed the acceptable intake levels by 200 per cent. Consumers were advised to top and peel carrots before eating them – scarcely reassuring. As a result demand for organically-grown carrots boomed. The Soil Association warned at the time that many other vegetables are also treated with OPs: parsnips, for example, are also sprayed. No warning about peeling parsnips was given, not because parsnips were necessarily safer, but because no safe level has been fixed, so no tests on parsnips were carried out.

Herbicides also cause problems. Not surprisingly, as they are designed to kill plants, herbicides can harm crops, even though they may have been designed to be 'selective'. Thus the Pesticides Trust reports research showing that winter wheat which has been 'weeded' with the herbicide isoproturon appears to be more vulnerable to mildew, which results in the farmer using fungicide as well. Herbicides are poisons to people too: no-one drinks Tumbleweed or Roundup on purpose, though herbicides are a common contaminant of drinking water.

Pests and weeds are becoming increasingly resistant to pesticides and herbicides, just as bacteria are developing resistance to antibiotics. Herbicide resistance is worrying a lot of arable farmers nowadays. Despite the constant supply of new and different pesticides, under industrial agriculture crop losses have been rising, not falling, warns the European genetic resources group GRAIN.

Growing in greenhouses and polytunnels often leads to particularly high use of agrochemicals. Many crops such as greenhouse sweet peppers cultivated in the UK and Holland are not even grown in soil, but simply in a chemical solution on mineral wool. Even if growers under glass wish to use the ordinary soil, highly environmentally unfriendly chemicals are used to sterilise it. Bacteria and fungi are a vital part of the soil as a rule, breaking down and digesting organic matter so that the chemicals are once again available to be used by a growing plant. Sterilising the soil means that these creatures are killed and the fertility will largely come through artificial fertilisers. The soil will mainly be used to hold up the plants.

One of the commonest fumigants is methyl bromide, a highly toxic substance which 'kills everything', as John Dalby of the Soil Association puts it, then evaporates away quickly. Unfortunately, once it has dispersed into the atmosphere the danger from this chemical has not passed: methyl bromide is a powerful destroyer of ozone, many times more destructive than CFCs.

Methyl bromide plays a big role in crop exports (and imports) as it is widely used to fumigate crops after harvest, preventing them from going mouldy in storage and transport. Grains, fruit, dried fruit and nuts are all commonly treated. It is demanded by importing governments in Japan, North America and Europe. Although some countries plan to phase out use of methyl bromide altogether, others, notably the EU and Canada, are only attempting small reductions in its use. Furthermore, according to the Pesticides Trust, many US environmentalists are worried that methyl bromide, which itself replaced DDT, will simply be replaced by something equally toxic.

Many of those sprays are used in the close confines of undercover growing – especially unpleasant and dangerous for the agricultural workers. In 1994 the Ministry of Agriculture warned consumers that banned fungicides and fungicides at above the permitted levels had been found in an alarming one in four glasshouse-grown (that is, out-of-season) lettuces the previous winter.

Awareness of pesticides and other residues leads many of us to wash or peel our foods. Special detergents have even been marketed to help us remove waxy and oily residues. But this is a rather unsatisfactory compromise. For one thing, some residues penetrate right through the tissue of our food: this is always the case with meat from chemically- or hormone-treated stock. Chemical residues are also present in processed foods made from treated ingredients, and it is too late for the customer to wash or peel them. And our attempt to get rid of poisons gets rid of nutrients too. Valuable vitamins are often concentrated in the skin and peel, and even washing foods leaches out soluble nutrients such as iron, calcium and B vitamins.

Although there are supposedly regulations about safe levels of residues in food, as we have seen, these are broken often enough for all of us to be exposed to illegal levels on a regular basis. And just as with additives, this year's safe pesticide becomes next year's DDT: chemicals which have been around long enough to show their dangerous effects are withdrawn, to be replaced by newer compounds about which less is known – for now. Even worse, safety levels are set for each pesticide on its own, when in fact each of us is exposed to a cocktail of residues every day. Not only do the poisons add up, they may actually multiply: a US study on cell culture reported in the *Guardian* found that a combination of dieldin and endosulfan was between 160 and 1,600 times more poisonous than either chemical alone. In other words this common combination has the effect of increasing the dose by several hundreds or even a thousand times.

Worrying about pesticides is no longer a cranky minority pursuit – after all the British government has been sufficiently concerned about residues in both lettuces and carrots that they sent out press releases to the newspapers. But no one seems to know quite what to do. Farmers blame supermarkets and customers for demanding 'cosmetically perfect' produce, consumers blame farmers, supermarkets claim they are working with farmers to reduce usage, yet still set strict growing regimes which include chemical use.

Unexpectedly perhaps, in Britain it is pesticide manufacturers who are sponsoring initiatives to educate growers to use lower dosages. The manufacturers are aware of public concern and would almost certainly prefer voluntary codes to stringent legal restrictions. Pesticide companies, and farmers too, in theory, risk litigation for damages from water companies who are struggling to rid the water supply of pesticide run-off from farms. However, none of these parties is primarily motivated by a desire to bring us safe food: they desire, first and foremost, to continue making a profit.

ANIMAL FACTORIES

Perhaps the strongest public feelings of all about agricultural techniques are aroused by intensive animal rearing. At the end of 1994 this became a hot political issue as ferry companies began to suspend the export of live animals to Europe, a practice widely condemned as cruel and unnecessary. By the first weeks of 1995, police battalions hundreds strong were being drafted in to contain groups of ordinary citizens angrily determined to end the trade altogether.

Live exports are just one unpalatable aspect of an industry which treats animals 'as if they were no more than plants' (and plants simply as combinations of chemicals). The great bulk of livestock is reared in massive 'units' that most of us would hardly recognise as a farm at all. In Europe, 80 per cent of the pork comes from just 10 per cent of the pig producers, and 10 per cent of poultry 'farms' produce almost all – 90 per cent – of the poultry we eat.

Producers are frequently tied into contracts with big marketing companies or retailers whose terms demand intensive systems, and may well specify every detail of production. Many farms in north Herefordshire, for instance, sport identical shiny new poultry sheds – all erected by one company on their contractors' farms.

On intensive beef, pig and poultry farms, thousands of stock are managed by just one or two staff. There is no question of individual attention to the animals. About 85 per cent of the eggs eaten in Britain are still from caged battery hens. As the Farm Animal Welfare Network describes the process: 'Battery hens spend their entire lives standing or crouching down on bare sloping wire mesh floors, often suffering severe damage to feet and claws. Cages are stacked three, four or five tiers high, and a typical cage for five hens measures 18″ by 20″.

'In the natural state, hens are rarely still. Pecking and scratching in the ground for food, dustbathing (to clean feathers) and nest-building are all activities denied to battery hens. Frustrated, they turn to pecking at each other's feathers, even to cannibalism ... Battery hens become aggressive and highly stressed because of the lack of privacy and nesting materials.

'When an egg is produced the vent becomes moist and distended, attracting the attention of the other birds. Vent pecking may lead to cannibalism and feather pecking of any kind is, according to the Ministry of Agriculture, "more likely to occur when chickens are kept on wire".

'Diseases and injuries go unnoticed in the gloomy, overcrowded cages ... impacted eggs, prolapses and disorders of kidney and liver plague battery hens ... often birds reach the point of death before farmers notice their suffering. Often, dead hens are dragged from their cages and left on the floor to rot ... caged conditions result in brittle and broken bones. Recent research indicates that 24 per cent of birds suffer broken bones when being caught for slaughter.' According to the Network, battery hens are slaughtered and used in chicken soup, chicken stock cubes, chicken pie, baby food and catering; and unlaid eggs are removed ('pulled') and used to manufacture biscuits and pasta.

MEAT

Meat production has also been driven to cruel and unhealthy extremes by the pressure for cheap and ever cheaper food, and big and ever bigger profits.

Poultry production is a particularly unpleasant example, with thousands of animals crammed into vast, airless sheds containing up to 10,000 birds or more. They are bred to grow so fast that their weight outpaces their strength, and they are frequently crippled with painful leg deformities. Although the deformities are invisible in the butchered birds, it is often possible to see 'hock burns', dark-coloured patches on the skin just below the drumstick, where the bird's knees have given way and its tender skin has been scorched by the concentrated, ammonia-laden droppings on which it spent its short, five-to-six week life.

Desperately frustrated, like their sisters in egg batteries, they peck at each other, and most have their beaks cut with a hot knife in an not-very-effective attempt to prevent this aggressive behaviour. This 'de-beaking' itself causes lasting pain to the birds.

Although poultry producers may hide the realities of their production methods from the public in anonymous metal sheds, tucked discreetly away behind screens of hedge or trees, there is no disguising the stench, an overwhelming, sickly odour which can sometimes be smelt for more than a mile downwind of these units.

The environmental damage spreads much further. According to the Worldwide Fund for Nature, approximately two-thirds of world production of fish meal is used for poultry food. WWF and the Royal Society for the Protection of Birds are concerned because this fish meal is harvested by indiscriminate hoovering up of small fish, such as sand eels, from the sea bed – fish which otherwise represent the main food for the millions of seabirds which nest around British coasts: puffins, guillemots, razorbills. In the winter of 1993/94 up to 100,000 seabirds are thought to have died of starvation in British waters. All over the world, fish stocks are in crisis, and increasingly tense and acrimonious squabbles break out between nations competing to harvest the remaining fish: yet a significant proportion of this fish is not even going directly to be human food, but simply to fatten industrial poultry (and cattle and pigs – and, ironically, farmed fish).

Even the apparently extensive, free-range life of the sheep contains hazards, for the sheep and for humans. Lambs are routinely subjected to tail docking and castration without anaesthetic, sometimes by the 'rubber band' method, which, the welfare charity Compassion in World Farming insists, is as painful as it sounds. The charity reports that male calves destined for sale as beef also receive rubber band or other forms of castration without anaesthesia, despite the fact that this is illegal.

Conventional farming has also required the regular dipping of sheep. The frightened animals are submerged in a bath of noxious insecticide, which soaks their fleece and gets in their eyes noses and mouths. These chemicals are so toxic that farm staff are now advised by the Health and Safety Executive to wear full-face masks, head-to-toe waterproof clothing, boots and gauntlets when carrying out dipping. But this is only after a long campaign by many farmers and agricultural workers.

PIG OF A LIFE

Many argue that intensive pig farming is particularly cruel, as pigs are highly intelligent and social animals. People who, defying conventions about which animals we include in family life and which we eat, have kept pigs as pets, have found them every bit as responsive, devoted and loveable as any dog. A pig was even featured in a TV show after rescuing a human child from drowning, diving into deep water and supporting the child at the surface until more help arrived.

Pigs, like hens, are naturally forest animals, rooting around on and under the forest floor for fungi, roots, invertebrates and other morsels. Yet the vast majority of pigs eaten in Britain have been confined in sheds, standing either on excrement-soaked straw (which like us, they would avoid if they could: with enough space pigs always use a particular area as a toilet and keep the rest clean), or on bare concrete or even metal grilles.

This animal, whose sense of smell is so exquisite it can detect a truffle deep below the soil, may have to live out its days in a nauseating, ammoniacal fug – temperatures are kept high to speed fattening. And sows, who have mothering instincts like all mammals, are imprisoned in cages barely large enough for their majestic bodies, only able to squat forlornly or to lie. They cannot make a warm, soft nest and curl up in it with their young, as mammals like to do.

DAIRY

Milk – the milk of human kindness, milk to comfort a child, creamy smooth, even milk-sop. What a pure, kind, gentle image milk has. How the cow suffers to bring it to us.

Although as a nation we are trying to cut down on our consumption of dairy products, and as a trading bloc the EU is desperate to limit milk production, where milk is still produced it is usually produced as intensively as possible.

Cattle, like pigs, have strong maternal instincts, yet in order for us to drink the milk the cow has made for her calf, those calves are usually removed at one or two days, and she is 'milked to capacity' twice or even three times a day for the next 10 months. She will give the dairy industry *10 times* what her calf would have demanded. So intensive is the demand on her body that instead of living out their natural lives to the age of 20, dairy cows are usually culled at five.

As a result of the constant strain on their udders, one-third of dairy cows already suffer mastitis; any woman who has suffered this infection of the breast tissue knows how excruciating it is. The genetically-engineered hormone BST (bovine somatotrophin), used in the US but still banned in Europe, forces the cow to produce yet more milk, and increases the incidence of mastitis, bringing more suffering to those cows still 'in work'. In a situation of milk surplus, higher production by some cows means other cows – and other dairy farmers – become redundant. For this reason, most farmers, as well as most consumers, oppose the licensing of BST in Europe.

Intensive dairying means that cows do not eat grass for much of the year, but processed fodder (cattle cake) made from a variety of materials, including spent agricultural wastes (sugar beet pulp and oil seed cake, for instance). The most notorious ingredient of dairy rations was of course ruminant remains: boiled-down offals and bones from dead sheep and cattle. This practice of forced cannibalism is likely to have been a factor in the origin and transmission of mad cow disease, BSE, which appears in turn to have caused fatal brain disease in some young Britons – and which devastated the whole European beef industry in 1996, when this link was first publicly accepted by the British government.

Although BSE triggered an acute political crisis, once again there was almost no acknowledgement by the government and the meat industry that the roots of the crisis lay in the remorseless drive for higher and higher yields at lower and lower costs. Yet this connection did not completely escape the public. There was horror at the 'unnatural' practice of feeding animal remains. It is also salutary to note, however, that the consumer reaction in Europe, and, in particular in France and Germany, where many more people retain some connection with small-scale farming than in Britain, was much stronger, although the incidence of BSE in these countries was lower.

Although beef farmers switched to more 'natural' feeds – grass, hay and silage (they had to to have a hope of sellimg their product in Europe) – in dairying there was less change. Concentrates – now minus the ruminant remains but still permitted to include chicken droppings, old chicken carcasses and fish meal – were still deemed essential for the gross yields demanded of the poor old cow.

Keeping cows indoors and feeding high-protein concentrates makes them liable to lameness, and their feet become too painful to bear their own weight. Although 'indoors' might sound cosy, it generally means cold, hard concrete floors and uncomfortable confinement, for all farm animals. Undersized stalls which prevent the cow from lying down comfortably also contribute to lameness: one in four dairy cows suffers a bout of lameness each year.

Until 1996, the carcasses of the worn-out cows were minced up for pies and high-street burgers. After the 1996 revelations that the government believed BSE from old dairy cattle meat had caused the fatal human brain condition Creutzfeld-Jacob disease (CJD), such carcasses had to be 'destroyed' (though there were reports that this meant boiling or rendering down the meat and spreading it over huge areas of ground to rot).

Meanwhile the cow must produce calves in order to continue in milk. These are, apart from the ones reared as replacement milking heifers, surplus to the dairy farmer's requirements. Many are sold to be fattened for veal. Calves being exported for fattening in other EU countries are one of the major elements of the live export trade which became such a controversial issue in 1994.

None of this is necessary. Cow and calf bellow in distress separated so soon; yet there is a milk surplus. Why then cannot the cow give her calf love, and milk, for a little longer? It is possible to milk a cow who has her calf with her – as we saw, the cow can produce far more than one calf needs. So why this cruelty and exploitation? The answer is dictated by the economics of scale and competition. When there is a surplus and prices are kept low, rather than every farm producing a little less milk from each cow, some farms must produce a little more from the each resource (the cow) in order to make a profit at the lowered price, while other farms must go out of business altogether. This is the process of intensification. It is inevitable if foodstuffs are traded on the anonymous 'free market', where price is the only distinguishing feature, rather than produced by individual farmers for responsible consumers.

DISEASE

It has been known for centuries that humans in overcrowded conditions were more prone to epidemics. Not surprisingly, the same applies to livestock. Disease is endemic in intensive animal systems, as Edwina Currie so memorably pointed out in 1988, when she said that virtually all British poultry production was infected with salmonella: honesty which cost her her job, and indeed her government career. Despite the regulations which were introduced after the 1988 salmonella scare, food poisoning is increasing rather than decreasing, and most of it is attributed to infected meat, as *New Scientist* reported in 1995. This was vividly confirmed in the Scottish E. coli outbreak in December 1996.

In 1996, the Consumers' Association found that 37 per cent of fresh and frozen chickens in a sample bought from eight supermarkets were contaminated with campylobacter and almost 20 per cent with salmonella. The risk to consumers is made worse by poor gutting and cleaning of the carcasses, which the Association attributed to the high-speed, high-volume slaughtering of factory birds.

Infection in intensive animal systems is kept down with frequent – and, often, regular – doses of antibiotic. Over twice as much – around £27 million per year – is spent on antibiotic feed additives as is spent on antibiotics for treating animals that are actually sick. Some of this antibiotic remains in the meat and milk; farmed fish, chicken, sheep liver and eggs have all been found in Ministry of Agriculture tests to contain antibiotics. We are therefore exposing the bacteria living in our throats, noses, guts and genitals to tiny but regular doses of antibiotic. When handling meat we may also contaminate our hands, faces – and other places – with antibiotic-resistant bacteria carried on the animal carcass.

As long ago as 1989, Bristol University's Professor Richard Lacey was warning that these possible routes of contamination could lie behind the persistent and troublesome antibiotic resistant infections suffered by so many: ear infections, throat infections, bladder and kidney infections. According to the Soil Association, children have died from infection with untreatable, antibiotic-resistant salmonella originating from antibiotic-treated dairy calves.

The Soil Association reports how researchers in Oxford, who became concerned about the outbreak in a kidney unit of a bacterial infection untreatable by one of the most powerful – and therefore most important – antibiotics available, did research to see if they could locate the source of the infection. This 'superbug' was traced to sewage outfalls, uncooked chicken carcasses, and other farm animals. This indicated that antibiotic treatment of farm animals was encouraging the formation of the untreatable 'superbug' which caused such havoc to vulnerable kidney patients. In this way a precious, life-saving medicine was effectively being made less useful by agricultural use.

WHAT CAN WE DO?

At the local shops and, in particular, at the supermarket it is almost impossible to confine your shopping to food produced on farms which are taking care of the environment, and their customers' health. Organic food is very patchily available, and usually very dear. The reasons for this are explored in the following chapters. Without a specific label, food from farms with high welfare standards and low usage of chemicals, or from farms which are taking care of the soil, water and wildlife is impossible to identify. You don't even know which county most food comes from, never mind which farm.

Because of this farmers have little incentive beyond their own personal concern, to take steps to protect the environment, unless they can manage to go completely organic. Sadly, there is often a strong financial disincentive to adopt more humane and sustainable practices, at least in the short term, as the economics of farming are so geared up to intensive production. Chapter six will look at this problem in more detail. Many farmers want to change, but find it almost impossible to do so – without help from consumers.

On the other hand, if farmers knew you could pick out their particular eggs, bacon, cauliflower and potatoes, then it would be worth them farming to please you. As we will see in chapter nine, you *can* pick out produce from particular farms by changing the way you shop. And those farms *do* farm in ways that consumers like, and produce good food into the bargain. Later in the book, growers who have rejected the intensive way describe how the consumers who buy directly from them make their ways of working possible.

5

THE ANAESTHETISED CONSUMER

We feel frustrated and angry when we hear how pesticides in our drinking water are harming our fertility, or that barn owls face extinction because the wild field-edges full of mice have been ploughed away; we may be particularly angry about the cruelty shown to farm animals.

And many of us are plagued by increasing traffic noise, annoyed by expensive and destructive roadbuilding, and increasingly aware that we need to eat less processed 'junk', as it tends to have more fat, more sugar and more additives, none of which are good for the health. Yet when we go shopping, as often as not many of us buy industrial bread trucked in from the other side of the country, ageing vegetables from hedgeless fields sprayed with poisons, and watery bacon from a pig which was tied up in a tiny stall. Why do we let this happen?

One reason, as we saw in chapter two, is that we are so often in a hurry. But the supermarket and food processors also play their role. There is usually very little to remind us of where the food came from, how it was produced. In supermarkets in particular, everything is clean, brightly lit and antiseptic. In this soothing environment we are physically sedated: our blink rate (a measure of alertness) drops by over one half.

Almost everything is in a package: the author of *The Total Package: The Evolution and Secret Meaning of Boxes, Bottles, Cans and Tubes*, accords packaging a 'heroic role' in the development of large-scale, self-service food retailing: packaging is 'the manufacturer's interception of the transaction between the retailer and consumer. In the modern age, food shopping in particular becomes a seamless compact, with as little human intervention as possible. In the package we trust.'[1]

1. Giles Foden, reviewing Thomas Hine, *The Total Package: The Evolution and Secret Meaning of Boxes, Bottles, Cans and Tubes*, Guardian, 9 August 1996.

As we saw in earlier chapters, the package enables longer journeys and rougher handling: but it also hides the contents from the consumer, presenting us with a carefully designed impression (or illusion) instead.

Even the unprocessed food is often 'packaged'. Fruit and vegetables have been washed and trimmed (even though this speeds deterioration and loss of vitamins), or even peeled and chopped. Bread is wrapped and ready-sliced; meat does not look like bits of animals but bits of recipes: chopped and trimmed into portions, fillets and cubes, and neatly wrapped and labelled. Everything else is in boxes or jars. There isn't anything to remind us of living fields or living beasts. It all seems very safe and easy.

Supermarket shopping may have made us into more passive shoppers, presenting us with everything ready done. And once you have abandoned your expertise and responsibility to the supermarket, it is hard to take the initiative again, warns cookery teacher Rosie Davies: 'I think one reason people like to go to the supermarket is they are frightened of making mistakes. When you see people buying pre-packed leeks at twice the price of the loose ones next to them it is surely not just laziness, not just because they are too busy to wash them.' It is almost as though people somehow fear the leek in its natural state. 'This is particularly true with meat,' Davies adds . 'People are just terrified of going to the butcher and asking for something, then finding it wasn't at all what they expected, and not knowing what to do.'

Supermarkets offer freedom from worry, effort and responsibility, in the same way that the processed food industry does. And they offer an illusion of abundance, too. Indeed, we have learned to believe we depend on the range of goods supermarkets offer. In a 'pro and con' feature in the *Guardian* examining the trend to supermarket shopping, the writer chosen to defend the practice claimed she 'needs' to shop in supermarkets because she 'needs' products like black bean paste, fresh coriander and screw-in light bulbs, and needs to be able to get them at once. An average supermarket presents us with 30,000 different packages to choose between. Choice: that's what the supermarkets sell.

Yet in some ways when we shop in big, impersonal stores we have very little choice at all. There might be country vegetable soup, spring vegetable soup, spring vegetable soup with noodle, chicken and spring vegetable soup, vegetable soup with pasta shapes and so on. but most tinned soups in Britain are made by one of two companies. Although we can choose between tinned tomatoes with or without added herbs, we might prefer a choice of tinned tomatoes with or without insecticide and fungicide, or tinned tomatoes from Europe not South America.

The information about how our food was produced is very minimal. In supermarkets, basic staples will name the country of origin, (though even this label can mislead: 'British' bacon may be from a Danish pig, salted and sliced in the UK) but that is it. It could be from one of thousands of farms: it could be from Dalbeattie or Dorchester. There is no way of knowing which variety of plant or animal, chemicals and other techniques have been used, and generally no hint of the way animals and the farm itself are being cared for.

In place of factual detail, there may be suggestions which are misleading, designed to lull and soothe; even the cheery smiling pig or cow is misleading, though it obviously isn't meant literally. Battery-produced eggs are called 'fresh' or 'farm fresh', sometimes the boxes even show traditional looking farm kitchens or country scenes. Broiler chickens come from 'Sun Valley' or 'Such-and-Such Farm'. These descriptions convey an idea – 'wholesome traditional country farm scene' – which is profoundly at variance with the realities of industrial food production. If packages were labelled 'Gloomy, smelly tin shed eggs' or 'The one that wasn't pecked to death' chicken, would we buy them? Similarly, with all traces of soil or of a complete growing plant cleaned away we are less likely to think about the field in which our vegetables grew, less likely to think about sprays and dressings, grubbed out hedges, or cold, exhausted labourers.

These are omissions rather then outright lies, but the effect is to help us forget about the things that worried us last night in front of the TV. In the supermarket queue, forgetting may be an attractive option: we do go along with it. Our trip to the shops is focused much more on what is needed this week by ourselves and our families, than on what we might be hoping for next weekend, when we go for a country walk, or for the next generation, when our children or grandchildren are growing up.

Lack of information is an inevitable consequence of the structure of mass retailing. Produce from a small, distinctive source is unlikely to be in steady supply, yet a steady, predictable, high-volume supply is exactly what the big supermarkets need so that shelves can be kept neatly packed with whatever the management believes is going to sell. Supplying on this scale is very hard for a craft producer – even one which produces in what looks, locally, like a large volume. One bakery firm in the Greater Manchester area supplies a very large proportion of bakers' shops in the area. Yet they found an order from one of the supermarket chains very difficult. Not only did they need to gear up their production, which meant capital outlay, they were also forced right down on price. While a few pence profit on several thousand loaves a day can amount to a satisfying income, if something changes (the price of the flour or electricity) suddenly you can be staring at terrifying losses. You need to be big to consider supplying supermarkets. A distinctive product from a small supplier *cannot* be sold in bulk, in every store in the land, so the logic of central buying means that it is unlikely to appear in any of them.

Since produce in supermarkets is selected centrally and distributed via large central depots, the staff in the store will have had nothing to do with the producer or manufacturer. On the whole they know no more about where it comes from and how it was produced than the customer who has read the label.

Independent butchers or greengrocers, by contrast, may buy direct from the producer; independent bakers may even bake their own bread. An independent butcher may well have selected the animal he sells while on the hoof, from a farmer he knows. But we only buy around a fifth of our meat from independent butchers now, and well over half in the anonymous cling-wrapped supermarket form.

Processed foods, which make up the majority of our purchases, are completely anonymous. They don't even tell us the countries of origin of the ingredients, never mind the county or the farm, or anything about the way they were produced. All you get is a list of contents and the address of the factory where they were assembled. As soon as we allow Marks and Spencer to put cheese sauce on our cauliflower or spaghetti with our mince, we lose the right to know if those cauliflowers came from Cornwall or Holland, if the beef was from Scotland or Germany. And we seem to lose the desire to know, as well.

Yet we do care. Most of us accept that if we were at the door of the battery shed or boiler house, we might not buy the meat or eggs; that if we saw lindane being sprayed over our strawberries, we would think twice before taking them home. In order to preserve the status quo the food industry needs to keep us remote and keep us passive. With meat products in particular the industry does not want us to think too much about the animals, because they know what will happen if we do. As the director general of the Meat and Livestock Commission quite honestly put it in a letter to *Farmers' Weekly*: 'Reminding customers of the origins of meat is likely to put further downward pressure on meat consumption'.

The need to conceal the realities of meat farming leads to a kind of ludicrous double-speak from the agricultural establishment. Interviewed for this book, Peter Rudman, advisor on animal husbandry to the National Farmers' Union, admitted to being a biochemist and zoologist by training and seemed uncertain of his ground on animal welfare matters. While applauding food produced to certified welfare standards (such as the RSPCA's 'Freedom Food') as 'a valid choice for consumers who wish to express their preferences in this way', he felt obliged to put up a robust defence against the notion that meat production methods not sanctioned by this scheme are cruel.

He also made the rather surprising claim that battery hens were 'bred for batteries': 'Rightly or wrongly, the birds we are talking about have lost the instinct to scratch and dustbath. If you let birds from an intensive system out, they would be lost and would probably scuttle back into their cages,' a claim dismissed as 'hogwash' by Philip Lymbery of Compassion in World Farming. 'It just isn't true. There have been numerous examples of animal welfare activists taking intensively reared animals and successfully keeping them in a more natural system. It simply doesn't stand up to examination, but it is part of the smokescreen of disinformation put out by the industry. They try to make us believe that the cages are better for the birds, but if that were so, why don't they label the eggs and meat as caged or battery reared – of course they won't.' (In fact a few supermarket chains now discreetly label battery eggs as 'eggs from caged hens'.)

Yet, having denied that any practices are cruel, Rudman went on to blame consumer indifference for the persistence of 'less desirable' practices. Talking about the fact that British producers would face devastating competition when sow tethering is phased out, he commented: 'In the end, for the majority of consumers standing in the supermarket, if they see one sort of bacon is 10p cheaper, that is more important to them than the way it was reared.' Yet of course this indifference is just what the industry wants, and Rudman is one of those responsible for downplaying the facts of production to the very public he then blames for being indifferent.

Manufacturers and retailers *have* responded to consumer concern about the way their food is produced, and what it contains, but these changes, such as new labelling and certification schemes, fall a long way short of giving full information and an active say to consumers. There is a rash of reassuring-sounding descriptions, but they sow more confusion than information.

There are two reasons for this. One is that retailers and manufacturers naturally try to modify as little as they can get away with to keep up their profit levels. They are not ashamed to say that their first responsibility is to their shareholders, not to their consumers, to farm animals, or the environment and society at large. The second reason is that labels and certificates have only limited capacity to convey real information and real consumer power.

LABELS

There are endless, acrimonious, and confusing wrangles over food labelling. This is not surprising when you think how much one label is supposed to do. One small piece of paper with a few carefully-defined words becomes so terribly important to consumers and producers, because this is the sole, tiny window through which the two sides can communicate. And labels are always, of course, a mixture of information and advertising.

A name which appears to give information about how something was made may only be telling us (roughly) what it will taste like: 'smoked' bacon, for instance, can have the smoke flavour sprayed on. Bacon used to be smoked to preserve and flavour the meat, drying it out, making it denser, tastier and more compact. But if the smoke flavour is sprayed on the bacon stays wet, nitrates and nitrites are still used as preservatives: a perfectly legal con.

Labels and descriptions suggesting a 'natural', 'traditional' and 'wholesome/countryside' product abound. Currently the fashionable area is meat: 'Traditionally reared', 'prime', 'Fourgrain' (does this remind you of a kind of health-food-shop muesli bread?), eggs reared, 'with welfare in mind' (although still in a cramped barn). 'Natural' is probably the commonest and most meaningless of them all. While we might not be taken in by 'natural' (at least not when we think about it), phrases such as 'sourced from farms operating high standards of husbandry and welfare' and 'reared outdoors and in large barns under strict welfare conditions', really do sound as though they mean something (descriptions of Waitrose and Safeway pork). Yet when the Soil Association contacted the chains to ask for details of the standards of welfare required, Safeway and Waitrose both refused to give any details, either of standards or of inspection procedures: there is no way of knowing whether or not practices such as tail docking and farrowing crates are employed.

And what are we to make of Mornflake porridge oats, 'Grown with conservation in mind'? Most of the packet is taken up with a drawing of heavy horses pulling a plough. Looking to the words for further elucidation, we learn that oats are a traditional British crop which has been declining of late. And that's it. Buy these oats and help conserve oat farmers; there is no conservation of soil, wildlife, or anything else.

John Dalby, technical director of the Soil Association is, not surprisingly, particularly concerned about labels which imply a production standard similar to organic, but which may in fact fall well short. He gives an example: 'There is an "Integrated Crop Management" label coming in, where pesticides are still used. Supermarkets are moving towards that because it gives them a cleaner image.' 'Integrated Crop Management' involves better planning to cut farm energy use (reduced tractor miles), and the use of non-chemical pest reduction techniques, such as unploughed strips or 'beetle banks', greater use of crop rotations, and so forth. These alterations make it possible for farmers to use fewer pesticides, and at the demonstration farms reductions of between 25 and 80 per cent in different chemicals were achieved. But ICM carries no guarantee of such reductions and an ICM label will certainly confuse some consumers and may divert custom from truly organic produce; understandably, the Soil Association finds this worrying.

The ICM label does give customers the chance to support a system which pays a little more attention to the environment. But as agriculture researcher Mark Redmond points out, there are no *rules* about pesticide use or pesticide reduction in ICM protocols (of which there are several, with yet more initials: LIFE, LEAF, LINK-IFS and FOFP). Farmers are obliged to stick within the existing legal requirements and recommended codes of practice, but beyond that usage is up to the 'discretion' of the farmer, who will use more or less pesticide depending on what they perceive the threats to the crop to be. There is no guarantee to the consumer that the produce is pesticide-reduced, just a likelihood. As Dalby suggested, supermarkets do advertise the fact that ICM systems such as LEAF have been used for some products. ICM is entirely compatible with intensive production and intensive retailing, and is enthusiastically promoted: indeed a 'charity' has been set up to do just that. It could be said that the retailers in particular are getting a lot of PR out of relatively small changes in practice, with no guarantee of significant benefits for the consumer.

Dalby makes a fair point when he says the variety of labels is confusing, and this confusion itself almost certainly suits those who profit from the status quo. It could even be argued that confusion has been encouraged as a 'best fallback' position for an industry which has tried to resist and oppose labelling of any kind. For example, when the Food Commission asked one supermarket chain why it did not indicate whether or not the apples they sold had been coated with insect-derived waxes, the reply was that the more information consumers were given the more chaos it caused, and that giving information causes customers to start asking questions!

The compulsory labels we have are not much more helpful. Some of them are apparently misunderstood by the majority of consumers. Ingredient quantities in percentages, for example, are meaningless unless you know what the normal or desirable level for that product might be; many people find the numbers too confusing and complicated to be bothered with at all. A study by MAFF showed that the format for 'nutritional information' finally agreed upon by industry was the one *least* liked by consumers. A generally agreed 'high', 'medium' or 'low' rating would be easier – if there was any prospect of reaching a consensus on such things.

But labels are not telling consumers what they want to know anyway. People want more than rudimentary 'nutritional information'. They want to know what happens on the farm or in the factory; they want to know about pesticides, welfare, pollution. A survey carried out by the UK Ministry of Agriculture found that 50 per cent of respondents wanted to know if pesticides had been used, with half of these wanting the pesticides named, and 40 per cent wanted information about the kind of farming methods used. As Tim Lang, one of the UK's most prominent food campaigners, points out, if customers had their way labels in the shops might read: 'these carrots have been sprayed with persistent insecticide at least seven times'.

CERTIFICATION

Certification schemes attempt to overcome the shortcomings of labelling. They are effectively sending a representative who, to some extent, is there on the consumer's behalf, checking on the farm that consumers don't have the chance to visit for themselves. Interested consumers can ask, for example, Organic Farmers and Growers to send them details of their criteria for certification, and this way can learn considerably more about the way their food was raised than they could learn from a label which just says 'pesticide free' or 'naturally reared'.

Organic certification is probably the most well known of those schemes. Organic standards for growers, stock-raisers, shopkeepers and food-processors require an exhaustive system of record keeping and tallying, confirmed by inspection, to demonstrate that no forbidden substances or methods are used on the premises. Growers must also be able to demonstrate that each organic product can be traced back to the field it first grew in, with no cheaper, more conventionally grown stock being slipped in under the organic label in the process. This elaborate system is very time-consuming and expensive to administer, and it accounts in part for the 'premium' that customers have to pay for 'organic' produce. The burden of this administration is too onerous for some businesses, and they find they cannot afford the certificate which would demonstrate to the consumer that they are, indeed, 'organic' – even though they do nothing the organic bodies wouldn't approve of.

The registration fee is not the only expense with certification schemes. To set up such a scheme, a uniform set of standards applicable to all producers has to be drawn up. The organic regulations are fairly rigid and some producers feel they cannot implement them in their particular operation. One of the organic certification bodies, the Soil Association, has been trying to find ways of becoming more flexible with growers and farmers, but at present many food producers still feel organic certification is not economically feasible for them.

The RSPCA's 'Freedom Foods' label has been criticised for precisely the opposite reasons: in its anxiety to include as many producers as possible, the scheme's basic animal welfare criteria seem rather low. 'Freedom Food' certification enables producers to charge a little more for bacon and eggs and chicken, in return for granting 'basic freedoms' to the stock. These are listed on the label as freedom from discomfort, pain, injury, disease, fear and distress, and freedom to express normal behaviour.

In fact, the Freedom Food regulations permit chicken stocking density of up to 15 per square metre: an improvement on the legal maximum, but this density may still require the birds to be de-beaked. Farrowing crates are also permitted, as are long journeys in crowded lorries, before slaughter, as Gail Vines reported in *New Scientist* magazine. According to critics, such practices are 'anything but humane', and the name of the scheme 'grossly exaggerates the freedom animals have'.

Those who set the scheme up claimed that a 'utopian' scheme beyond all criticism would have been too expensive, or even that it would simply be impossible for farmers to produce enough animal products if more stringent criteria were applied. RSPCA campaigns director Jerry Lloyd commented: 'we want to get farmers on board and lead them to better practices', while his colleague Martin Potter argued: 'we would not achieve anything for animals if it's so damned expensive that no-one buys it'.

The cost arguments may be exaggerated (as chapter eight explores the myth of 'cheap food') however, even if it were true, the RSPCA is missing the point: people are being misled. It is hard to see how the freedoms promised on the 'Freedom Food' labels can be guaranteed. The RSPCA itself concedes that the first item on the printed list, 'freedom from hunger and thirst' will not be feasible at all times. The implication is that the RSPCA feels it is necessary to dupe consumers to achieve welfare improvements – a patronising attitude, that 'they know best'.

When we are so completely cut off from our food's producers – in many cases they are not even in the same country – we are forced to fall back on labelling and certification systems, good and bad. But no scheme is going to look at everything you worry about. A welfare label may not guarantee anything about the diet, which means that animals may have been fed antibiotics and egg dyes; but on the other hand, hens on a guaranteed fourgrain diet may well have been crammed into a barn where pecking and cannibalism are rife. And none of the schemes tell you if farmers are good to their staff, or whether they have uglified great tracts of countryside (even organic farms may have huge open fields and hideous metal packhouses). It is also hard to imagine a scheme or even a range of schemes, which would suit every single farmer.

Tim Lang has followed arguments over food labelling for years. Though he is in favour of customers having as much information as possible, he despairs of a satisfactory, non-misleading system of labelling ever being agreed on. He has come to the conclusion shared by a growing number of consumers, producers and commentators: 'The endless arguments over labelling just show how vulnerable the consumer is when they are distant from the source or production of their food. There is no way labelling can ever be a substitute for going and seeing for yourself.'

WAKE UP SHOPPERS!

Many people love the countryside and animals so much that they pay for membership of one or several environment, wildlife or animal welfare charities. Yet isn't this an absurd waste of money, when such a huge part of their weekly shopping budget is spent destroying the very things they want to save?

The way most of us shop and the way that most of our food is presented to us, makes it difficult for us to get meaningful information about what we are buying, and difficult to tap in to better farming systems. Organic food is not reliably available in supermarkets, and it tends to be off-puttingly expensive. Other labelling systems are of limited use. Even when we do know the facts in our heads, the whole conventional shopping experience effectively detaches us from the realities of the field, factory and shed, and what we *feel* about our food is brushed aside.

Supermarkets now suck in an astonishing 78 per cent of consumer spending on groceries: independent retailers are left with just 12 per cent. Since 1972, 103,000 small shops have closed, more than half, leaving only 85,000 open. Yet small retailers buy their own stock: greengrocers, bakers, fishmongers and butchers in particular. They can tell you a great deal more about what you are buying, sometimes down to the particular farm something originated from, as they have a personal relationship with the producer. This vital lifeline of information is narrowing to a thread, sadly, as these kinds of stores are closing before our eyes, their trade eaten up by the big anonymous superstores. We can choose to go on shopping where the source of our food is identifiable, and support these smaller shops.

Better still, many of the best producers are going out of their way to meet us, to sell their produce to us directly. Small, craft producers in general and organic producers in particular know that, in contrast to the industrial sector, the more we see of them, the more we'll like them. They are not ashamed to have you roll up to the farmyard and talk to the pigs.

6

THE COUNTRYSIDE IN TROUBLE

Modern intensive farming has caused enormous environmental damage and tremendous suffering to animals. Not surprisingly, farmers are blamed for this. Indeed, farmers have a very poor public image in Britain. We tend to think of them as greedy, sucking up public subsidies and destroying the countryside in order to extract yet more yield to reap yet higher support payments.

Of course, ultimately they are responsible for what they do. Yet for all their proud image of fierce independence, British farmers have been pushed into the practices we now worry about by a combination of powerful actors wielding rules, policies, prices and subsidies. It is no simple matter for any individual farmer to change the way a farm is run. Rather like the shopper caught up in going to the supermarket, farmers have been caught up in a huge intensification machine. The financial odds in the existing market place have forced farmers onto a 'treadmill' of intensification, and, trapped by debt, most are convinced they would be unable to change their practices without going completely bankrupt. For many, only a whisker away from bankruptcy anyway, this may well be true: thousands fail each year. But even if they could change, the culture surrounding farmers – their organisations, their press, the government advisers – assures them that they *would* suffer financially if they changed tack.

The following pages explore the way that the intensification process is a near-inevitable consequence of the way food is sold: via EU support prices, and to large retailers and wholesalers. It seems increasingly clear that the best, and perhaps the only, way for the face of agriculture to change is for food to be sold more directly to consumers, giving consumers a closer role in the production process, and farmers more flexibility.

Of course, there are those farmers who are very happy to be brussels sprouts barons or milk magnates, ripping out soil and hedgerows, confining their animals in gloomy sheds and turning out tonne after tonne, gallon after gallon for the big buyers. But there are plenty more who are not happy about it at all, and are being driven to fury, despair and bankruptcy by the massive, and overlapping forces in European agriculture: the drive for intensive farming and intensive retailing. Increasingly, food producers the world over are powerless under the pressure of artificially structured pricing systems, 'free trade' and the near-monopoly buying power of huge food firms. And they are miserable.

British poultry farmer Christopher Turton voiced his disquiet to food writer James Erlichman: 'It distresses me. I would prefer to be seen as a craftsman, not as a commercial exploiter of animals, but I feel I am being turned from one to the other ... I am just a small cog in big industry ... today poultry management is dictated by the company accountant not the stockman.'

THE ENDANGERED FARMER

Bigger farms have prospered in this system, growing and growing as they swallow up the smaller farms. Indeed, there have been grants to encourage amalgamation of holdings in the name of efficiency. The kind of small, mixed, family farm that features in children's toys and books, and lives on in the popular imagination is an institution heading rapidly to extinction. As industrialisation and intensification have advanced, small family farms have collapsed, and been swallowed up by big concerns, who sell off the farmhouse to rich incomers, and as likely as not lay off any staff.

Herefordshire dairy farmer Jeff Glyn Jones explains the process: 'The way that production has been supported [through the subsidies and support prices in the European Union] means that the smaller farmers have suffered. And the farm next door which has managed to be a bit more successful takes over, and you end up with agribusinesses on a large scale with thousands of acres; and nobody cares too much about individual fields or individual animals because there are just too many of them'.

The income of Welsh hill farmers plummeted by almost 40 per cent in the five years before 1990. In that year, 6,000 British farmers gave up the struggle and sold. In 1991, it was 12,000. Many farmers have committed suicide. The Ministry of Agriculture estimates that another

100,000 farmers' jobs and 25,000 related rural jobs will go by around the year 2000. These figures were compiled before the BSE crisis, which is certain to make things worse. The Church of England Archbishops' Commission on Rural Areas found in its study of rural England: 'Everywhere we met the same apprehension and uncertainty for the future. Amongst the agricultural and older rural community, morale is often low, family continuity queried and in the saddest cases suicide has occurred'.

Farmers are well aware of the public criticism levelled at them. As the commission put it: 'With this growing [environmental] protest coming at a time of increasing financial pressure, many farmers reported that they felt their standing in the community had fallen'. One couple, for instance, felt that a combination of local criticism and abuse, much of it from urban 'incomers', and the fact that they were no longer employing the four staff that the farm had supported when they began, had undermined their role in the community. The Archbishop's Commission found they ended up feeling they were 'strangers in the church in which they and their ancestors had worshipped for centuries'.

Many farmers now say they would not advise their children to continue in farming, and this advice is being heeded: the average age of farmers is now 55. The position is exacerbated because young people wishing to start out in farming can seldom afford a holding big enough to make them any kind of living. As older farmers die or retire or, sometimes, go out of business, their farms are not taken over by young farmers, but are sold to bigger holdings. In thirty years perhaps one-third of all farms have been swallowed up in this way, according to government figures. It is almost exclusively smaller farms which disappear like this, and one-eighth of them vanished in the 10 years prior to 1993. About 10,000 agricultural jobs disappear each year. Our agricultural community is about to be lost for ever.

Poignantly, the farms which are most vulnerable to failure or amalgamation are often the very farms which so many of us understand to be at the heart of the countryside, often with beautiful buildings, and maintaining the features of the countryside we love. How many city dwellers revelling in a walk through stunning hill country realise that behind the doors of those picturesque stone farmhouses, an elderly couple may be struggling on an income of less than £5,000 a year – the reality for one third of hill and upland farms.

Small farms which would not recover the economies of scale from, or simply cannot afford, the machinery and capital investment to intensify, are slower to remove the stone walls and hedges, trees and copses, ponds and winding streams that make the landscape so attractive, and harbour much of its wildlife. DoE figures show small farms have more woodland, particularly deciduous woodland (big farms are more likely to have conifer plantations), smaller fields and more hedgerows. On an intensive farm such features stand, literally, in the way of the monster machines and giant sheds which represent efficiency and progress. When a big farm swallows a small one, landscape features are almost inevitably removed.

Even the local planning system discriminates against smaller farmers, (and in favour of mechanisation). Under the general development order, a large farm is permitted to put up any huge hideous shed it likes; but for farms under 5 hectares, the holder must apply for planning permission. Alarmingly, there was talk in 1996 of extending this limit up to 50 hectares (125 acres) – immediate discrimination against all the smaller farms in this country. Planning authorities do not distinguish between genuine smallholders and urban 'incomers' who buy a few acres for a horse. If people want to live on their holding authorities tend to insist on a minimum income before granting permission: once again, clear discrimination in favour of intensive production methods and big holdings. Even the bigger farmers face difficulties if it is human workers they wish to accommodate, rather than big machines in asbestos sheds, because housing (unlike sheds) requires very elaborate planning procedures, with expensive architect's drawings.

The image of the big, rich farmer as the pinnacle of desirable efficiency has a powerful grip on the farming and food establishments' minds. Sometimes, farmers who face ruin receive not sympathy but contempt: they 'would probably have gone out of business anyway' is a common comment from those profiting from the present system.

Yet just a cursory examination of the way agriculture is financed shows that this is unfair. Forty per cent on average of farm income comes from EU subsidies, under the Common Agricultural Policy or CAP, but it is not distributed evenly between farmers. Big, intensive farms attract big subsidies – the richest 20 per cent of farmers hog 80 per cent of the subsidy payments – and they are in a better position to make more profit out of the subsidies, too. Payment is based on a combination of factors: there are guaranteed prices for tonnage of crop or meat plus acreage or 'headage' compensation brought in when support prices were lowered in 1992. This is simply reward for scale and intensity, nothing to do with 'efficiency'. Thus a large farm can make a very comfortable living for its owners though CAP payments, while under the same system, small farms struggle and disappear.

Ian Hutchcroft of Devon County Council Environment Department points out that the milk quota for a 200-acre farm may represent a reasonable living for a family, but the herd on a 50-acre Devon dairy farm will hardly pay one salary. 'It's an incredibly hard way to earn a living: running a small dairy farm is the best way to break your back that has been invented. When the farmer on a small farm dies or retires, the young generation just don't want to live like that. The farms get sold, and it is only the bigger farmers who have the cash to buy the land and the milk quota. The farmhouse will probably be sold to incomers. In one area, in the Blackdown Hills, we found that the number of holdings under 50 hectares had fallen by one quarter in just 10 years.'

Subsidies in Britain boomed after the war to secure our food supply, but surpluses and the introduction of set-aside payments show how far things have rocketed out of control. The system of guaranteeing a good price for a crop ensures that crop will be grown in quantity, whether or not any consumers actually want to buy it. Many of us have ended up paying through our taxes for large quantities of agricultural produce (wine, butter, grain, milk, fruit), then paying again for these goods to be stored.

This situation has got so far out of hand that subsidies are now being paid to farmers to *reduce* the level of production. Under the set-aside scheme, farmers are obliged to leave a percentage, usually 15 or 20 per cent, of land uncultivated, in return for a farm-wide subsidy. Set-aside will not simply reverse the process of intensification and labour-shedding, however. If anything, farmers have an incentive to make production even more intensive and 'efficient' on the land remaining in cultivation. Meanwhile, most set-aside land is ploughed and sprayed to keep down the weeds, so it is of little benefit to wildlife or the environment, either.

There is certainly disenchantment with the money spent on farm subsidies, not least because so much of it seems to be wasted on surpluses, handed to staggeringly rich landowners, or fraudulently obtained. UK contributions in 1996 were £3.5 billion: £200 or £300 for many households. Another estimate, from the OECD suggest EU taxpayers pay as much as £200 a head per annum for the CAP, with half of it spent on surpluses. Arguments about contributions to the EU sparked a furious row within the governing Conservative party in Britain in 1994, leading several Tory MPs to vote against the government. In France, businessman James Goldsmith set up an anti-EU political party and won a seat as a member of the European Parliament, and in 1995 he set up the Referendum Party in Britain to campaign against 'Federal Europe'.

There are some measures which attempt to set limits on subsidies paid to bigger farmers, and one or two which attempt to aid small farmers directly, but the big boys are still the ones making the serious money out of the CAP system. Massive price support has been replaced by quotas and compensation payments, which in some cases have discriminated against smaller producers even more. Attempts to protect smaller farmers in the 1992 CAP reforms were voted down by the British government, urged on by the large farming unions, the SAFE Alliance reports.[1] In fact, large and medium sized farms in the mid-1990s were doing extremely well, with these payments funding a boom in land buying, even while small farms continued to struggle.

The sheer burden of paperwork involved in claiming subsidies, weighs heavily on the smaller farmer. Several days (or, more likely, nights) are needed to understand the main form, not to mention the 80 pages of accompanying notes; and payment is on a field-by-field basis, so smaller fields equals more work. The large farmer may receive a cheque of £250,000 for filling the forms (making it well worthwhile to employ a financial advisor, who may even be able to increase the level of subsidy), while a small livestock farm may receive £10,000 or less for almost the same amount of administrative work.

Although the financial waste has angered many, fewer have made the connection that their own money is being used to sponsor the kind of environmental and social destruction that worries so many of us. As Bill Mollison, enthusiast for 'permanent agriculture' or Permaculture puts it: 'We are obliged, by entrenched bureaucracies, to pay for the destruction of our world, regardless of the long term costs to be borne by our children and our societies'.

It is also not widely recognised that, despite the fact that there are frequently enormous surpluses in milk, beef, wheat and other crops which receive guaranteed prices from the CAP, Europe remains one of

1. 'Farming Foundations', Tracey Clunies-Ross and Stewart Turner, SAFE Alliance, Dec 1995 (see resources).

the largest importers of food in the world. We import oilseeds, protein and starch grains, fruits and vegetables which could in great part be replaced by equally tasty and nutritious crops grown at home.

With such enormous funds available in the EU budget, and an estimated 40 per cent of farm incomes paid as subsidy by taxpayers, we ought to be able to buy the kind of farming we want. The SAFE Alliance and many other bodies are calling for a total rethink of the structure of the CAP, oriented towards supporting employment and the rural economy. Because of the huge size of the CAP budget, political pressures are mounting for some sort of reform, but unless the needs of the small farmers and the wider issues of sustainability are included, there is always a danger that reforms will remove the last feeble lifeline from small farms, while bigger ones, cushioned by the capital reserves represented by their land and stock, may be able to hang on through a 'CAP shock' and clean up when the dust has settled. For these reasons, bodies such as Devon County Council are looking towards direct marketing to consumers as a way to support the livelihoods of smaller farms – directly.

INTENSIFY OR BUST

With enough capital for big machinery and enough chemicals, even a crop grown on unsuitable land for a very narrow profit margin can be profitable. The bigger the acreage the bigger the profit. Big fields, big farms and big profits support big harvesting machines needing fewer workers and fewer wage packets: profitability increases again. A margin of a few pence on a bag of corn which never adds up to a living on a small farm, can add up to hundreds of thousands on a large, intensive one.

Higher yields sound as though they ought to be good news for farmers. But they aren't necessarily. By increasing output using expensive, industrial techniques, big suppliers, producers and buyers can between them drive down the unit price and at the same time stay profitable. As prices for crops go down, so intensification becomes necessary for survival. Farmers are forced to squeeze more and more out of their land in order to make the same relative income. 'In 1971, I could sell five bullocks to buy a car; it would have to be 20 now,' says Herefordshire stock farmer Bill Philips. 'Once the fleeces from 200 ewes would have bought me a tractor: the price for wool is just the same now, and that money wouldn't even buy you a wheel!'

Once the unit price is so low that anyone operating on a slightly more expensive system can no longer make any profit and is driven out of business, the market share for the big holdings goes up, and profitability jumps up again. As if this wasn't advantage enough, there is active discrimination by the subsidy and quota system in favour of 'efficient' producers. For example, British Sugar, who buy all of the sugar beet produced in the UK, publishes a league table of all sugar beet growers, ranked in order of 'efficiency' – measured in terms of yield in tonnes per hectare.

The justification for this, according to *Crops* magazine is that, 'for the UK sugar industry to argue its case for beet quota in Brussels, the UK has to be able to show that its claims of efficiency are justified'. Farmers wanting to save money, or reduce environmental damage, by using lower inputs and accepting a lower yield, find themselves slipping down the league table and coming under pressure to give up their quota – the right to grow and sell sugar beet – to more 'efficient' farmers who can 'increase our national efficiency rating in Europe'.

On a low profit margin, yields have to be maximised, using all the machinery and chemicals available, to ensure the farm runs at profit and not loss. Farmers cannot afford to do things just a little more gently than their neighbour, if it means they then need to charge a penny more to avoid making a loss. One Midlands turkey farmer who raises high-quality turkey meat in relatively humane 'traditional' conditions, was suffering from price-undercutting by an intensive operation nearby. Most of his meat is sold through large retailers, where there is no room for a detailed comparison of the two farms' husbandry practices. 'I haven't had such a good year, and so I fear I may have to go over to the other techniques,' this farmer admitted.

The emphasis on competition mainly by cost, and the increasing specialisation of farms so operations can be scaled-up, has horrifying consequences. BSE is probably the most notorious example. Cattle cake has long been the cheapest way to increase animal size and milk yield. Indeed, for the kind of yields and composition (flavour does not come into it) of milk considered 'economic' today, a cow simply would not have time to gain her nourishment from grass, hay and silage alone. Mixed into this cake, together with the soy from Brazil and oilcake from France, and perhaps the fishmeal from the Pacific or the North Sea bed, is 'animal protein'. Dead animals or those parts considered unsuitable or unfit for human consumption – chickens dying in battery cages, chicken droppings and feathers, and in the 1980s, sheep and cattle bones and guts

– are all boiled up, ground, and added to the mix going into cattle cake and other livestock rations. Once sheep remains were suspected of being the source of BSE, they, along with cattle remains were banned from cattle feed, but they continued to go into chicken and pig feed until 1996. There was evidence that ruminant remains were still slipping through into cattle feed up to that date, because of sloppy practices and sloppy inspection at the feed plants.

Specialisation means most livestock units long ago ceased to produce all their own fodder on-farm, and many were sold cake by reps from the big, often multinational firms. Farmers had little idea what was in the sacks, as Herefordshire dairy farmer Jeff Glyn Jones recalls: 'Naturally farmers assumed that companies specialising in producing animal feed were selling them a wholesome product. The manufacturers were under no statutory obligation to tell us what was in the feeds and many of the big companies would not tell us. So we simply did not know what was in the cattle cake'.

Just like consumers buying ready-meals, farmers have ceased to be responsible for selecting the ingredients in what they feed to their beasts, handing this over to the big corporations. And like us, the farmer gets scant information but plenty of promotion and bland assurances. In 1996 a number of feed manufacturers, including Dalgetys, one of the largest multi-national grain merchants and feed manufacturers, announced that post-BSE it would be listing all ingredients in order of weight. Before then, a sack of Dalgetys' Sheep Feed would read: 'A compound feed designed to ensure optimal animal and financial performance. Energy level and type is specific to production level and system. Protein supply reflects a specific ratio of RDP and DUP [whatever they are] to balance energy and optimise performance. Formulated using selected raw materials to ensure excellent palatability ...' and so on. All implying: you don't need to worry about what's in this, trust us, we are the scientists.

Some farmers don't even get to choose whether the feed will be from Dalgetys' or the feed mill down the road, but instead are tied into the exact production methods by their customers – not us, that is, but the big meat companies (like Sun Valley for chickens) or the retailers. One way or another, the majority of meat, eggs, and indeed most of the vegetables, are being grown to the order and specification of the food industry. Very often the producer is tied into a contract specifying exactly what is to be done and when. For example, Marks and Spencer food technologist Andy Clappen admits that 'the specifications covering a calf's life from birth to dinner table cover about 300 pages'. The farmers and growers themselves have very little say in the way animals are kept and fed, crops are sown and sprayed, if they want to keep these large contracts. As the comment by Christopher Turton at the start of the chapter showed, this is a demoralising process, degrading a craft into an assembly-line job.

A FARMER'S VIEW

Geoff Hawkins has farmed all his life in Pitstone in Buckinghamshire. He is an enthusiastic conservationist and wildlife lover, and shares his interests with fellow farmers in the Farming and Wildlife Advisory Group. He knows his colleagues cannot change overnight. 'Farmers are under tight constraints. Their first responsibility is to make a living or they will be out of business. The difference between putting on an extra £5 bag of fertiliser might be £50 or even £100 worth of crop. In that situation there is no doubt about what you have got to do.

'In order to make a stock farm pay you have got to keep so many more animals. You used to be able to keep just a few animals and make a good living, and of course this was much better for the livestock. Nowadays you have got to keep hundreds in order to stay in business.

'Labour has become more and more expensive relative to what you get paid for the crop. My grandfather used to say if a worker took home the equivalent of a sack of wheat at the end of each week that was about right. That certainly wouldn't be enough now, as other prices have all gone up so much more.

'Of course you can get a lot more for organic produce, but it is difficult to convert. Unless the subsidies were changed, there is no way you could just grow using less inputs and make it pay. In theory customers might well be prepared to choose lower-input produce, but they would have to be able to identify it first.'

CULTURE OF BIGNESS

The mouthpieces of the industry: the farming press, the National Farmers' Union, and the Ministry of Agriculture (described by Edwina Currie on Channel 4 as 'little more than a trade union for the worst kind of farmer'), do not help farmers to challenge the status quo. The bigger and richer producers are the ones who can reach positions of influence. They have time to sit on committees. To sit on the council of the National Farmers' Union, for instance, you have to get to London once a week. Conservative MP Richard Body describes these council members as 'the men who have almost by definition been the beneficiaries of the system which has amalgamated tens of thousands of small farms. These are the men who have enjoyed the lion's share of the grants, subsidies and tax allowances.' They 'advise' the government on what kind of national and European policy would be best for 'British farmers' – like themselves. They represent 'farmers' on TV and radio programmes.

When the NFU, which has a permanently staffed office in Westminster, was asked if it represented small farmers the information officer said 'Oh no, they have their own organisation. I can give you the address, but they're not on the phone.' (There is in fact an association for small farms, the Family Farmers' Association – with a phone number – but it has no paid staff at all, while the NFU has full-time paid officers in each region and its own headquarters.)

Agriculture schools and agricultural research, government agriculture advice, and the agricultural press all stress the intensive, high input, high volume approach. The bias begins at agriculture college, with colleges running farms on high-profit, 'modern' lines. And as soon as the young farmer begins work, similar advice rains down.

The government agricultural advisory body ADAS has always been oriented towards intensive farming, to some extent a hangover from the post-war panic to reduce dependence on imports. It has been charging farmers for individual advice for the past few years, and is due to be privatised. Farmers are likely only to want to pay fees for advice which make them more profit than the advice cost.

Meanwhile, of course, the reps from agrochemical firms advise individual farmers for free. Pesticide is a big business indeed, and a booming one. The Pesticides' Trust reports that in 1994 sales worldwide topped US$27,800 million – up 10 per cent on 1993. The British Agrochemicals Association (the industry's lobby group) not only produces a 'training pack' for use in agricultural colleges, it has even targeted primary and secondary schools with a pack on 'the agrochemical industry's contribution to feeding the world'. Such firms also sponsor agricultural research, and support the farming press by buying advertising space.

Articles in farming magazines are geared towards maximising yield, by heavy use of chemicals and machinery in order to maximise profit. 'Hit wheat disease accurately, with the right product, and you are quids in,' urges *Crops* magazine. Farmers are told when to spray in anticipation of diseases. That week's *Farming News* was meanwhile passing on the government advisory service's advice to 'count the orange midges on the [wheat] ear in the evening and spray the fields at risk next morning with chlorpyrifos, fenitrothion or triazophos' (all insecticides). And so it goes on. According to the Soil Association's *Living Earth* magazine the biggest farm journal of them all, *Farmers' Weekly*, is sometimes known by its readers as 'the Caged Canary' 'apparently because it is distinctively yellow in colour and allegedly obliged to sing the praises of its major advertisers'.

THE FARMER AT WAR

The farmer's job is depicted as a battle, rather than a matter of co-operation and co-existence. His (they are all men in the adverts) tools have names like Dominator (a harvesting machine), while pesticides are Invader, Falcon, Panther, Fusilade, Challenge, Stomp, Tigress ('arm yourself with Tigress'); even the innocent seed varieties are lumbered with names like Hussar, Fighter and Brigadier.

Not only are farmers encouraged to believe they are battling with nature and the banks, according to the language used in their media they are battling with the rest of us too: standards on effluent disposal or animal welfare sought by wider society are invariably 'punitive'. The British media, who tend to think a news story must involve conflict of some kind have only exacerbated this situation. The farmers upon whom consumers depend for food, and the consumers upon whom farmers depend for a living, are each for ever being reminded of how selfish, greedy and ignorant the other group are. This hostility reached particular heights during the BSE crisis in 1996, with public amger directed again and again at 'greedy farmers' (many of whom had no idea of the ingredients of the now-suspect cattle meal), rather than at the renderers, millers or indeed the food companies who forced down the prices paid for beef.

Environmental groups are portrayed to farmers as a particular enemy. When the SAFE Alliance – an umbrella group of consumer, environmental and other organisations – was established in 1991, *Farming News* declared war at once. Under the headline 'Yeomen of England a Call to Arms' the newspaper urged: 'There must be no unilateral abandonment of scientific agriculture. There must be no surrender'.

THE CRAZY WORLD OF SUPERMARKETS

If the EU, with its guaranteed prices, is one powerful customer, the other giant in the market is the retailer and in particular, the supermarket. It is big farmers who have contracts with the big retailers. And you have to be very big to flourish on such a contract, where once again, margins are vanishingly small but volume is colossal.

Because more and more consumers are visiting them, supermarkets have risen to a position of tremendous power over farmers and growers. Supermarkets represent such a large portion of the market that most producers dare not lose their custom. As their share of the market rises, there are fewer alternatives for farmers to sell to. Between 1983 and 1991, for instance, while the big retail multiples increased their share of the fresh produce market from one-quarter to one-half, independent greengrocers' share declined accordingly, down to less than a quarter.

Retailers reinforce the pressure for intensification by shaving down the prices they pay to the absolute minimum. On top of this supermarkets only deal with companies who can supply large quantities to big, central depots, for distribution to stores all over the country. Furthermore, growers supplying the supermarkets have to have packhouses, washers, chillers; packaging, labelling, and transport, all of which have to be altered every time the supermarkets say so, to keep up with innovations such as bar coding, or even 'restyling'. Once again, small growers are the hardest hit. They simply cannot afford this kind of outlay.

'Green' technologies, such as biological control with specially bred insects, or packing vegetables in bags containing inert nitrogen gas as a preservative and substitute for post-harvest spraying, are also expensive technologies. Salads packed in bags of nitrogen enable supermarkets to claim to be selling a 'greener' product without having to alter their patterns of purchasing, distribution, or presentation. But equipment for packing salads in nitrogen is not cheap. Biological control involves using natural predators to kill crop pests, systems available which offer so much control that the end product is as supermarket-perfect as anything which has been sprayed. For example, glasshouse peppers grown for one supermarket chain are protected with specially bred insects air-freighted in from the Netherlands, with eggs that hatch on schedule, at carefully timed intervals. This kind of service is only for the rich producer.

The way that supermarkets transport and present produce involves the growers in even more expense. Transport to ever fewer 'regional distribution centres' has to be undertaken by the supplier – who bears the cost of the longer journey (and, incidentally enables the supermarkets to claim that they are transporting goods less, which is true because they're getting other people to do it for them).

And the supermarkets are fussy. Have you ever wondered what that farmer would have done with his massive plantation of pineapples if the man from Del Monte had said 'No'? A vegetable grower whose harvest has been rejected by a big retailer, for the most trivial of reasons, cannot watch that advert without a shudder of recognition. Fanatical cosmetic standards result in huge waste. Government figures reveal that around one in eight apples is thrown away, and with other crops as much as 20 per cent may be rejected and dumped. One large intensive indoor pepper grower dumps an industrial-sized skip of gradeouts every day – before they are even looked at by the supermarket buyer.

The insistence on perfection drives growers to use more pesticides than they otherwise would, as Cornish grower Gillian Body told Judy Steele of *Living Earth* magazine: 'We dare not have one aphid or slug in a consignment of lettuces, or the whole lot could be rejected'. Although the supermarkets make great play of using 'integrated crop management' and 'biological control', ironically, as Steele reports, thousands of pounds worth of cauliflowers were rejected and dumped by Sainsbury's in 1995 because of the presence of those same harmless parasitic wasps which had been keeping aphids off the crops without poisoning the consumer.

Rejection is not always for reasons related to the produce; as sometimes orders are cancelled arbitrarily, before the crop is even harvested. Once again, supermarkets are so dominant that growers cannot often take their produce elsewhere. Simon Brenman, who was a member of the Herefordshire Green Growers co-op before becoming an organic farming adviser, has suffered the waste of an entire crop – an entire season's work. 'I got interested in selling direct to consumers after I had really been screwed down by the supermarkets. I had grown two acres of organic red cabbage, exactly to their specifications. We had spent a long time discussing it beforehand: exactly the size on exactly what date. And I did it, because I'm a good grower. Then when they were ready to harvest I was told, 'we have decided to get out of red cabbage'; they thought they could get more money for the shelf space by filling it with something else. I either had to sell them wholesale at an appalling loss or just disc them in and keep the fertility in the field. I couldn't afford to do anything else really. It was shattering. The supermarkets just don't care if a 12-acre smallholder goes out of business.'

Growers dependent on contracts with big retailers speak bitterly of the way they do business. This bitterness surfaced in correspondence in the weekly journal, *The Grower*. When the journal ran a feature on 'Supermarket abuse of growers', that journal was inundated by 'letters, phone calls and faxes, all in broad agreement ... few correspondents were prepared to be identified, testimony to the awful power these companies wield.' Correspondents feared having orders cancelled in retribution for their criticism, perhaps for a few weeks, on some trumped-up excuse usually at the last minute – in their experience 'this is the punishment meted out to those who offend against the rules or over-step the mark'.

The low prices paid to growers by supermarkets are not passed on as low prices to consumers. Supermarket fruit and vegetable prices, for instance, are higher than those in independent greengrocers and market stalls. In fact, the prices paid by consumers for fresh produce in supermarkets enable fruit and veg to make 'one of the highest fully costed profits contributions per foot', according to one City retail analyst.

ORGANIC GROWERS AND SUPERMARKETS – A CLASH OF CULTURES

Like Brenman, many farmers and growers who have made a primary commitment to turn their back on industrial farming find working with supermarkets particularly difficult. Organic meat production faces similar difficulties to fruit and vegetables: some supermarkets will carry organic meat, but are fussy about matters like carcass conformation (the exact shape of the animal) and so reject a high proportion of what is produced. As John Dalby puts it: 'Supermarkets have not always got what they wanted in terms of consistent supply, carcass conformation and so on, and this has tended to put them off.' As a result, about half of the organic meat produced in this country is turned down by supermarkets and butchers, and just goes to market with all the rest. It is hard to see how this is offering consumer choice.

The British organic movement has worked hard to supply the

supermarkets, seeing them as the likeliest outlet to large numbers of consumers. Many producers are now disillusioned, feeling that what supermarkets demand: big volumes of homogeneous produce, mass transportation, packaging and cosmetic perfection, are not only difficult and expensive (as they are for regular growers), but go against the philosophy they follow.

A colleague of Simon Brenman's commented that to sell his potatoes in a supermarket they had first to travel to West Wales for grading and packing – 'ridiculous! for such heavy bulky things'. Increased lorry transport and increased packaging go against the grain for most people either growing or buying organic produce. Yet, organic growers complain, supermarkets have made no attempt to modify their demands to accommodate these ideals, despite the fact that organic farming is *specifically* about diversity, responsiveness to nature, care and environmental friendliness.

As organic farming researcher Lawrence Woodward put it: 'I fear that the mainstream is changing us more than we are changing it. By and large our successes ... have been based on accommodating the essential character of conventional approaches to food production, processing and distribution.'

Worst of all, some organic growers feel that supermarkets have deliberately 'ghettoised' organic produce as a luxury product, and, indeed, that smaller stores have done the same. The way organic food is sold, they feel, ensures that it never grows past being a minority, luxury item in a similar bracket to the West Country lamb or delicatessen items. Why something as basic as a potato or a pint of milk which just happens to be uncontaminated by poisons should be regarded as a 'luxury' is hard to explain. And very revealing about our society, and what we expect for ourselves.

Supermarkets did bring organic food to a wider market than health stores were reaching in the early 1980s, but they have never offered a complete organic 'shop'. Furthermore, prices have always been spectacularly high, and, by the mid-1990s, many supermarkets had ceased stocking more than one or two lines of organic food. The dream of organic produce being the norm on all the supermarket shelves – lettuce, lamb, parsnips and pork sausages, from Colchester to Carlisle – has fallen a bit short.

Supermarkets cite lack of demand. Consumers reply that of course demand is not high when organic food is so much more expensive. Although organic growers do rely on a certain 'premium' to cover some of the extra costs of their style of farming, they argue that fussy supermarket grading has raised the price far more than was needed. Ten or 15 per cent more on the price and people might feel they were paying for quality, but at 40 or 60 per cent more, it becomes a luxury that even the better-off now balk at.

Organic food now has such a reputation for being expensive that when Oxfordshire farmer Julian Rose opened his farm shop which sells mainly organic produce: 'The word "organic" was put in quite small writing on the sign. If it said "ORGANIC SHOP" people would just think it was expensive and wouldn't come in,' he says.

Organic milk producer Dirk Bauer points out that, in comparison to conventional milk, 'organic dairy production is slightly more expensive, because more land is used for the same number of cattle, and their feed is organic without fishmeal or other animal remains, which puts up the costs slightly. The producer of the organic milk only receives a slender 2½p per litre – 1½p per pint – more.' So why does the customer pay an extra 22p?

'What is dreadfully expensive is the enormous burden on transporting because of the economics of scale,' Bauer explains. 'If you try to transport one pallet of milk it costs a lot more per pint than a forty foot container full of milk. In the shops the tremendous difference in price is because of the logistics of transporting a product in relatively lower volume.'

Furthermore, the discounting of 'ordinary' milk has exaggerated the difference, and put off consumers still more. 'To make things worse, supermarkets are selling milk as a loss-leader', Bauer says. 'They are prepared to support conventional milk with large sums of money to sell it at a low price to tempt customers in. With organic milk they say to us: "That's a luxury product so we must have our 35 per cent mark-up." This leads to the enormous gap in price: 70p a litre for organic versus 48p for conventional. On the other hand, Bauer points out, 'If people decided to buy organic milk on a large scale they would find prices were comparable to ordinary milk – it would be something like 57p for a litre instead of 55p.' Of course, another way to avoid this mark-up would be to avoid the long distance transport and use local suppliers instead, but this simply does not fit in with the centralised, total-control buying structures of supermarkets.

For all their fussiness about the reliability of their suppliers, supermarkets themselves do not offer a regular supply of organic produce to customers, making it hard for anyone to get into a habit of buying there regularly. As Julie Alderson reports: 'A friend of mine couldn't get to the organic market one week so she rang round the supermarkets to see where she could buy organic veg. One supermarket said to her, "The such-and-such store sells it but you'd better get there on Tuesday because it's usually sold out by Thursday".' As Alderson commented, 'You can't imagine them saying "the strawberry yoghurts always sell out by Thursday", can you!' To this, supermarkets will reply with complaints about 'sourcing difficulties' – that organic growers don't produce perfectly size-matched carrots week after week come flood or frost, with never a blemish, which, of course, they cannot do, because they are farming with, rather than despite, nature. They can always produce *good* food, but it is hard to produce food that is identical week after week.

Smaller retailers have similarly failed to embrace organic produce wholeheartedly. Once again, many greengrocers, butchers and bakers do stock some organic lines, but they are in a minority, and are unlikely to be as prominently promoted as the 'bargains'.

Are retailers deliberately sidelining organic produce? Does the label 'organic' raise too many awkward questions about 'mainstream' produce, simply by sitting there on the next shelf? Some people believe so. Will Taylor, who raises organic beef, potatoes and other crops, has always found that the best way to sell his produce was direct to consumers. To begin with, local shops had no idea what 'organic' meant so weren't prepared to offer a penny more for it. Then a butcher in Cambridge did start to take his meat. 'They liked the product, but they didn't like the mark-up, and they didn't like admitting the rest of the meat in the shop was not raised naturally.'

Simon Brenman has come across this too: 'It does sound funny and you may laugh, but actually it's very serious. When people know what the other, not-organic stuff *is* on the shelves, know what's really in it, there is a problem. So conventional grocers won't make a big thing of organic. Even so, when they do have to explain the difference, their bread and butter produce gets into problems.'

Supermarkets can make money from a product by selling at a competitive price on a low margin, at very high volumes with little wastage. Or they can opt to 'position' a product as a high-margin speciality, which means that it is high-priced, appealing to a minority of customers and so with a high risk of wastage, but a high mark-up to compensate. And as long as it remains a 'speciality' item, prices suffer further upward pressure because there cannot be economies of scale.

Supermarkets seem to have relegated organic food to this latter category, along with fancy biscuits, and frozen pigeon (and why on earth should pigeon be expensive?). Is organic food 'too good' to fit into a system built on large-scale and industrial farming and distribution? The supermarkets, the food industry, the haulage industry might have too much invested in the status quo to be open to – or even, perhaps, to be capable of – radical change.

Tesco supermarket has accepted that the high margins added to the price of organic produce in supermarkets puts people off. In October 1996 Tesco announced that it would experiment with selling some lines of organic produce at the same price as conventional produce, in some of the more affluent parts of the country. This could apparently be done without making a loss, but simply accepting 'substantially reduced margins', according to a press release. The object of the exercise was to bring 'economies of scale and lower production costs' to what has been 'almost a cottage industry'.

While welcoming the move to make organic produce more affordable, organic growers pointed out that such a sudden leap in the market could not possibly be met from existing UK organic producers and so much would be imported, at least to begin with. There were also concerns that Tesco might put the 'squeeze' onto growers, forcing down the prices paid, 'though they have promised they won't,' said Soil Association president Patrick Holden. It will be interesting to see whether, when many more shoppers get the chance to choose organic carrots, potatoes, lettuces, milk and bread, will they start to wonder about everything else on the shelves?

AN EXPENSIVE WAY TO EARN A LIVING

The organic movement believes that the fair trade criteria required by the International Federation of Organic Agriculture Movements (IFOAM) of 'a reasonable return for the produce, and no exploitation by middle-men', cannot technically be met by the organic sector in the UK. The Soil Association's John Dalby says: 'I proposed including these fair trade criteria in our own policy statement, and I was laughed out. It just is not possible, with supermarkets screwing the price right down, for fair trading to apply within the market. The only way is to go outside the market and buy and sell direct between grower and consumer.'

In a Consumers' Association survey seven in eight kinds of

supermarket organic produce were pre-packed. Although supermarkets claim this is to avoid the produce getting mixed up with conventionally-grown goods, many stores display the conventionally grown produce loose in the original box, with the origin clearly marked – so why not do the same with organic?

Packaging just adds to the cost paid by the consumer and it pushes up the investment required of the growers. Organic fruit and vegetables are sold in pre-packs, usually washed. Packaged vegetables are easier and quicker to load and unload, to put on shelves, to sell at the checkout. The supermarket has to spend less on warehousing staff if the job is faster, more mechanised. This cost cut is paid for by the farmer who buys the packing equipment. And because each supermarket requires a different kind of package, growers or co-ops either have to buy several kinds or tie themselves in with one buyer, which can leave the grower extremely vulnerable.

WHO WINS THE INTERNATIONAL COMPETITION?

It is particularly galling for farmers who are struggling to sell their produce to find imported food on the counters and supermarket shelves. As Tony Edwards of the Herefordshire Green Growers co-op put it: 'There is nothing more demoralising than to see good produce wasted. We were supplying courgettes to a supermarket and had agreed the amount, but they didn't take the produce. We were cutting them and throwing them away. Then what did we see but French courgettes at a very high price in the same supermarket, very inferior quality to what I was throwing away. It was just crazy to me.' Independent retailers have more or less followed the trend, if less dramatically. A visit to any wholesale market – including an organic one – will show the same range of countries of origin, from all five continents, that is familiar to anyone browsing the supermarket shelves.

Imported food has led to a UK food trade deficit, which in 1995 stood at around £7 billion. We do export food, mostly grain, but not as much as we import. Some imports are tropical products like cocoa, tea and coffee which we can't produce here. But why, when we export a respectable £30 millions' worth of Cheddar cheese to the EC – a British speciality, after all – do we also import £27 millions' worth of Cheddar cheese each year from Holland, and a staggering £124 million-worth from Eire? Two-thirds of the tomatoes we import come from Holland: over half the tomatoes we eat. Much of the meat we eat in Britain is from Holland, much from Denmark. Apple consumption is rising, but the EU is paying British farmers to grub up orchards of attractive old apple trees. Why? Because we eat more French apples than British ones.[3]

According to SAFE, 70 per cent of Britain's food trade deficit is accounted for by trade like this, with EU countries with climates similar to our own: Belgium, Holland, Denmark, Germany, Ireland, France. In other words the UK spends 4.7 billion pounds a year on food which could have been grown or manufactured at home. The UK also exports similar goods to these same countries. Exports and imports are both rising: a crazy 'food swap' mirroring the growth in domestic food miles at the international level. Cheap imports are undercutting local produce and putting British growers out of business. The SAFE Alliance reports that UK salad growers are 'facing ruin because of competition from cheap imports as a result of oversupply within the EU': cheap cucumbers and lettuces from Spain, produced in an EU-sponsored drive to create employment there. Ten thousand hectares of horticulture have been lost in this country in recent years. The land use which replaces horticulture is almost always less labour-intensive, and probably less nutritionally sound: fresh, locally-grown fruit and vegetable crops are being replaced by the grains and oilseeds which go into animal feed and processed foods. Less valuable, but more profitable. The official response, apparently, is to tell UK producers that they must export too.

Yet, bizzarely, some importers of produce are in fact growers themselves. At first sight, the idea that British growers are importing foreign produce seems illogical. In fact, the biggest growers can profit out of this situation. They are importing out of the domestic season to keep up the round-the-year supply demanded by supermarkets (who in turn of course insist that this is demanded by consumers).

Growers who supply the big retailers have often found it necessary to invest heavily in washing and packing premises and equipment, so they are under financial pressure to keep the investment busy. As agricultural economist Sean Rickard (formerly of the NFU) put it on the BBC Food Programme: 'The horticulture industry invested millions of pounds in holdings. If they can keep packing houses and

3. Figures from *Food From Britain*.

employees working throughout the year, they lower their costs of production and therefore provide their products more cheaply to the supermarkets in what is an increasingly competitive world.' Thus, once a grower has gone down the road of growing for the supermarkets, they actually *need* us to buy out-of-season produce to help them pay back the investment they have made to get into bed with the supermarket in the first place. Though it is not so much the 'free market' which causes this as the scale of the supermarkets' demands, for volume, continuity and capital- and resource-expensive preparation and packaging.

Sean Rickard's perspective is echoed by Lincolnshire vegetable grower Tony Worth, a member of the working group which drew up the *Food From Britain* report on vegetable trading in Britain, published in 1992. 'There is nothing wrong with imported produce,' he insisted. When asked if British growers would benefit if the public ate more seasonally the reply was, 'Why should they?'

'That is the whole point of the free market: consumers can have what you want when you want it as long as you can afford it. We are part of the European Union now, if other people can produce the stuff, why shouldn't we eat it?' He did not see any need to encourage British consumers to eat more British vegetables. 'Europe is a single market. We should be eating more vegetables from wherever. We should not think we have any rights to the job at all.'

Pressed on the plight of British growers who are going out of business – many of them smaller growers who never dared borrow the money for pack houses in the first place – he replied: 'Well, some are going out of business for other reasons to do with their own financial and managerial inefficiency.' Indeed, he did not seem to want other growers active in the marketplace anyway. 'If demand went up what it would do is open up the market to those growers who are not doing vegetables at the moment and do not know the ins and outs, and they would come a cropper.

'With an increase in price you start getting in people who have no idea what is going on, what it's all about, they're the ones who will fail. They will overproduce and the price will come down. It's not a gloomy picture though, because if you manage it properly and do the marketing properly there is no reason why you can't make a living.'

Doug Henderson of the Fresh Produce Consortium – another committee man, this time on the government's Nutrition Task Force – was no more enthusiastic in defence of the average British grower. The way forward was bigger organisations, tighter discipline, efficiency. 'Much of the domestic sector remains fragmented, and so it is much more difficult for growers to reach the critical mass to properly satisfy the demands for huge retailers. A number of large co-ops have been successful, for example ENFRU, marketing English apples, have nearly 50 per cent of our apple output through the co-op.' He dismissed one of the (few) regional vegetable marketing initiatives as 'not a shining example', preferring larger farming organisations with central control of vast acreages of land.

The death of seasonality is not just relevant to fruit and vegetable producers. It would make life easier for farmers like John Armitage, who has a small sheep farm high on Exmoor. 'Local butchers do not take all our stock, meaning we have to sell surplus into the markets at the low prices they set. Yet of course at other times of the year, butchers in this area are buying lamb from elsewhere, for instance New Zealand where the sheep are reared on an 'easy care' system,' – that is, not really looking after the sheep like we have to here. The public would not tolerate the way New Zealand sheep are reared, here in the British countryside! Yet if only consumers decided to buy lamb when it was in season, from June up until Christmas, and buy other meat like beef at other times, demand would fit in more closely with our production.'

THE FREE TRADE WINDS BLOW CHILLY

Though the supermarkets' insistence on year-round availability of seasonal produce is an important factor, probably the biggest threat to British farmers and growers is simply the pressure from imports which, despite transport costs, are cheap. Just as British workers are having to exploit themselves and their families more and more in order to stay in work, British producers are having to exploit themselves and their land more and more to remain 'competitive'. This situation is likely to worsen as international free trade, under the GATT – the General Agreement on Tariffs and Trade, finalised in 1994 and policed by the World Trade Organisation – really gets going.

Some countries have much lower land and labour costs than our own. One expert on the international pig trade has warned British pig farmers that China, the world's biggest pig producer, could soon be looking for other markets, 'developments in Vietnam, Taiwan and Thailand needed watching', and a major pig-keeping revolution was taking place in the US, with massive 50,000-sow breeding units being set up.

Suffolk pig farmers James and David Black, who hold a supermarket contract, and rear both indoor and outdoor animals, are already taking this threat seriously. David Black joined a party visiting South America to inspect pig production. A foot-and-mouth scare in Denmark meant that at the last moment the Europeans were barred from visiting one operation – which is British-owned – but they still found out something about it. According to nephew James: 'There are apparently 22,000 sows there, and they're finishing pigs with their own feed, milled on site, and they have their own slaughterhouse. With those kind of comparative costs of production they could drive us all out of business, if the supermarkets decide that price rules and the only criterion they look at is price.

'The capacity for production in the US is also phenomenal. British vegetable producers are being squeezed very hard by cost competition from imports at the moment, but with our markets open to the world, America could zap UK production in more than just vegetables. We were talking the other day here, and we were seriously wondering whether we would be in business in 10, 15 years time. If consumers don't make a positive decision to support us, it will be: well let's open up a golf course instead, really.'

Free trade favours the largest, most powerful organisations, those able to move to where land and labour are cheapest and those who cut prices until competitors worldwide are driven out of business, leaving the field clear for them to make all the money there is to be made. These largest operators are not countries, as a rule, but companies, frequently transnational ones.

A GLOBAL GOODBYE TO LOCAL STANDARDS

Clearly there is tremendous commercial pressure to drive down production standards to the lowest common level, even when local standards have been set for domestic production. Local laws still apply – for example to pesticide use or animal welfare – but these laws cannot usually be applied to imports, so the overseas producer is immediately at an advantage.

British fruit and vegetable growers feel it is unfair that compounds banned to them are permitted to their competitors. Fruit and vegetable growers are lobbying to be allowed to use the same chemicals as their

European competitors – or alternatively, for banned chemicals to be banned on imports too. Import bans would be a breach of free trade regulations and would have to be defended to international free trade bodies with watertight scientific evidence. Therefore liberalisation of local laws or continuing commercial difficulties for domestic growers are the likelier outcomes. Blanket 'liberalisation' is what happened with food additives: when the European 'single market' was inaugurated in 1992, an additive allowed in one European country became allowed in all, regardless of pre-existing local bans.[4]

Sometimes standards are improved all round. Animal welfare regulations in Europe are, on the whole, becoming tighter. For example, sow tethering is to be banned throughout the EU. Currently, pregnant sows may at present be held on a very short tether on a concrete floor. The sows often thrash their heads, crash against the stall sides and scream in the struggle to free themselves. Sow tethers are to be outlawed throughout Europe in 2006. The problem for British producers is that the tethers are due to be outlawed in Britain by 1999, anticipating the European ban by seven years. Many observers predict that, with 'tethered' pork perfectly legal to import – since it would not represent a notable threat to public health (unlike, say British beef was deemed after BSE) – seven years is all it will take to drive British producers out of business altogether.

Even when there is a public health argument, it can be hard to impose an import ban. Because of safety worries Denmark recently banned seven pesticides widely used in other countries in the EU, including atrazine, lindane and paraquat. The bans have been welcomed by Danish trades unions, but because the banning 'may conflict with EU legislation', it is being examined by the European Commission.

This is a classic example of the way free trade makes a mockery of local standards. James Black is infuriated. 'There will be pork in products on the shelves of UK supermarkets from Denmark and Holland where tethering and stalls are still being used. It a complete unlevelling of the playing field.'

If British consumers always chose 'raised without tethering' pork,

4. In 1996, the Food Commission reported that the committee advising the government of whether or not to license Olestra no-fat fat (see chapter two) were allegedly warned that is it was not licensed in the UK Olestra's manufacturer would 'simply get it approved elsewhere in Europe then Britain would have to accept it anyway'.

bacon, sausages, luncheon meat, pork pies and ham, the British producers wouldn't be worried. But, unfortunately, no pork products carry such a label, nor do we see a picture of a miserable tethered pig on imported meat, labelled: 'The pork in this sausage was raised according to strict standards of cost control, in pursuit of which its mother was tied up on a short leash'.

As a final irony, by the same token a further threat hangs over all European pig production after 2006 if – and why wouldn't it – tethering were to remain legal elsewhere in the world.

This is exactly the fate predicted for European poultry farmers by proponents of low-cost intensive production. According to an industry spokesman quoted in *Poultry World*: 'Ethical' considerations and animal welfare regulation would leave the European poultry industry 'operating with its hands tied behind its back stuck in the twentieth century and reduced to producing antique, niche market chicken ... unable to compete with the up-to-the-minute Third World industries with access to all the animal health products (sic) banned in the west.' Allowing for the obvious desire of a poultry feed additive manufacturer to promote his own products, there is still a certain ring of truth in those observations.

The General Agreement on Tariffs and Trades, or GATT, was designed to promote maximum trading between countries. The theory runs that each country is best at doing particular things (selling insurance, growing soya), and can do those things more cheaply than everyone else. So if everyone does what they are best at, and everyone can sell their product more cheaply to the whole of the rest of the world, we will all be greatly enriched by a world fuller and fuller of soybean cake and insurance policies.

Traditionally countries have, by and large, tried to protect their own industries from 'cheap foreign imports' by imposing import duties, or tariffs, on rival goods from overseas. But such tariffs are against the spirit of free trade, and the world's nations have by and large signed the GATT agreement to do away with most of these and, further, to bow to the authority of the World Trade Organisation which enforces the GATT. Anyone who doesn't want to play may find that their exported goods are refused entry into other countries. As the world's economies have been deliberately encouraged to become more and more dependent on export trade, nations are reluctant to take the risk of falling foul of the rules.

As the GATT stands at present there is very little room for

individual countries to refuse to import a product because of something that has happened outside its borders. For example, the US banned the import of Mexican yellowfin tuna because so many dolphins are caught and drowned in the tuna nets. But in 1991 Mexico objected to the ban. A GATT dispute settlement panel found in Mexico's favour, ruling that the ban contravened the GATT agreement.

The panel's reasoning should worry all those many consumers who, as opinion polls have repeatedly shown, do care about the way their food was produced. The GATT panel stated that Article III:4 of the GATT agreement 'calls for a comparison of the treatment of imported tuna as a product with [the treatment] of domestic tuna as a product'. 'Regulations governing the taking of dolphins incidental to the taking of tuna,' the panel insisted, 'could not possibly affect tuna as a product'.

If this attitude remains entrenched in the international free trade process it bodes very ill for those wanting to maintain and improve standards of food production. If, for example, the battery cage were banned in Britain (which itself would probably not be possible unless it were banned Europe-wide) – as Philip Lymbery of Compassion in World Farming warns, European producers could face devastating price competition from non-European battery egg producers. Eggs, after all, last quite long enough to withstand a lorry journey from, for instance, the former Soviet Union or North Africa. The GATT administrators could rule that the eggs, as products, were the same, and that a ban on battery eggs was therefore in breach of free trade.

Lymbery warns that local democratic control of these issues has become meaningless as regional and international trading bodies are given more and more power. 'In this country we have always looked to government to ban this and ban that, for example, the battery cage. What has happened since the single market came in is that the government has fallen back absolutely on the European argument: "we would disadvantage our producers so we will have to wait until EU does it as a whole". GATT does the same thing on a global scale. So we have the prospect of Europe saying: we will have to wait for the whole world to change.'

The Codex commission is being set up within GATT to arbitrate on whether a food standard set by a particular nation, for example a pesticide limit or a ban on an additive, constitutes an unfair barrier to trade. There is no room at all in this structure for ethical criteria. If

Codex deems a particular standard to be unjustifiable, any country perceiving that its trading interests are damaged by the regulation can apply retaliatory trade sanctions. As Tim Lang and Colin Hines wrote in *The New Protectionism*: 'If decisions about your life and environment ... are taken by far-off people and bodies, it is almost impossible to affect those decisions directly.'

There is theoretically some scope for flexibility, at least within Europe. For instance, according to Compassion in World Farming the Treaty of Rome makes allowance for suspension of a trade which harms animal health or offends public morality. In practice, however, governments reluctant to act have an almost perfect smoke-screen to hide behind when they tell their discontented subjects, 'we would love to change it but Brussels/the World Trade Organisation won't let us'.

THE MAD OFFICIALS

Like the requirements of the big retailers, the requirements of food hygiene regulation often suit large producers better than small. Impossibly expensive regulations have forced delicious and wholesome locally produced foods towards extinction – along with their producers. The UK's reputation for red tape certainly holds up in food retailing. Food marketing researcher Harriet Festing warns that, 'Farmers considering selling direct may be put off by some of the most stringent food hygiene regulations in the world'.

Regulation is a double-edged sword, very much like labelling. It may serve to prevent shoddy practices and in a world where consumers have no idea where their food comes from, then regulations may clamp down on the worst of the unhygienic 'cowboy' producers who might otherwise be cheating and harming unsuspecting shoppers. However, reputation and customer knowledge can perform a similar task, while permitting producer and consumer more choice. Many small producers feel that they are perfectly capable of controlling cleanliness and other standards without the need for the expensive capital equipment so often demanded by regulations: stainless steel floors, or automatic taps which come on without being touched or separate rooms for this task and that task, or changing rooms and showers for staff.

Small producer Julian Rose, whose 'green top' unpasteurised milk round was wiped out by supermarket competition, is cynical: 'I'm quite sure the body imposing these ludicrous standards is lobbied by those larger organisations who can afford this kind of equipment, and can also get to Brussels. They are using their influence in order to wipe out the opposition.' Cheesemaker Humphrey Errington agrees. After soft cheese came under attack in 1989 in a scare over listeriosis, Errington commented: 'The reason the government seems to be directing its big guns at unpasteurised milk producers has more to do with the big dairy industry's concerns at the erosion of their share of the market'.

European regulations have closed down a great many smaller, local abattoirs in Britain. For instance, abattoirs are now obliged to have a vet present at all times. Economies of scale mean this cost is affordable for the huge industrial 'meat plants', but wipe away all profitability of smaller, local abattoirs. This trend, coupled with 'rationalisation' in the large meat processing firms, means that farmers are having to drive further and further with their animals: a journey of 70 or 80 miles by lorry may now be necessary instead of 10 or 20. This is expensive in time and fuel and greatly increases animal suffering. For smaller producers, the whole business is sometimes no longer worthwhile.

One mixed organic farm in Wales has already stopped rearing pigs because, with the closure of the three nearest abattoirs, the journey has become simply too long for it to be worth their while. 'The abattoir requirements have forced the three nearest slaughterhouses out of business. We used to do a few pigs – organic – and as we only had to take them 10 miles to the abattoir it was well worth it: our local customers were happy to buy the meat. Now they can't get it from us any more, as the journey to the nearest abattoir is so long it just isn't worth it.' They fear they will also have to give up producing organic lamb. 'We may end up just having to sell next year's lambs to the market, where nobody will give a damn that they were organically reared.'

This producer agreed with Julian Rose. 'I do feel strongly that small producers are being penalised. The number of regulations are ludicrous, yet at the same time the government is telling us to diversify and add value. Well an obvious way to add value is to sell produce direct. This is becoming impossible.'

As a final irony, the presence of vets at slaughterhouses and markets did not stop BSE infected cattle getting into the food chain, nor has it succeeded in reversing the rise of food poisoning. This rise is indeed attributed by the World Health Organisation to the very high demand for meat and to 'enormous quantities of animal feed ... imported'. This would seem to suggest that large, rather than small, operations might be behind the problem, stainless steel floors or no stainless steel floors.

Infections are endemic in many large intensive animal units, and the situation is exacerbated by large scale catering, fast-food and restaurant outlets where corners are cut for speed and profit, and clientele may not be regular. One US burger chain is known to have killed several of its customers through food poisoning. Whereas the Welsh meat producer quoted earlier pointed out that she did not need rigid regulations to force her to maintain scrupulous hygiene. Her buildings and processes are already as clean as any inspector might wish. She has a more rigorous quality-control system than any inspector: 'If one of our customers got food poisoning, everyone would know about it,' she points out.

This same grower is now worried about her mixed salad bags, extremely popular with the local people on their 'round' of vegetable boxes. They may technically be illegal! 'By making up the bags it's possible this could be classified as 'food processing', then we might be required to set up all kinds of expensive premises complying with hygiene regulations, which would of course be out of the question.'

Farming researcher Mark Redmond regrets the effect of rigid regulation on local marketing and local economies. 'For meat some of the regulations are ludicrous. It is so difficult for farmers to meet them all. One effect has been to drive it all underground – everyone is doing it [selling meat privately], of course. If you want half a pig, there is always someone who can fix you up. But people are selling to people they know – they wouldn't be comfortable with a stranger, after all, they might be the environmental health officer. 'The local community has always had links to farmers, which ought to be perfectly legitimate and are now covert.'

Many British egg producers were also hit, because they were unable to meet the costs imposed by salmonella testing regulations brought in in 1988. Salmonella spreads rapidly through large, densely stocked poultry flocks, but for a couple of years small, carefully kept, healthy flocks had to be salmonella tested equally as often as the thousands-strong battery populations.

But an example from Australia shows how determined consumers and producers can have the last laugh. A group of farmers and growers around the Australian city of Brisbane got together and started selling direct to customers, firstly via a box delivery, then by setting up their own shop in town. The organic free-range eggs they produced fell foul of one of Australia's food hygiene regulations, and it turned out it was illegal to sell them without expensive and burdensome changes to the way they were produced and sold. The shop, however, continued to sell the eggs clearly marked as 'unfit for human consumption'! Because the customers knew the growers, they were able to make up their own minds about whether or not these eggs were fit, and, thus, to secure for themselves the kind of eggs they wanted at an affordable price.

Some regulations do not seem to have any point at all, most notably, the cosmetic regulations determining the size, shape and colouring of fruit and vegetables. In reams and reams of regulations, more reminiscent of something from Kafka or George Orwell than anything connected with the realities of growing, eating and enjoying food, EU regulations specify the permissible stripiness of striped apples, curvature of bananas, length and diameter of carrots, and variability of apples. Produce failing to make these grades is classed down and will fetch a low price or be considered unsaleable (especially through supermarkets) – however delicious and nutritious it may be.

The effect of these regulations is to oblige producers to choose varieties which produce yields of consistent size, shape and colour, rather than to think in terms of other criteria, such as flavour, nutritiousness, disease resistance (meaning less spray needed) which consumers might consider more important. Once again, identical sizes and shapes of produce suit huge growers who raise their crops with chemicals and harvest by machine, but are a complete nonsense to the craft producer.

THE ORGANIC OFFICIALS

Julian Rose does not exempt the organic movement when he complains of red tape. 'You should see the amount of paperwork we have to do here to keep our symbol,' he protests. 'It's out of this world.' He isn't the only one to object. Retailers wanting to sell produce marked 'organic' must comply too. Detailed regulations about separate counters, storage space, containers, and extremely painstaking record-keeping are demanded of anyone who wishes to register.

Qualifying for a symbol can be particularly onerous for retailers who want to sell some organic produce alongside a majority of conventional produce. Bakers, for example, need elaborate schedules in order to be able to sell bread as organic. It is not just a matter of buying in a sack of organic flour.

These requirements, the Soil Association insists, are to prevent fraud

– it would be possible to substitute cheaper, conventional produce without these safeguards. Unfortunately, while fraud may well have been prevented, the regulations are too much for many, and so customers are denied the chance to choose organic produce.

Happily, in small, local systems, where people know and trust one another, these obstacles have been overcome by replacing the symbol with personal knowledge and personal trust, as we will see in chapter nine.

THE RURAL NOT-SO-IDYLL

The rural community is desperate for some change, some new life. Employment and economic activity in general is in desperately short supply. Increasingly, what paid work there is casual, seasonal, extremely badly paid – and offered mainly to women. Although as a whole agricultural employment provides only about 2 per cent of jobs in this country, in rural areas such as the West Country, the northern uplands, Wales and Northern Ireland, agriculture is a significant employer, with 20–35 per cent of people depending on farm work. In such areas, trends towards agricultural mechanisation, which have led to a 26 per cent drop in farm labouring jobs in 10 years, are felt very keenly indeed.

The countryside can be a particularly difficult place to be poor or unemployed, and in rural areas, these problems affect people in different ways from people in the inner city. Poverty in the countryside tends to be less visible. Such statutory 'safety net' provision that does exist, may only be available in an office that is just too far away to get to. Rural culture can make claiming benefit such a source of shame that if people cannot do so secretly, they prefer to go without. As the Church of England reported in *Faith in the Countryside*: 'Work done by the Citizens Advice Bureaux ... has shown how difficult it is ... to ensure those who have a right to entitlement first appreciate that fact, and secondly feel able to apply for it without their peers being aware of it.'

Everywhere in Britain, people would on the whole far rather work than sign on, but this seems to be especially true in the countryside, and people seem prepared to tolerate even higher levels of poverty and deprivation, and even lower wages, rather than seek out benefits. Thus, while unemployment may be at lower percentages than in cities, low pay is rife, and for women, the norm. In 1985, 77 per cent of female manual workers in rural areas were earning below low-pay thresholds, and rural incomes continue to be even more inequitable than those in the cities. Low incomes and rich neighbours mean housing problems for many. In 1990, average weekly earnings of a couple in Shropshire would no longer anything like support a mortgage on a modest three-bedroomed semi. In that year the housing survey showed that 606 households needed affordable rented accommodation, but only 36 such homes were available.

Income inequality is greater in rural areas than urban areas. The idea that poor people in the countryside have more social stability and social support than those in the cities is largely myth. The reality is that at least half the population in rural areas has no close family living nearby. Rural people – rich and poor – have become increasingly isolated. A Herefordshire man who still lives in the village where he grew up told his local paper that in his youth he knew most of the people in the village, but now 'I hardly know anyone.' A neighbour commented that people now 'keep themselves to themselves much more.' As rural populations have ceased to be workers in and customers of the rural economy, the opportunities for social contact have evaporated.

Young people in the countryside who can find neither jobs nor housing do what the dispossessed rural poor all over the world do: they drift to the cities in the hope of finding work. The homelessness charity Centrepoint says more housing for young rural people is needed to stop them gravitating into city centres. As Jules Pretty and Rupert Howes wrote in a report on British agriculture: 'Rural culture in Britain would now appear as fragile as any in the poor countries of the third world'.

The fact that the urban population wants to – and does – move out of the cities to the countryside is doing little to help the rural economy. Many who move in are rich, contributing to inequality and the squeeze on housing, and living and shopping quite outside the local economy. Money is earned in the cities and spent in the supermarkets. Some even buy up rural housing then only use it at weekends, arriving on Friday night from the city with the boot of the Peugeot already stocked up at Sainsbury's the night before.

The Church of England reports that 'the ongoing repopulation of the countryside by the more affluent has done little to improve the lot of the less well-off. As the countryside is "repopulated" with older people without children, richer families with cars who shop at supermarkets, not in the village, who may educate their children outside the state system, vital services such as buses, village shops and schools decline. Centralisation has also moved essential services, such as local hospitals, further out of reach.'

Supermarkets have been enabled to penetrate into rural areas by roadbuilding and road-widening – which makes it economic for them to transport goods so far – so that even when people shop in a supermarket in a rural area, most of the money they spend is 'repatriated' to the centre: to the big chains, national suppliers, and associated haulage and packaging operations. Meanwhile village shops, which are in a much better position to buy from local producers, and which are a lifeline to those without cars, lose business and close down. The number of Devon villages with a shop dropped by 31 per cent between 1967 and 1991, with 9 per cent going in the last four years of that time. As Ian Hutchcroft of Devon County Council's environment department puts it: 'the trend is for money to flow out of the county in ever increasing amounts, and food is one category of business where this has been very noticeable. Even for food produced in the county, much of it will be transported for pre-packaging and warehousing and transported back to Devon to sell, so most of the economic benefits of the value added go to businesses in the centre rather than our own economy.'

Hutchcroft, like many others, is also concerned about the social effects of these trends: 'Farmers are becoming increasingly isolated, partly through lack of trading with local people, partly because of incomers in the population. There is a mental health aspect to this, which concerns the health authority'.

People too poor to afford a car are relatively much poorer in the countryside than carless people in towns, or people in the countryside a generation ago. Today, there may be nothing at all within reasonable walking distance: no school, no shop, no doctor – and no work. Yet one in four rural households has no car. People dependent on public transport are in a cruel poverty trap: employers have refused jobs to those dependent on rural public transport as, even when the route joins home and workplace, timetables do not permit flexible working, and services are thought to be unreliable. If people do get the job, they might spend up to 40 per cent of their earnings getting there and back, the Church of England found.

With the increasing squeeze on services, including those particularly vital to the rural poor, such as subsidised public transport, the responsibility that all community members have to one another to keep the local economy alive, is thrown into sharp relief. State provision is essential, but it can only complement, never replace, jobs and wages. The countryside needs buses, and it needs jobs at the end of the bus route.

What is needed above all is a thriving local economy. Money spent in the countryside should be spent in local businesses – so that local people can earn a living. And since one of the main sources of wealth in the countryside is food production, and since all of us eat food, we can all contribute to the local rural economy by ensuring the maximum possible of our food spending goes direct to local producers, both of primary commodities (joints of meat, sacks of potatoes) and locally processed cheese, bread, sausages, pies, preserves – whatever it is that local firms produce.

Money earned by local farms tends to go back into local businesses. In an NFU document which signals a recognition that all-out intensification may not always be the answer, the union estimates that each £1,000 of farm income generates £2,000 in the local economy. Money that farmers can pay to labourers is equally valuable, with each £1 generating £2.20 in the local economy. On the other hand, the NFU points out that money earned by 'incomers' in urban-based work ('telecottaging') is far less valuable to the local economy, because of the urban shopping habits that go with this lifestyle. Less intensive farming creates jobs. Local food processing creates jobs. And as we will see in chapter nine, buying produce direct from farms boosts farm incomes. So: well-produced food from farms which do not exploit chemicals, plants and animals to excess, locally processed and locally purchased, is not only good to eat, it means a job and income lifeline throughout the rural economy.

HELP US OUT OF THIS HOLE

Many farmers are now stuck. They have followed the advice and intensified. They have sunk large amounts of capital – often borrowed against the land – into sheds and slurry pits, machinery, packhouses, automatic feeding systems, and now need to produce mammoth yields to earn enough to pay the interest.

In 1991 the agricultural sector collectively was £10 billion in debt to banks; a horrifying 70 per cent of net farm income was going to service debt – a situation worse even than that faced by most Third World countries. Such profound economic dependence may give farmers little mental space to question the techniques they are obliged to employ. Farmers in this position cannot risk any change – like going organic – which would lead to even a temporary fall in income, as this could lead to defaulting on debt repayments, which would push the farm straight into the hands of the bank.

As Buckinghamshire farmer Geoff Hawkins says: 'If it were possible for farmers to make it pay to grow differently, I'm sure they would be prepared to do it. I work with a farming and wildlife group and I have noticed that farmers are much more concerned about wildlife these days. Farmers are in a way very conservative and want to do things the same way they have always done them, but also if you can show that it pays, they are willing to try almost anything. And I think they would enjoy working in a way that was less damaging to the environment, if they could still make a living.'

Dirk Bauer, who set up the British Organic Milk Producers, agrees: 'I had a stand at the Royal Agricultural Show and I explained what I was doing to the farmers. 90 per cent of them said they would go organic if there was an outlet, they would start tomorrow.

'They hate to put fertiliser on the land and inject the cows with antibiotics and chemicals to keep them on their feet. They'd rather do away with all that. They know their grandad did without it and he brought them all up that way, but they're forced into it. I am convinced the conventional farmer is not at fault. They have no choice because of the banks and so forth, changing over is impossible. I am 100 per cent convinced the majority would turn organic tomorrow if society allows them to do so. If consumers are willing to have healthy food, they should be going out and screaming for it.'

Even an outspoken critic of modern farming like Compassion in World Farming's Philip Lymbery is ready to point out that farmers are not the villains of the piece. He too feels that farmers on the whole would welcome the chance to make a decent living, using more humane and environmentally friendly techniques. 'The desire is there. But if you have been brought up through college education and beyond with all the research, the reps and advisors telling you to farm in a particular way – then told by the public: "it's wrong", it does feel like a kick in the teeth. The system has ensured we don't see eye to eye.'

The need to continue to make a living forces many farmers to defend their practices, he suspects. 'When we do get rid of a system such as the veal crate you won't find a single farmer to defend it, though it was a different story 20 years ago when so many were using them.

'I don't think we're so far apart. Farmers have been encouraged by the system to take up intensive animal rearing and now they have a lot of money sunk into it.' Lymbery adds that retailers risk stifling the move to more humane rearing by pricing 'humane' meat as high as the market will bear (the 'luxury ghetto' again). 'Although it may cost 15 to 30 per cent more to rear meat humanely, why are consumers charged 50 – 100 per cent more? In many instances it is the retailer who makes the profit and not the farmer. This doesn't help either the farmers or the animals.'

One option for a farmer wanting to escape from the intensive farming 'treadmill' is to convert to organic production, so that increased production costs can be recovered with higher prices paid for organic produce. There is, however, a 'changeover period' where income can fall drastically before picking up again – and this may be too much for the fragile farm finances to cover. Although MAFF now offer a subsidy to farms in conversion, and one day's free organic husbandry advice, this is widely condemned as inadequate, especially when compared to the massive resources pumped into conventional growing.

Other 'reduced input' techniques seem to have only small impacts on income, but the information and encouragement from farming advisory bodies is missing, meaning that farmers have to cling to methods they understand. Consumer pressure is feeding through, but we certainly all need to make more fuss. Unless 'reformed' farmers can signal their intentions and practices to sympathetic consumers, and unless consumers can find them and support them, they will simply be eaten up by the competition. However, of course they can signal to consumers. They can sell to them directly, or through outlets where the farmer's identity is respected and valued.

The majority of farmers probably still fail to conform to the efficient industry ideal. Perhaps we haven't got the climate – or the subsidies or the obedient temperaments – to win the international competition. The NFU's Marketing Advisor David Bawcutt could barely conceal his impatience with, and his low opinion of, the average British vegetable grower when he grumbled that 'they don't like being told what to do'. He would not see independence and individuality as an asset. But perhaps consumers do.

It seems that a great many farmers still believe that food production really should be about quality, value, sustainability, individuality. Small farmers want to keep their small farms viable, and if possible, viable for their children. They don't want enormous debts; they don't want to be cogs in a machine. Consumers are equally unhappy about industrially-produced food and about an industrial-looking countryside. Mammoth efficiency-mad organisations stand between the two (and get rich in the process). They can, however, be bypassed.

Those farmers not quite so close to the establishment are indicating that they want to talk, and they want to hear. They suspect, perhaps quite rightly, that the only way for them to survive is to offer a personal, quality service at a reasonable price. Although cheap food does no-one any favours, there is no need for good food to have Harrods prices, either, as later chapters will show. Without the middlemen, prices to consumers can stay low or even fall, while the money available to the farmer rises and wastage drops, freeing her or him to farm more flexibly, responsively, carefully. This book contains many examples of farmers and producers doing just that.

Consumer contact would make it clear to growers that this is what people want. Devon County Council's environment department is interested in direct marketing as a financial lifeline for farmers, and research overseas has suggested to them that a more sustainable farming style would flow naturally from such links. As spokesman Ian Hutchcroft says: 'In the United States experience shows that once the link with consumers has been made, the farming style tends to go towards organic.'

Exmoor stock farmer John Armitage feels sure people would like to buy his meat, knowing where it came from, and that if he could sell it directly he could get a better return and protect his holding. And he would be more than happy to accommodate customer wishes in return. If he and his colleagues were able to sell directly to customers: 'we would have no problem signing an undertaking to use no chemicals, for example. A completely organic system might not suit the way we farm, but we would certainly be keen to give quality assurances, and I would certainly be happy to talk all day with customers who wanted to ask about how the meat is produced.'

Charles Peers, who runs a part-organic mixed farm in Oxfordshire, also regrets the distance between farmers and consumers. 'We don't really get customer feedback. We would really like to know what customers do want, instead of being told by the supermarkets. It is very difficult for smaller farmers to know what to do; a clear mandate from customers would be very valuable.' Peers feels it is wrong that consumers cannot identify the source of most of the food they buy, wrong that it is hard to choose food from a 'kinder' system unless it is under a specific symbol such as organic. 'Ask more questions as to the origin of what you buy,' Peers urges. More consumer interest would automatically favour 'better' agricultural systems, by indicating to retailers that these factors are important for trade.

Like many farmers, Peers is concerned by the mismatch between the realities of his job, and the way we have been encouraged to shop: ever changing, subject to fashion, getting whatever we want when we feel like it, unconstrained by any hint of the seasonal rhythms outside the supermarket doors. A 'free trade' future in which cost competition is allowed to make all the decisions could mean financial tragedy for farmers and a landscape tragedy for us. If current trends continue, we could see our working landscape, potential source of fresh, healthy, delicious, life-sustaining food for all generations, reduced to infinite acres of the three most profitable crops, interspersed with theme park attractions, windsurfing lakes, off-road vehicle circuits, golf courses, and 'country parks'. The logic of the free market and comparative advantage – of which British farmers apparently have very little – could finish off British agriculture as we know it, very rapidly. On the other hand, if consumers were prepared to adapt a bit to the realities of nature, many growers would be willing to go more than half way to meet them.

7

TROUBLE EVERYWHERE

The troubles faced by British farmers are faced by farmers all over the world. Intensive production on a scale big enough for bulk export has only ever suited the few, but it has managed to harm the many: the smaller farmers, the environment and the consumer. This is as true overseas as it is in Britain – and in some other countries, the damage is even more acute. Agricultural 'progress' – high yields, mechanisation, commercial success – has shut out many farmers, especially poorer ones, and driven them into mushrooming third world slums. In Europe, too, gearing agriculture away from local needs towards international buying and selling trends is threatening the distinctive and beautifully adapted cultures and landscapes which make countries unique, and which distinguish each region, each county, from the next.

Traditional, sustainable methods of farming everywhere are under attack. The dry centre of Spain, the Extremadura and New Castile, has been the granary of the country for centuries. A careful, labour-intensive style of cultivation developed, growing wheat and other crops in rotation with grazing livestock, under oak and olive trees. This system stabilises the soil and maintains fertility: animals manure the land, and the trees protect against erosion and provide valuable fruits, including acorns to raise the pigs for Spain's uniquely delicious pork and ham.

The system has continued sustainably for centuries despite the great harshness of the conditions – reflected in the region's name. But the arid climate and poor soils mean farmers cannot produce bumper yields at low prices. They cannot compete with the grain prairies of other European countries and are being driven out of business. Farther north, near Spain's rainlashed Atlantic coasts, family farms have for centuries produced top-quality meat for the home market. They too are being squeezed out by lower-quality, intensively-reared, cheap imports from the Netherlands and France.

One by one the farmers are giving up, they or their children are drifting to the cities to look for jobs, all too often ending up on unemployment benefit; Spain's unemployment rate is one of the highest in Europe. The stunning countryside, shaped by careful, continuous husbandry over the centuries, featured in a hundred travel posters and loved by Spaniards and foreigners alike, will eventually fall apart. In its place will come intensive, irrigated, chemical agriculture, and eucalyptus and poplar plantations. People's culture and livelihoods will be destroyed, and so will their environment.

Those who remain in the countryside do not all find work in the new rural industries. The bulldozers, engineers, pesticide salesmen and sprayplane pilots employed in intensive irrigated agriculture and forestry are mostly outsiders. One group, CEPA (*Coordinadora Extremena de Proteccion Ambiental*, a federation of environmental organisations) reports that some of the fires which periodically occur in eucalyptus and pine plantations 'are possibly started on purpose by country people who would rather see the timber burn in the hope of gaining back their grazing land'.

In order to keep these farms viable today, farmers would have to receive some kind of financial support. But this would not need to be as much as is spent supporting them unproductively on social security payments: at the time of writing, Spain's 1997 unemployment budget was 1.5 trillion pesetas (£7.6 billion) and unemployment was estimated to be running at 22 per cent. But such an allowance, unlike unemployment benefit, would count as a subsidy to individual farmers, and such subsidies are frowned on in the free-trade belief system. They would be considered 'inefficient' in a system which sees efficiency only in the narrow terms of yield per hectare, with all other benefits ignored. Instead Spanish farmers must stand disconsolately in the dole queue, surely the worst possible buy for Spanish taxpayers' money. It is hard to see how money paying someone to exist while they endure the humiliation of constant unemployment is better spent than money subsidising wheat grown in a dignified, traditional, environmentally-friendly way. But those are the rules.

Meanwhile, European money is being poured in to 'modernise' and 'develop' the Spanish countryside. Public money spent on the infrastructure (roads, irrigation, drainage), which is proportionally far more useful to huge mechanised enterprises than to small, labour-intensive ones, is not seen as subsidy. Infrastructure on this scale also devastates the environment. Tree-clearance for mechanised growing, and crude river 'management' for irrigation threaten the habitats of numerous rare European species: the black vulture, the imperial eagle, the Iberian lynx. In the *Ecologist* magazine CEPA describes the EU 'Operational Programme for the Improvement of Farming' in the Extremadura as 'environmental and economic madness'. More money will doubtless have to be found before long for 'conservation' – a job which the farmers had been doing for centuries.

There are farms in the south of Spain which look as though they, at least, are benefiting from international free trade: the vegetable farms of Andalucia. These farms have provided employment for some of those displaced from more traditional almond, olive and wheat farming by mechanised monocultures. However in Andalucia unemployment is if anything even higher than in the rest of the country. And the riches from the nurseries do not all stay in Spain: nurseries are often owned by foreign companies, for instance from the Netherlands.

Spanish vegetable growing is unashamedly chemical: irrigation pipes supply water and fertiliser to plants standing in little more than sand, beneath acres of plastic shadecloth and greenhouse. And there may be an environmental price to pay. Perhaps it is a coincidence, but in September 1994, at the end of a year of drought, the water in the taps in Castell de Ferro, a coast town in the midst of these greenhouses, was so salty it was impossible to drink or even to wash in. Could the pumping of groundwater for irrigation have allowed the salty Mediterranean to seep into this town's water reserves? A horticulture labourer's income – which must stay low to contribute to the 'competitive advantage' over, say, Britain – does not go so far when water must be brought in by lorry in plastic bottles, and paid for at 100 Pesetas a litre.

The idea behind the single European market is to exploit 'comparative advantage' within Europe to a maximum, so that each country concentrates on growing the product it produces most 'competitively' (that is, cheaply). Quality is not a prime consideration here. As the Spanish environmental network CEPA puts it, according to this belief system: 'All other produce, however traditional' [and indeed, I would add, however delicious]) should be gradually abandoned in favour of cheaper imports.'

Quality producers, not just in Spain but all over Europe, suffer as a result. So although French food is renowned, France's rural populations, vigorous and self-sufficient for centuries, are unable to compete on price with cheap imports rushed into the country on the Euro-highways. 'English meat, Spanish fruit and vegetables, and Italian wine have all succeeded in supplanting home-grown produce over the last 25 years.' As a final insult, the British approach to intensive cattle farming brought BSE, and a Europe-wide crash in the price of beef which looks like being the final blow to many small European farms. The French agriculture ministry has responded by offering an early retirement package, which has angered farmers: 'The government is telling us to quit at 50. It is telling us we must pay for all those years of intensive farming which we resisted in the first place.'

Setting up this single market requires vast expenditure on communications, irrigation schemes, and so forth. Rampant road-building is obvious to anyone who has visited southern Europe recently. The three EC (then) structural funds involved in this kind of project disbursed around 14 billion ECU of taxpayers' money per year in the late 1980s. Motorways have ploughed through a national park in Portugal, and are tunnelling into unspoiled valleys in the Pyrenees. CEPA, who are concerned with the farmers' plight all over Europe, warns that such a policy can mean death, rather than 'development', to rural areas. Others are equally concerned: 34,000 Galicians have signed a petition against the construction of two pulpwood factories, to be fed by endless plantations of pine and eucalypts.

TROUBLE IN THE SOUTH

In the international free trade world, the 'doctrine of comparative advantage' rules. Instead of seeing food as an integral product of a land, a soil, a culture, a climate, a palate, a way of cooking and living, nations are presuaded to buy their food from whoever produces it most cheaply. US agricultural secretary John Block apparently believes that the world should live from US wheat and maize. He described the idea that developing countries should aim for food self-reliance as 'a romantic anachronism'. Instead, according to a report in the *Food Magazine*, he urged them to 'adopt a more realistic food strategy based on the ready availability of cheap US cereals'.

Governments in developing countries often pressurise farmers and industries into producing commodities and goods for export: cash crops. They do this because they in turn have been urged to do so by the big banks and agencies as conditions of loans. Urban elites in third world countries are often keen to 'buy into' the western lifestyle: cars, skyscrapers, designer clothes, all of which come with a large foreign-currency price-tag. But the main engine driving the dash for exports is the debt – initially incurred in the 1970s by so many Third

World countries. Through a combination of rising interest rates and falling prices for traditional exports, these debts are like the credit card bill from hell. No matter how much the countries pay back, the debts just seem to get bigger.

One of the things that countries with a lot of space and a lot of sunshine can do is grow tradable bulk commodities: palm oil, cocoa, sugar, groundnuts, soy, manioc. They can also grow fresh produce – fruit and vegetables – out of their European and North American seasons. Such production is often carried out on plantations; it almost always involves expensive chemical inputs and irrigation, and often requires expensive, imported seeds as well. Developing-country governments end up promoting intensive, export-oriented farming, and condemning small-scale, traditional, and frequently more environmentally-friendly peasant farming, more likely to be growing food for home consumption, as 'backward'.

The pressure on farmers comes in the form of advice, education, rules for getting government loans, publicly-funded infrastructure projects (for example in transport, irrigation or river diversion schemes geared to help large-scale cash cropping), and enforcement of regulations. Direct or indirect government help almost always favours the farmers who are better off to begin with. This has led to a two-tier pattern of agricultural development in Third World countries, with better-off producers and landowners attracting government support and doing well, and poorer ones, without the means to begin on the modernisation path, being further and further squeezed.

Farmers producing local foods for domestic consumption have been further undermined by the policies of importing cheap grain from the industrialised world, in particular from North America, which encourages tastes for wheat and other 'northern' foods, and further squeezes producers of local staples: maize, sorghum, manioc or rice. In Latin America this process has reduced the majority of small farmers to 'semi-proletarian' status, according to David Goodman and Michael Redclift, specialists on the international food system. According to Goodman and Redclift, less than one-third of all producers in Brazil – the largest ones – have access to government credit to 'modernise' their production: most of the rest have ceased to be independent farmers, but have become agricultural labourers (which is what Goodman and Redclift mean by 'proletarianisation'), or they have migrated to the small towns and big cities as shanty-town dwellers.

Government agriculture and development policy is just as

discriminatory in other continents. In Bangladesh, plans are being advanced to spend a sum equivalent to several times the country's Gross Domestic Product on embanking the mighty Ganga and Brahmaputra rivers. The annual floods of these rivers bring fertility and fresh fish to the poor, but the flood waters are too deep for commercial, fertiliser-dependent rice varieties, so huge sums of money are to be spent to stop this annual recharge taking place.

At the same time, shrimp farming for export has destroyed the mangrove forests which protected the low-lying Bangladesh coasts from cyclones. It is the floods caused by cyclones which are mass killers: 140,000 people were drowned by a cyclone in 1991, and there have been several since. Yet while money and energy are poured into the river flood plan, infinitely cheaper cyclone shelters which could save lives on a spectacular scale, are not built.

Official encouragement of foreign currency earning has been behind the rapid growth of shrimp farming. Shrimp farming does not only expose people to cyclones – it exposes them to destitution. *Panoscope* magazine reports how Bangladeshi shrimp producers, anxious to cash in on the international demand for shrimps, attempted to rent Abdus Sabur's small subsistence plot in Khulna, in the south-west of the country. Sabur refused, as the rent offered was not enough to live on. However, the neighbouring shrimp barons would not take no for an answer: they dug through the embankment surrounding Sabur's land, and flooded it with salt water, making it useless for rice. 'I dropped to my knees and broke down in tears,' Sabur told Bangladeshi journalist Inam Ahmed. 'I could not believe they could do this to me ... they made me a beggar overnight'. His land ruined, like numerous small farmers in coastal Bangladesh, he has been forced to accept a rent from the shrimp farmers which cannot replace the food he used to grow.

People believe the authorities are on the side of the shrimp farmers, failing to take action against those who grab land illegally and even violently. There have been reports of beatings and even shootings of local people trying to protect their land. After all, shrimp farming is a lucrative export business: *Panoscope* reports that earnings rose ten-fold from 1978 levels to US$ 170 million in 1992-93. Forty per cent of exports went to the EU, 38 per cent to the US and 10 per cent to Japan. We buy a lot of Bangladeshi shrimps, but by doing so we are not helping poor people in Bangladesh very much. Similar social and environmental havoc is caused by shrimp farming in many other countries: Ecuador, Malaysia, Thailand and the Philippines.

Thus, far from providing a livelihood for farmers in poor countries, food exports frequently take those livelihoods away. Some, like Abus Sabur, owned their land but lost it through force or financial failure. Others who are displaced are tenants. The opening of a new market can mean a landlord sees a chance to get rich, and throws people off the land to make way for plantations or ranching. This happened to British peasants in the eighteenth century, during the enclosures and the Highland clearances: world prices for grain and for wool were soaring so landlords threw off the 'inefficient' tenant farmers, replacing them with acres of grain, or with sheep. The same is happening now to peasants in Latin America whose landlords decide that soya, beef, cut flowers or whatever, will make them more money than the peasants pay in rent.

THE HUNGRY EXPORTERS

All over the world, small farmers who do hang onto their land have been tempted or cajoled into growing crops for cash themselves. This does not always work out well for them. Farmers who replace traditional food crops with crops for cash often end up with less on their own tables. In a report commissioned by the British Overseas Development Administration, tropical health expert Martin Birley warns: 'Malnutrition is frequently a serious problem among the dependants of plantation workers and cash croppers'. The World Bank has also warned that cash cropping could harm the nutritional status and health of families: in its book *Disease and Mortality in Sub-Saharan Africa*, the Bank cites a study from Tanzania which shows that subsistence farmers and the economic elite have the lowest prevalence of malnourished children, while those growing cash crops but not outstandingly prosperous, have the highest.

'Cash cropping can result in poor nutritional status for children for a number of reasons, many of which have to do with the allocation of resources, decision making and monetary control within the household. Cash cropping may actually reduce food production by diverting labour and [often the best] land into cash rather than subsistence crops, and financial and food resources away from women. Cash crops, unlike food crops, are more likely to be controlled by men, and increased monetarisation tends to increase male cash-in-hand, especially lump sum cash. This may produce expenditure patterns that are dominated by so-called male preferences, which may not include household food or children's welfare,' the Bank report explains.

It is not just Third World governments who pressurise their farmers into growing cash crops: international 'aid' agencies do the same. A major part of the so-called structural adjustment imposed on many Third World countries by none other than the World Bank and the International Monetary Fund, is the promotion of export production. Yet as Martin Birley wrote: 'Crop development programmes ... neglect staple root crops and coarse grains in favour of high protein or fine grain export crops. ... Crops with a high value, high yield and high protein content may represent a health hazard to poor farmers by paradoxically increasing malnutrition.'[1]

Birley adds to the reasons given by the World Bank for why this happens. He explains that poor farmers have different needs. They need: subsistence rather than cash crops (they either cannot afford to eat cash crops, which are an expensive source of calories, or these crops may not be a normal part of their diet); extra energy rather than extra protein; reliable yields rather than high yields; a stable market demand rather than fluctuating prices, which may be high some of the time but may also plummet unpredictably; varieties that are resistant to drought and disease, easy to store, and which do not require labour in quantities or at times which conflict with other key activities. For those without land, who have lost it or never had it, the situation is even worse. Food crops are generally displaced onto poorer land, or displaced altogether. There is less food available, and prices rise.

In the late 1980s and early 1990s horticulture (luxury vegetables and flowers) in Kenya boomed, overtaking coffee to become the country's second biggest export after tea. Those with land to take advantage of Safeway's demand for 'picked on Mount Kilimanjaro yesterday' green beans now have a higher cash income than they used to (though their children may or may not be better fed). Those without land are facing soaring prices for ordinary local food: maize, cabbages or potatoes. For instance, as Kenyan journalist Pamphil Kweyuh reports in *Panoscope* magazine, in the Maagoli area of Kenya's Western Province, one of the most densely populated regions in the country, more or less every single field has been converted to growing crops for export, and no food for local people is grown at all. Maize now has to be trucked in from 200 km away, and prices have been doubling every two years.

1. *The Health Impact of Development Projects* (see bibliography).

If a local food staple is being grown for export, producers are not interested in selling to local people if more money can be made in export markets – which of course is exactly the intention. The World Bank has accepted that this is happening in Vietnam (where child malnutrition has been estimated at 50 per cent): 'Consumers in food deficit areas do not have the purchasing power to bid up the price paid for foodgrains from the surplus regions. In fact at present it is financially more rewarding to export rice outside Vietnam than to transfer it to the deficit regions within the country,' as they put it.[2]

SAKARAMMA'S STORY

Sakaramma, a woman from a small family farm in Karnataka, Southern India, told the Oxfam project officer there that her family had suffered since they began to grow crops to sell, rather than to eat. The family had replaced the traditional grains and pulses grown without pesticides, for their own consumption, with groundnuts grown for cash.

Sakaramma said that the variety of cereals and pulses such as millet, lentils, pigeon peas, that they used to eat had diminished, and so had the quality – by which she meant more pesticides had been used. And they were eating less: 3kg of the staple grain *ragi* used to be cooked up for the family every day; now, it was only 2kg. She had some familiar-sounding complaints about her present food supply: 'Everything has to be bought, and has been produced by others, no one knows where and by whom'. She added that the older, tastier varieties had been replaced by high-yielding hybrids, and that she was unhappy about the pesticides and insecticides used in their production.

The balance of control between the genders in the family had shifted away from the women. When the farm grew food, it was Sakaramma's to harvest and prepare. Now she must ask her husband for money to buy that same food – and he sometimes refuses. She also has a harder, longer working day. For instance, the traditional crops supplied some cooking fuel and cattle fodder from the stalks and husks, now Sakaramma faces a long trek to collect wood and fodder from elsewhere.

There is also a new element of uncertainty in her family's life.

2. Cited by Michel Chussodovsky in 'Vietnam's New War', *Third World Resurgence*, no 47.

Before, they existed almost completely outside the world of money. When their own harvest ran out, they would work on larger farms in return for food, rather than cash. Now they earn cash, but they also need it, not only to buy food but also to buy the inputs: fertilisers and pesticides, for their groundnuts. If the money is not available at the moment the crop requires the input, the family is forced to borrow at high interest rates from money lenders, or risk losing the whole lot and having neither food nor money to see them through the rest of the year.

The high-risk existence endured by families like Sakaramma's does indeed lead to disaster, time after time, all over the world. A farming family goes into debt, then the crop fails or the price falls and they cannot meet the repayments so the only thing left is to sell their land to a bigger, richer operator. They must then become landless labourers on the same land, or, by their thousands and millions, drift to the cities to camp out in a slum and try to find a living there. In countries of the North the farmers do not so often end up in slums, but dole is not uncommon. The trend for small farms to go out of business and be sold up to bigger and bigger holdings is universal, driven by very similar forces everywhere.

North and South, the farmers are not only losing their livelihood, they are also losing their identity, autonomy, and pride. Their countries lose too, as the supply of locally-distinctive food is replaced by uniform, lower quality and often more expensive substitutes. And the world loses unique knowledge of particular crop varieties and agricultural techniques – techniques that will have to be painstakingly re-invented, if and when the need to use less fossil fuel and fewer chemicals in agriculture is finally acknowledged by all.

Sakaramma and her neighbours now all agree that they have not benefited from cash cropping. Sakaramma believes it was mainly propaganda from government and development workers, promising them a better standard of living, which persuaded them onto the treadmill; now with debts and degraded lands, it may be impossible for them to escape from it again. This, too, is a familiar story.

SHOPPING FOR JUSTICE

Buying anonymous imported food is rather like buying anonymous British-produced food. The chances are you are enriching a large organisation, not a poor family. Buyers, traders, processors are the bodies who make money from Sakaramma's groundnuts (see also the table on bananas, below). But at least Sakaramma's family own the produce and the land: most poor agricultural workers do not. Most of the food imported from the South has been grown on plantations or farms (like the shrimp farms) owned by large companies, by the government, or even by overseas companies or multinationals. For example, the pioneers of horticulture in Kenya include Britain's Brooke Bond and the US firm Del Monte. It has been said that only when there is no work on these plantations do the labourers' children eat properly, as it is only then that their parents have time to grow food.

In Kenya, even those farmers who are trying to continue growing staple food crops face difficulties because land clearance for new horticultural plots high on the slopes of Mount Kenya has interfered with the flow of water from the mountain into local rivers. Traditional farmers lower down are being deprived of water for their crops, and once again, prices rise steeply.

Trade in most foods is controlled by a tiny handful of huge corporations (for instance, 70 per cent of all banana trading is carried out by three companies) who are therefore more or less at liberty to fix the price paid to the farmer at one end, and by the consumer at the other. Generally, most of the money disappears in the middle, with only 10–15 per cent returning to the country where the crop originated.

Prices paid to producers are usually very low. The table, produced by the Third World Network in Penang, shows how much of the £1 spent by you in the shop on bananas gets to the person who did the work in the field.

Supermarket/wholesaler and shop	31p
Ship and Lorry Companies	11p
Ripening shed owner	19p
Packaging, dealing, taxes, duties and miscellaneous	27p
Landowner	10p
Agricultural worker	2p

But even bulk food items like bananas only represent a small proportion of the export crops grown in Southern countries. The biggest trade is in raw materials for food processing: palm groundnut and coconut oils for margarine and other processed foods; and soya, sorghum, manioc and other bulk crops for animal feeds. Intensive pig and poultry units in Europe are built on farms producing nowhere near enough food for the number of stock so farmers must rely on cheap imports from South Asia and Latin America. In the Netherlands, where land is in even shorter supply than it is in the UK, stock farms are situated near to the ports since most of the animal feed comes from over the sea.

The widescale cultivation of animal feeds has caused severe social and environmental disruption in Third World countries. Many areas of tropical rainforest have been cleared for fodder crops: soy in Brazil, cassava in Thailand and Indonesia. Groundnut residues from drought-plagued Senegal, palm nut residue and coconut cake from once-forested Malaysia and the Philippines are also fed to our animals and poultry. European famers buy these feeds because the price is low, but the cost to the environment is high. The *Financial Times* reports that 12 million acres of the Cerrados plateau in Brazil was under soy cultivation by 1989, three-quarters of it destined for Europe; one-fifth of the area's natural forest has been lost already. Soy cultivation contributes to galloping soil erosion, estimated to be around 70 times faster than from land covered with natural forest. It also requires heavy use of pesticides and herbicides, which have contaminated the water, and the soy is believed to have encouraged the whitefly which have been plaguing the traditional bean crops, reports the *Farmers' World Network*.

Cash crops to be grown for export will almost certainly need chemicals: fertilisers, pesticides, fungicides, particularly if they are destined for human consumption; supermarkets do not want pineapples with nibbles taken out of them. Heavy pesticide use on horticultural holdings is very common, because of the demand for 'perfect' appearance in a crop not adapted to the climate, and with which farmers are unfamiliar. The pesticide affects the farmers and their labourers, the labourers' families, those dependent on any water supplies which become contaminated – and of course, they affect the consumer. Producers in industrial countries use plenty of poisons, but, sadly, growers in tropical countries tend to use even more. There is also a chance that produce imported from tropical countries will be contaminated with pesticides banned in the purchaser's country.

A WHO/United Nations survey of various food importing countries found that among the produce most frequently rejected because pesticide residues exceeded WHO recommended limits were asparagus, blackberries, cocoa, dates, chilli peppers, paw-paws, peas, pears and strawberries. The survey focused on imports from Third World countries. One of the contaminants reported to the WHO was DDT, traces of which appear on cocoa beans. Though DDT is banned in Mexico, DDT residues have also been found in high concentrations 'suggestive of continuing use' in that country, source of much out-of-season produce in the USA.

Even produce from Southern Europe may be hazardous: Greenpeace in Spain reports that lindane, known to cause nerve damage and fatal anaemias at high doses, and possibly a carcinogen to boot, is 'widely used' in Spain, where residues have even been found in baby food.

Imported produce will almost certainly not have been checked for residues, partly because tests are incredibly expensive. The House of Commons Select Committee on Agriculture heard in 1987 that only one chemical analysis was conducted for every 6,500 tonnes of imported produce; and most of those tests would have been for something other than pesticide residues.

Supermarkets do their own tests, too, even though much of their produce is grown under contracts which specify every single spray and pretty much which day to spray it on. As Stephen Ridge, quality control manager for Somerfield, explained, the routine quality control is a visual check, which will not detect pesticide residues. 'With £300 million worth of produce going through our stores we can't possibly test everything, neither can the government. Our approach is to put our effort into working with producers to keep levels low, and if we know what is being sprayed, then we know what we are looking for. We then do a blitz every three months and buy 60 or 70 lines in store and test those.'

The trouble with imported produce is that it is harder to monitor the use of chemicals; with farmers so far away, retailers can't be sure what is really going on on the farms. The UN environment programme found that Kenyan fruit, vegetable and flower farms were using over 1,500 different pesticides. Most of the pesticides were unregistered. One very popular chemical, sprayed on vegetables, citrus and mangoes, is the carcinogenic compound Carbosulfan 25EC. This pesticide was denied registration in the US eight times. However, it is manufactured in the US, exported to Kenya – then eaten by US citizens on imported Kenyan produce.

Toxic chemicals are particularly dangerous where workers are not literate in the language in which warnings and instructions are written.

Protective equipment is provided for Third World agricultural workers even less reliably than it is in Europe; and poor workers in hot climates wear little clothing of their own, making them even more vulnerable to absorbing pesticides through the skin, for example, through the skin of bare feet. The World Health Organisation estimates that three million people round the world are poisoned by pesticides each year, around 90 per cent of them in the South. A staggering 220,000 people probably die.[2] The WHO calculates that around one in sixteen agricultural workers in Malaysia is poisoned by pesticides *each year*. Other organisations have made even higher global estimates.

As in Europe, chemical-intensive monocultures damage the environment. The natural balance between soil, plant, sun and rain is quite different in different parts of the world; tropical countries are even more dependent than temperate ones on trees and perennial plants to protect the soil. But European agricultural techniques have been applied unthinkingly by northern 'advisers', although these methods can do even more damage, even more rapidly, than in cooler parts of the world. Monoculture is the order of the day: plough, sow, fertilise, spray, harvest. No permanent leaf cover or root structure protects the fragile soils from the extra-heavy rains of hotter climates, or from their extra-drying winds. Once again, it is not only cultivation for cash crops that leads to this kind of damage, but as a rule, the more profit-oriented the enterprise the more likely it is to involve monoculture, chemical and machinery use. And the more machinery and the more chemicals, the more damage to the soil.

Adrian Friggens of Farmers' World Network, who has been studying these issues for many years, agrees that there are no clear and simple answers, but that when it comes to the customer standing in the greengrocers, butcher, or at the supermarket shelf, the 'safest' bet is to choose home-produced food where possible, if you want to protect the basic livelihoods of the world's poorest people (rather than richer minorities within poor countries). And he agrees that this decision to choose food grown locally is greatly reinforced by the environmental and health benefits to consumers, and the planet as a whole.

Slightly more circumspect, the Council for the Protection of Rural England and the Worldwide Fund for Nature say in their report *Growing Greener*, that imported cash crops 'may provide significant benefits for the farms and communities where they are grown,' but go

2. *New Scientist*, 23 November 1996.

on to warn that 'in practice the benefits for developing countries of growing cash crops for the export market can be outweighed by the costs. Accurate information is essential before judgements are made about the merits of increasing or reducing trade.'

Friggens agrees that the main difficulty is lack of information. This is why he supports the development of fair trade arrangements for produce which we can't grow here and won't do without: tea, coffee and chocolate are the most familiar examples. By fair trade, Friggens means produce sold directly from growers (who may get together in a co-op) to ensure that producers and not middlemen, receive the profit. The job of the bodies running the fair trade labels is to check to ensure fair treatment of producers, to promote the products and inform customers. Other foods available, or due to become available on such schemes include bananas, jam and honey.

Fair trade aims to bring a taste of the direct contact their customers seek when they buy from farm shops or box schemes. While of course it cannot be one-to-one direct (despite the name of one highly successful 'fair trade' coffee brand!), it is more certainly direct than the alternatives. Fair trade brands set written standards about the kind of returns to workers and landowners, and try to increase the share of the price you pay which goes to the people doing the real work, cutting out the rich traders and import/export companies. They generally try to buy from small family farms, often organised into co-operatives. This system enables small farms to be financially viable, enabling families to remain autonomous and self-supporting. Fair traded goods generally tell you something about these issues on the packaging – certainly more than you usually find on a label – and further information can usually be had by contacting the organisation.

Members of a Nicaraguan co-op selling coffee to a co-op owned exporting organisation who supply, among others, Cafédirect in Britain, told *Guardian* newspaper reporter John Vidal what difference it made to them to sell their coffee in this way: 'The profits come to us, not the traders; now we have an alternative ... fair trade has meant we have paid off our debts ... we are more content, life is better. We have clothing, food. We can buy things we could not before.' These co-op members are still extremely poor, but at least they have stopped getting poorer, and according to Vidal some co-ops are even able to invest in education and retirement provision.

There are problems with fair trade labelling, as with all certification schemes. There is the inevitable argument between those who want to set a really high standard, so that customers can be entirely happy and confident about buying the product, even though this can mean a high price and limited supplies; others would prefer to set the standards more 'realistically' so that more can join in and the scheme is better able to make an impact on the whole market. All blanket schemes that aim to supply workable regulations to many farmers on the one hand, and to satisfy many consumers on the other, run into these kinds of problems. Where direct contact with producers is impossible, as it is for those of us who want to go on drinking tea and coffee or eating bananas, we have to accept 'fair trade' as the next best thing.

Alistair Smith of Farm Link points out that, when assessing the fairness of a product, it's worth ensuring that terms and conditions of trade have been negotiated with growers as opposed to unilaterally imposed by the company selling the product to consumers. Organisations running these fair trade labels are also beginning to take an interest in the kind of agriculture practised, favouring more sustainable or even organic methods. Similarly, bodies certifying organic products from overseas are beginning to realise that they should make some attempt to find out if a fair return is going to the original producer, in other words, to ensure that the production is socially, as well as environmentally, sustainable. Smith warns that there are currently some ecological 'labels' which are purely technical, such as using biological control rather than pesticides, with no safeguards on employee terms and conditions.

The Soil Association confirms that imported organic produce that they certify tends to have some fair trading criteria incorporated into the deal: 'We would not accept the product if it was obvious workers were being exploited,' a spokesman said. 'A lot of producers we work with ourselves are independent producer co-ops who have got together and decided ours is the market they want to sell to, so it isn't imposed. One crop which does come from larger plantations is tea, but in fact the workers on the big organic plantations are pretty well looked after, too, with detached houses, hospitals, and so on.'

John Dalby of the Soil Association reports a certain amount of 'cross inspection' between organic and fair trade marques. In the end it seems likely that, on the whole, imported organic goods will be fairly traded and fair trade goods grown at least in an ecologically sensitive way. 'The issues are closely allied, and the same consumers tend to be concerned about both. Ideally we would like to see them both together, all fair trade also organic, but we understand that the fair trade organisations are very anxious to get things going and get fair trade on the map. They do have lists of banned chemicals, and they do check to ensure workers don't get exposed to dangerous chemicals. It's a different agenda. It would be nice if one day it could be the same.'

Fair trade enterprises must also be sure they are offering long-term social and economic sustainability. Helena Norberg-Hodge urges that anyone setting up a fair trade scheme should ask themselves whether they are enabling producers to achieve a *lasting* improvement in their lives, or whether they are in fact being attracted into a new dependency on foreign markets which, while initially attractive, may in time fall foul of the vagaries of consumer fickleness and see-sawing exchange rates. 'I do worry that these schemes are set up without proper account being taken of the profound structural inequalities of the international markets,' she comments. 'They should really ask: "are people being drawn into a less secure, more dependent situation?" Obviously if they were previously mining asbestos, or even producing coffee but for the international traders who gave them a bad price, and now they can sell direct and get a better price, that is all right. If on the other hand people have been engaged in subsistence production or production for local markets, even at very low levels of cash income, and are diverted into producing something like cosmetics or ornaments for a fickle northern consumer market, even at a 'fair trade' price, I really do think there is a danger that in the long run people lose their security and end up worse off.'

By these criteria the injunction by the campaigning group Farm Link and others to buy the small, smallholder-produced Windward Island bananas rather than the cheaper, larger, corporation-owned plantation-produced 'dollar' bananas, fits the criterion of promoting independence over dependence. Windward Islanders already have banana trees, are already dependent on an export market, and they practice mixed cropping. Dollar bananas are gown in vast monocultures, drenched with pesticides, on land that may well have been either natural forest, or alternatively, peasant farmland.

Fair trading is important, and indeed we should try not to buy anything which is not fairly traded, at home or from overseas: and we should endeavour to find out as much as we can about who produced it and under what conditions. But the majority of imported produce – bulk animal feeds, glasshouse vegetables and fruit, vegetable oils and so forth – is viable for export precisely *because* it undercuts the same product in the receiving country: in order to compete on price, environmental and wage considerations are scotched. Where there is no direct trading arrangement, the primary producers tend to get a very poor deal. Commodity prices have fallen, certainly in relation to the prices of everything else, and in some cases, fallen absolutely. People producing bulk commodities for the world market have to run faster, plough deeper, spray more often and still they fall behind. By not buying such products we are reducing the incentive for the rich and powerful to turn topsoil into foreign currency, and we are leaving local landholders with more control over their lands. By choosing fair trade and direct purchase we are participating in a new model of development, where gross exploitation is replaced by responsible, informed, participatory self-reliance.

8

CAN WE AFFORD
CHEAP FOOD?

One of the most common justifications given for the industrialisation and centralisation of food production, distribution, processing and retailing is that this is the only way to ensure cheap food for all. Poor people, in particular, we are told, need access to the cheap products of factory farming, cereal monocultures and plantations.

If by cheap, we mean low-price, low-quality and carelessly produced, then yes, we do have access to cheap food. But it is not low-cost. The way industrial agriculture, processing and retailing are subsidised means it is possible to have food in the shops with a very low price, and there are several million people in Britain on such low incomes that they do indeed need to buy this kind of food, in order to avoid starving to death. Many people who can afford better food are also seduced into eating a degraded diet by the forces described in earlier chapters. But this food is most certainly *not* the food that people on low incomes – or anyone else – *need*. The fact that there are people in this country who cannot afford a basic healthy diet but can only survive by buying highly-processed, nutritionally impoverished rubbish is a political, not an agricultural issue.

But of course cheap food is not really cheap at all. It costs the nation indirectly in any number of ways.

HIDDEN COSTS

The price of the British diet may be relatively low at the check-out, but we pay at other times and places. Among the many costs of current systems of food production are: environmental damage, damage to our health, loss of pleasure, loss of jobs, water and insurance charges, taxation to pay for EU subsidies for unwanted crop surpluses and set-aside schemes, spending on road construction, health care, unemployment benefit. Others are paying too: The last chapter described the price paid by people in some of the countries we import food from. Animals too pay with their suffering for our 'cheap' food.

No one has sat down and added up the entire cost each household pays for the present style of food production and distribution. But we can find some pointers. For instance, as mentioned in chapter six, the EU's Common Agricultural Policy – one of the chief sponsors of industrial farming – has been estimated to cost each taxpayer £200 a year. A single mile of new motorway may cost £100 million, which means that each new road costs every household upwards of £100, whether they ever use it or not. And many of us have also noticed how much water charges have gone up in recent years: according to Ofwat water companies are spending £121 million a year monitoring and removing pesticides in drinking water, and investment of around £1 billion is needed in the coming years.

These costs flow from the food production system as a matter of course, even when it is functioning as intended. When things go wrong, as they have so spectacularly with BSE, the costs really pile on. It was estimated in 1996 that the EU would have to spend over £1 billion in 1997, and nearly as much again in 1998, buying up beef from condemned animals, or simply beef raised but no longer wanted by nervous European consumers. No compensation was even considered for exporters, or packing and processing plants dependent on beef. Similar blows to the national exchequer and/or to employment and profits have come with other disasters: salmonella, E. coli, antibiotic resistant superbugs, and so on.

FREE RIDE

Chapter three described the way national and international food distribution and car-borne shopping contribute to congestion, and to the drive to build new roads. Worsening congestion, and the idea that roads promote growth and trade, have been driving road-building programmes – which we pay for. The European proposals to build another 12,000 km of motorways are set to eat up 60 times what the EU plans to spend on rail in the same period.

Motoring and road freight as a whole has been estimated by environmental economist David Pearce to cost Britain £50 billion per year, in pollution, congestion and accidents – about three times the revenue collected from road tax. Food shopping and especially food freight produce more than their share of this burden, as we saw in chapter four, and the share is set to rise if the pattern of food retailing does not change. The Environmental Transport Association, whose own calculations also show that road transport makes a net loss for the country, points out that conventional costing of roads tends just to consider construction and maintenance costs of the roads themselves, and takes no account of the costs they impose on non-motorists and the country as a whole. The cost of rising road traffic is often borne by individuals. For instance, people whose homes are on increasingly noisy roads lose not only in terms of quality of life, but find their houses become harder – if not impossible – to sell. There are other costs which, though measurable, would be hard to put a cash value on: such as the loss of independence for children who are no longer allowed out to walk or cycle on their own, and the loss of neighbourliness on noisy streets.

Supermarkets are carrying our food across ever greater distances, and customers, too, are being drawn further and further to do their grocery shopping. As supermarkets have got bigger, they have tended to favour out-of-town locations, which are exclusively geared to the car-borne shopper doing a big family shop. As Sainsbury's once boasted: 'We would not open a store which did not have a large surface level car park'.

All those journeys increase congestion. In the past 15 years, the SAFE Alliance reports, shopping mileage by car increased dramatically, almost doubling. The difference in shopper miles between an out-of-town store and a town-centre equivalent has been estimated to cost the community almost £25,000 *a week*, in pollution, accidents and noise nuisance compared to a town-centre equivalent.[1] Extra congestion, the single largest burden of the community, probably costs as much again on its own.

A concrete example of shopping-related congestion can be found in the East End of London. In 1994 Sainsbury's opened a new store, complete with large car park and cut-price petrol station, on the junction of two main roads, Cambridge Heath Road and Whitechapel Road. Because these roads are both so busy, a special traffic light was installed to permit entrance and exit from the store, which means that people in buses, cars and vans going about other business now have to wait while shoppers are allowed in and out on their own green light. An inspector for the local bus company confirmed that the lights were delaying their buses and causing them problems. An extra one or two minutes on each journey means fewer complete journeys each working

1. *Off Our Trolleys*, Tim Lang and Hugh Raven, IPPR 1994.

day – or the company has to buy extra buses and pay extra crew. The service to the public either gets worse, or will cost them more. This is how hidden subsidies work: bus passengers pay extra so car drivers can shop at Sainsbury's.

Road traffic increases not only have immediate costs in terms of congestion, air pollution, health damage and loss of quality of life, but burning motor fuel is a major contributor to the greenhouse effect. Energy used in other parts of the food industry – agriculture and processing – add to greenhouse emissions. Tractor fuel is a significant cost on most farms, and with ploughing, sowing, harvesting and six or more trips to spray pesticide and more to fertilise, up and down every row, every season, the mileage is considerable. Artificial fertiliser is particularly energy intensive to produce, using electricity or gas to fix the nitrogen from the air (a process which can alternatively be carried out by clover!). This is added to all the energy used in processing and packaging.

Global warming is now accepted as reality. Unfortunately many people still think of global warming as an entertaining novelty, bringing fields of sunflowers to Kent and Sussex, rather than a dismal reality of repeated storm damage, extortionate water metering, dying bluebell woods and deserts in southern Europe. One sector which is, however, already paying for climate change is the insurance industry. A spokesman for General Accident told an international climate convention summit in 1996 that, 'We are losing increasing amounts of money through extreme weather'. As the global atmosphere warms up, more energy in the systems means more hurricanes in the tropics, and unpredictable shifts in weather systems everywhere. Insurance companies in Britain are paying an average of £5 million each year for property damaged when drought shrinks the sub-soil; and in 1995 Yorkshire Water found out just how expensive it can be when the pattern of rainfall in an area alters. Insurance companies, water companies and, of course, farmers will all have to pass increased costs onto their customers – us.

MEDICAL BILL

Congestion and pollution harm our health, as we know. But the cost to our health of eating our 'cheap' national diet is also enormous. The foods which producers have most incentive to grow are fatty (meat, milk, vegetable oils), full of sugar, or made from grains and potatoes (to be mixed with the fats and sugar for processing). Furthermore, food produced by intensive industrial techniques may also have a lower nutritional value per kilo than well-grown food, as we saw in chapter three. Heart disease, cancer, obesity, bowel disorders and diabetes are all more likely if you eat mostly processed, fatty food and not many fresh fruits and vegetables. The suffering caused by unhealthy eating habits extends from the nagging misery of constipation to the horror of losing a loved spouse, parent or grandparent, twenty or thirty years before their time.

This human cost is mirrored by the financial burden to the country. Perhaps the commonest of the many illnesses to be brought on or exacerbated by poor diet is coronary heart disease. The British Heart Foundation estimates that around one-third of the coronary heart disease in this country is attributable to poor diet: too much fat, too few vitamins. Each year this translates into 18 million working days lost, costing £150 million in invalidity benefits, and losing industry £1 billion, says the Foundation. Medicines and operations prescribed to those suffering diet-related coronary illness cost the NHS around £300 million a year. Meanwhile, the Office of Health Economics calculates that obesity costs the nation around £200 million annually. Cheap food begins to look more pricey.

Growing and buying food differently would save us a lot of money. Yet the way we run our lives at the moment, we can't afford to make the savings that healthier habits would bring.

The British way of eating is tied up, in part, with the British way of earning. Working adults feel they cannot afford the time to prepare and cook fresh food for themselves and their families.

Adults outside full-time work on the other hand are very short of money, on the whole. So don't these households need food at rock-bottom prices in order to eat properly? The appeal to the needs and rights of the very many poor families in this country is an obvious way to silence critics of the food industry – especially those coming from somewhere vaguely on the left, as many do.

Cheap and nasty food has been a feature of the life of the urban poor throughout the industrial revolution. In his book *Sweetness and Power*, Sidney Mintz writes that the colonies, amongst other things, provided 'low cost food substitutes, such as tobacco, tea and sugar, for the metropolitan labouring classes.' The industrial revolution diet of the 1850s is described by Mintz as: suet pudding and golden syrup at midday, while, in the evening, 'sweetened tea probably increased the workers' readiness to consume large quantities of otherwise unadorned complex carbohydrates'.

In the 1990s nothing has changed. As the late and much-missed East End GP, David Widgery, described in his book, *Some Lives*: 'I see a good deal of old-fashioned low-intake malnutrition, especially among ... the long-term unemployed; people who will survive on sweet tea, toast, chips and biscuits. Bread and margarine is a dietary staple.'

As diet and poverty campaigner Suzi Leather points out, the 10 per cent of the population living at or below the level of income support are simply too poor to eat properly. They have perhaps £10 per person per week to feed a family. It is impossible to produce or to buy proper food that cheaply, therefore these households are below starvation levels of income, and are only surviving because they can just about afford the most injurious and degraded sources of calories – a diet not really fit for human consumption. Because these foods are available, people seldom die of frank starvation in this country, but plenty of people are stunted, malnourished and suffer and die from nutritionally-related diseases.

Families on these incomes have to buy the cheapest calories available simply to stop their children losing weight from calorie deficiency. That means high-fat, high-sugar foods, the National Food Alliance points out. Biscuits give you 500 calories for 10p, carrots only 50. Sausages give you 100 calories for 10p, cod only 10. Biscuits and sausages are cheap because the sugar cane, palm oil and pig meal are produced by ruthless chemical agriculture which uses up tomorrow's soil fertility for today's profits, and by paying agricultural workers, particularly on Third World plantations, appallingly little. Much meat production is subsidised, too, and different subsidy structures would make different, perhaps healthier calorie sources cheaper. But no one should be expected to exist on such a low income that even carrots and potatoes are too expensive.

The very environment inhabited by low-income households seems to conspire against a healthy diet. Even those with a bit more money may find that there is little healthy food in the shops they can get to that is affordable or remotely appetising. Fresh fruit and veg are often completely unavailable in low-income areas, or priced very high and offputtingly old and tired. The brown cauliflowers and wrinkled oranges characteristic of many inner-city stores are obviously not worth parting with money over-the-odds for.

Time and again, research among low-income households has found that when asked 'what do you want' people don't say 'the biscuits are too expensive' or 'we can't get pork pies here'; they say 'The fruit is too expensive' and 'we can't get fresh vegetables here'. Over half the low-income mothers questioned in a National Children's Home survey would buy more fruit and fresh lean meat, a quarter more vegetables and fish, and only one in 10 more cakes or ice cream, if they could find and afford them. One woman interviewed by Lancaster University's Jo Malseed about how she'd *like* to feed her family commented: 'Fruit. I'd give them fruit. And fresh vegetables. And brown bread instead of white'.

Of course there are other forces at work. Culture often dictates that a meal must include meat to be a 'proper' meal, and meat costs more, even low-quality meat. Parents have to be particularly careful that whatever appears on the tea table will be eaten, as there is unlikely to be the money for one dinner to be thrown away and another produced.

And although it is well-known that people in work in Britain have ludicrously little time left over for their lives, people with little money by no means have a lot of time. Being poor is expensive and time-consuming. Poor people are made to wait: in bus queues, at doctors' surgeries, in benefit offices. Their time is believed to be worth next to nothing, because that is what they are paid in pounds per hour.

As cookery teacher Rosie Davies points out: 'You may not need much money or time to prepare good food, but you do need time to think and plan, and I think that is what people often find so difficult: most women with children in particular are very busy always. You can eat very well for little money if you plan and think carefully, but it does require thought.'

A diet composed of cheap calories is sadly deficient in other vital nutrients, in particular vitamins and minerals. According to *New Scientist* magazine, iron deficiency, which leads to lethargy and difficulty in learning, is common in inner city toddlers. In the Third World, where industrial farming has been introduced under the banner of 'the Green Revolution', there are now serious worries that the lack of nutrient content in an industrially-produced diet is holding back the ability of the new generation to study and learn – and holding back the development of these nations. Very low income communities in this country may well be facing the same problem.

These problems begin before birth. Babies born to women on low incomes have a much greater risk of being of low birth weight. This is almost certainly due to poor maternal nutrition: calories, but little else. Low birth weight in turn increases the risk of all kinds of health problems, increases their chance of needing special care, and increases the risk of the baby dying. Health problems such as diabetes and heart disease are thought to dog people born at low weights right through life – almost certainly exacerbated by continuing poor diet. According to a report by the Maternity Alliance and the National Children's Home, babies born with low birth weights are likely to suffer illness, disability and behavioural disorders throughout childhood: all unwanted in themselves, and all likely to interfere with schooling, and thus with all future life chances.

For those with enough money in theory to buy the basics, cooking at home with good-quality ingredients should work out cheaper than buying the more usual processed foods, ready-meals and take-aways. But insufficient availability, time, confidence and skill still stand in people's way. Fortunately, these obstacles are being tackled in some places. Food co-ops, food growing projects and direct delivery schemes – described later and in the following chapters – can overcome availability problems; and as people make contact with each other through such schemes, they share skills and knowledge, and gain in confidence.

SUPERMARKETS SQUEEZE OUT THE POOR

It is not just the intensive farming apologists who claim to be bringing cheap food to the masses – supermarkets claim it too. The centralised buying and distribution, the 'one-stop-shop' are supposedly efficient, and we are always being told that 'good food costs less' when you buy their 'low price essential no frills value savers'.

In fact, bargains in supermarkets are really aimed at the penny-pinching rich. Shopping in a supermarket can be humiliating if you are poor. The shop is laid out to give an impression of abundance, luxury. 'You see people with trolleys, throwing things in, and there I am with my basket, hunting for the cheapest things,' said one low-income woman interviewed by Jo Malseed.

We are all familiar with the discovery that we have spent more than we intended to in the supermarket. This is one way the chains have made so much money over the years. For poorer customers the pressure to spend can be disastrous. Another of Jo Malseed's interviewees told her that she had once spent her entire giro in Sainsbury's. 'It all looked so lovely. I just couldn't resist the temptation.' She dared not go there again after that.

Although people believe supermarkets are the cheapest place to shop, for some of the healthiest foods, fresh fruit and vegetables, they are more expensive than independent greengrocers. But they get away with the mark-up because they judge, correctly, that many people will come in for cheap milk, cereals and ready meals, and won't want to bother going elsewhere for the rest. Supermarkets also recognise that they are now chiefly in competition with each other and the super-cheap discount stores. This pressure has led to competition not on quality but on price and other cash-related benefits: 'loyalty' cards, which promise that if you spend several thousand pounds in their particular supermarket you will earn yourself a toast rack or a sports bag and matching beach towel.

In the 1990s the supermarkets also began a 'price war', advertising cut-price 'essentials' – even selling at a loss – in an attempt to woo shoppers. But rather than bringing basic healthy food within reach of customers, the 'essentials' have frequently been fatty and sugary foods. Tesco has offered free chocolates, sweets and biscuits as inducements to buy other goods, whereas Sainsbury described sausage rolls, cola drink and sugar as low price 'essentials'. As the Food Commission reported, potatoes, onions and carrots were discounted by only two of the 'big four' in the 1994 price war, while fatty and sugary products like biscuits were discounted by all of them.

Even the dubious benefit of these cheap offers is not available to truly low-income customers, as supermarkets do not site their branches in the lowest-income areas. City centre stores a walk or short bus-ride away have been closed and new superstores on the ring road are opened up. Yet of the several million households in this country managing on £150 a week or less, only one in three have a car, and in urban areas, the proportion will be even lower. Out-of-town stores are out of reach for these families. It is wildly impractical for them to shop there. Even if a bus goes out to one of these stores, it is such a long journey, and such a long walk round the shop, that the trip is too time-consuming and expensive unless you can afford, and can carry, a whole week's shopping at a time. Superstores are quite explicitly geared towards shoppers in cars.

If a supermarket chain does open a store in a deprived area, it is usually because the site happens to offer convenient road access and space for a large car-park. The Sainsbury's store built in Whitechapel in East London is set *behind* the car park – which could well deter customers from straying onto the main street and spending in the other shops – and even deter on-foot shoppers from straying into the store and blocking up the checkout. A spokesman for one supermarket chain (Somerfield) spoke for them all when he admitted that 'basket shoppers do cause problems' for stores because they cost more in staff time for the same amount of turnover. 'Of course, what we really like is the shopper with two trolleys,' he said.

Sainsbury's are so keen on the shoppers who come by car and fill up two trolleyfuls at one go – and preferably fill up on petrol at the same time – that they managed to find an out-of-town site even in the inner-city borough of Hackney, and proposed to build a superstore and petrol station there: right on a motorway interchange. The nearest homes were 1km away, and few of the many local bus routes passed the site. So this store would not have been troubled by too many 'basket shoppers' (the application was eventually withdrawn).

'Points' and 'loyalty card' systems are also geared to two-trolley shopping: if you are only spending £30 a week in a store your child will probably be potty-trained in the seven months it would take you to qualify for a bumper pack of nappies.

Even better-off customers are starting to feel that supermarkets might offer a bit too much of a good thing. Many people object to all the plastic and packaging, and that is before they know that how much they are paying for it. Around 10 per cent of the average food bill is devoted entirely to plastic, aluminium, glossy waxed card, glass, metal and the like: money which goes straight into the bin. Some packaging is obviously necessary: butter needs to be wrapped up, and you couldn't take loose flour or sugar home. But the majority of customers would be happy to return and re-use bottles, and the same can in theory be done with jam jars and yoghurt pots.

Supermarkets don't like the idea. It's not particularly in their interests to reduce domestic waste; after all, they don't pay for landfill – we do, in our council tax. On the other hand, if the stores had to make space to store returned containers this would cost them valuable retail square footage. So they do no more than put a token bottle bank in the car park – a solution that's several environmental steps down from re-use, as we have seen. Large amounts of packaging also cuts down on the need to employ locally: packaging advertises the product (there are no staff in the shop to tell you about it) and protects it against the rigours of a trans-national or even intercontinental journey (which replaces local sourcing and loading and unloading carefully by hand). At its starkest, the difference in cost between something minimally packaged and over-packaged can be double: apples in plastic trays with film wrap cost twice as much apples sold loose in some stores.

A large supermarket shop might have a kilometre of aisles to walk along. Customers tend to put more in their trolleys if they are in the store for longer, passing more goods. Once you have made such a mammoth expedition you are less inclined – and will have less money left – to make a separate outing to the town centre, even if you can still get cheaper veg at the market there. By moving away from the town centre, the supermarket is able to steal most of the town trade. Trips to the town centre may have been made conveniently on foot or by bus, even by car-owning households. These households almost all switch to cars if they switch to the superstore.

In 1980, only 5 per cent of shopping was done in out of town centres; in 11 years this rose to 17 per cent. 'All over Britain shops in the centre of towns have been boarded up and high streets have become more deserted. Until the pronouncements in 1994 by the department of the environment, and then the Commons select committee, urging an end to out-of-town developments, Britain was well on the way to an American model where the vast majority of shopping is done in super stores on ring roads. 'This,' as the *Guardian* newspaper put it, 'is madness.'

The change in retailing and shopping patterns has two effects. Smaller businesses, often those in town-centre sites, close down. This is a grave loss of service to people dependent on the town centre, particularly people who are elderly or on low incomes; without cars, or without the income to contemplate a mega-shop at the superstore – these are people the megastore doesn't go out of its way to attract, anyway. As a result of falling trade, town centres feel less welcoming, more run-down and dangerous.

Supermarkets do little or nothing for the local economy. Although when applying to open yet another store they always claim to be 'creating jobs', supermarkets employ fewer people per £1 of turnover than smaller shops: this is another way they make their money. It therefore seems inevitable that at least as many jobs will be lost as surrounding small shops go out of business, as are created. Of course, supermarkets buy little or nothing of their stock from local businesses: around 95 per cent of stock is centrally sourced and around 95 per cent of takings are siphoned away from the area to the shareholders and company HQ. By contrast, small local shops are much more likely to source a good proportion locally: a survey in one town found 80 per cent of town centre shops and market stalls did so (see chapter ten). Small local shops are also much more likely to employ local businesses for services such as decorating and repairs, servicing the van, and so forth.

CUSTOMERS ARE DOING IT FOR THEMSELVES

Some of the people most completely excluded by the supermarket culture are finding other ways to get the affordable healthy food they need. Some of the most successful initiatives are food buying co-ops. Once a little 'priming' finance has been found, the buying power of clubbing together enables even lower-income consumers to go direct to wholesalers and buy basic foods at cost prices.

Fruit and vegetables are generally a priority for co-ops, along with other basic items. Andy Hill and Eddie Gorrell have been working to help a group of co-ops in Glasgow's Castlemilk area, and what they find is typical of many low-income, urban areas: 'We survey people to find out their needs, and the biggest bugbear is that the shops are awful. There is no choice and the prices are extortionate. In one place where there is now a co-op, people hated the nearest shopkeeper so much they were walking past him and going a mile to the next shop.

'People do get pissed off hearing what an unhealthy diet people eat in Scotland when it really isn't possible for them to buy healthy food. The shopkeepers are just screwing as much as they can from the locals, then they're away in their big houses when they shut the shop. The co-op keeps the money in the community.'

The Castlemilk co-ops do something like £4,000 trade a fortnight. Their shops might be open 8 or 12 hours a week, in tiny premises; one is in the former changing room of a gymnasium! 'There is certainly a market for fresh fruit and vegetables. We sell about £300 or £400-worth a week: a big proportion of the total. We're actually the biggest supplier of fruit and veg in Castlemilk already. We supply to schools (half-price fruit and juice through tuck shops, thanks to help from the local health project) and some cafes as well.'

With this scale of success, the co-ops feel it is realistic to look into buying directly from growers. 'We are looking to form a federation of co-ops throughout Scotland, and then we might be in a position to negotiate direct with growers.' Such deals would enable the co-ops to secure a better price, by using collective purchasing power to bypass middle men. In order to encourage members who feel unsure about cooking, the co-ops sell packs for making a fresh soup or stew, with a carrot, an onion, a turnip and stock cube, plus a recipe, 'because some of the younger folks especially don't know what to do with the stuff otherwise, since they stopped making cooking compulsory in schools'.

Not only do co-ops bring a better choice at a better price to where people can reach it, they also offer a sense of cooperation to the people involved. One Castlemilk co-op member commented, 'They are there to serve you, not just to take your money'. The National Food Alliance comments in its document 'Food and Low Income': 'For people desperately lacking confidence and company, the benefits of five minutes at the co-op and a good laugh is not to be underestimated'.

SURELY WE'D ALL STARVE IF FARMING WENT ECOLOGICAL

Even if the many constraints on poorer people were removed, and the fresh fruit and vegetables were available at fair prices, surely most people couldn't afford ecologically-produced (for example, organic) food? And anyway, there wouldn't be enough to go round, would there?

When he was Agriculture minister, John Gummer asserted that 'organic farming can never feed the nation'.[2] This statement mischievously implied that conventional farming in Britain feeds the nation – which it most certainly does not. As we have seen, more food is imported than exported. But more specifically, Mr Gummer was referring to the widespread belief that organic farming is less productive, in terms of kilograms per hectare and pounds (sterling) per kilogramme, than conventional methods.

One reason for this impression is that when organic farmers first take over soils ravaged by chemical farming, yields are, not surprisingly, lower in tonnes than they were on the chemical diet. As the years go by and organic matter and fertility is patiently returned to the soil, and the earthworms, soil fungi and soil bacteria gain in strength, the crude weight of yield can match anything raised chemically. Research by soil scientists at Washington State University showed that a farm in the USA which has been cultivated organically with rotations and green manures for 80 years matched the wheat

2. Quoted by Will Best in, *A Future for the Land*, (see bibliography).

production average for the region, and beat one conventional farm on similar soil by 13 per cent. The organic farm had a full six inches more topsoil, so the high yields were hardly surprising. As we have seen, the yield in terms of nutritional value may be still higher.

Studies of farms like these in the US were examined carefully by the Committee on the Role of Alternative Farming Methods in Modern Agriculture, set up by the US Board of Agriculture in the early 1980s. In the report they published after five years of deliberation, the committee concluded that a holistic, biological approach to agriculture is the only way the world will maintain sustainable food production.

On a global level too, sustainable farming is indeed more likely than chemical farming to feed the South as well as the North. Care, attention and thoughtful practices such as growing compatible crops side-by-side in the same field can entice far more out of a given hectare than the crude application of chemical fertilisers ever can, and this is every bit as true for the developing world as it is in the North.

Henk Hobbelink of the European genetic resources group GRAIN reports Mexican research which shows one hectare of maize, beans and squash together produces as much as one-and-three-quarter hectares planted separately. One small plot in the Philippines, lovingly tended for 12 different crops in one field, and fertilised only with chicken manure, yielded a staggering 50 tonnes of food per hectare. Even high-yielding green revolution rice with two crops a year can only manage about 8 tonnes. Farming like this requires labour, of course. But labour isn't something that most Southern countries (or any countries, these days) are short of. Hard cash to buy tractors and chemicals of course, they do tend to lack.

In our own third world, the impoverished inner cities, labour-intensive farming has also shown top yields: Fresh Start Farms is a vegetable garden worked by homeless people in San Francisco. 'Its biointensive gardening methods require more labour than a conventional farm, but yield a far greater return per acre,' according to a report in *Sierra* magazine.

Vandana Shiva, in her book *Staying Alive*, eloquently describes the way that so called 'high-yield' agriculture is nothing of the kind. 'With the green revolution [the introduction of new rice varieties requiring pesticides and fertilisers to give bigger rice harvests], edible fish in rice fields [the little fish which swam in the flooded paddies and ate the rice pests] are destroyed by poisonous pesticides, and the reeds for fibre- and rope-making are destroyed by poisonous weedicides (sic). The little spaces which ensure sustenance are slowly closed ...'

More 'efficient' harvesting machines were introduced by International Rice Research Institute scientists because they discovered that up to 10 per cent of the yield was being 'lost'. In fact this grain was not lost at all, but gleaned, usually by the poorest people in the village who did not have rice fields of their own.

Similarly, in Indian wheat fields, 'productivity' (in terms of wheat yield, and in terms of reduction of labour costs) has been increased by replacing the job of hand weeding, done by women, with chemical weedkillers. However, one of the commonest 'weeds' in wheat fields used to be a plant called *bathua*, which is actually more nutritious than the wheat and rice for which it was forced to give way. Gram for gram, it contains more iron and calcium than either, far more protein than rice and virtually as much as wheat. Rather like spinach, bathua is also very rich in vitamin A.

After their day's work, the women used to take this 'weed' home and cook it for their families. Since the widespread introduction of weedkillers in wheat production, *bathua* has almost disappeared. And forty thousand children in India go blind each year for lack of vitamin A. It looks as though industrial agriculture has at least as much potential to starve or blind, as it has to feed the world.

The results reported here have been noted by the relatively few academics and researchers who study organic farming. By contrast, the effort and expense ploughed into 'improving' chemical, intensive agriculture has been immense. If as much effort was applied to adapting sustainable farming techniques to the needs of contemporary farmers, there is no reason at all to suppose yields could not be matched or even surpassed – and farm profits too, for that matter. Yet at present, government support in Britain for sustainable agriculture is minimal. Organic farming, for instance, receives an annual subsidy of £1 million, as opposed to the estimated £2 billion spent on conventional farmers. As the Soil Association points out, £500,000 a year – half the entire subsidy for organic farming – is spent simply on testing foods for pesticide residues!

It is not proven that organic, or sustainably-produced, farm yields are much more expensive than the conventional equivalent, even before the externalised costs, such as water treatment and landscape damage, are included. Jules Pretty and Rupert Howes from the International Institute for Environment and Development studied the results of four research projects and found that in sustainable farming (greatly reduced chemical use, more crop rotations, encouragement of hedgerows and other wildlife habitats) yields were between 20 per cent less and five per cent more than yields on conventional farms; and because many costly inputs were avoided, profits were mostly higher. Pretty and Howes are very keen for more research of this kind to be carried out, because if these findings were repeated they would suggest large-scale change in the UK might be possible without either us or the farmers starving, contrary to the entrenched views of the establishment, which farmers have come to believe.

Happily, the world has had centuries of experience of sustainable farming. Communities in China, Japan and Korea have farmed the same fields without loss of fertility for 40 centuries. But perhaps not for much longer. Unhappily, that knowledge is being lost fast, as around the world agricultural colleges, government extension workers, loan companies and chemical reps spread the gospel of chemical intensification. All over the world, organic farmers do carry out their own research, mercifully, and the more they are supported by their customers, the more they can do.

THE HUNGRY HAMBURGER

The differences (either way) in yield per hectare between organic and conventional systems pale into insignificance beside the most dramatically inefficient form of agriculture there is. Which form of agriculture is only one-tenth as efficient as the lowest-yielding wheatfield? Why, a field growing wheat to feed to livestock.

Raising meat intensively, as we do it now, is an extraordinary waste of land and resources. While a tonne of wheat harvested from the field will make pretty nearly a tonne of bread, it certainly won't convert into a tonne of beef on the butcher's slab. In fact it takes between 10 and 16 tonnes of grain to produce just one tonne of beef.

Livestock do have a valuable role to play in many farming systems. They can be a useful way to convert the otherwise inedible grass from poor land (waterlogged meadows or windswept hillsides into food); stock are also valuable members of the farm community, resting and fertilising land between arable crops, producing top-quality manure for key sites like the vegetable patch. And delicious locally-fed meat can easily be part of a healthy, locally sourced way of eating. However, as a nation we eat far more meat than can be provided by animals integrated this way into the farm cycle. There is no way that the number of sheep, cattle, pigs and poultry raised in Europe and North America is in balance with what our countryside can support: any more than the amount of meat eaten is in balance with the needs of our arteries or our waistlines.

In Europe we don't have the land to feed all the animals we believe we 'need' to eat. Most meat is not locally raised at all. The cattle and pigs may be standing in sheds in Britain or Germany, but the food they are eating comes in large part from as far away as Thailand and Brazil. The EU imports around 75 per cent of the fish and soya meal, which are the main protein sources for intensive animal feed. (CPRE/WWF, *Growing Greener*, June 1996). In order to feed our cattle population, the UK needs to farm an estimated two acres overseas for each one farmed at home, as well as to devastate uncalculated areas of sea bed. Clearly, conventional farming as currently practised is not feeding us without considerable help from overseas. In effect, rich northern purchasing power (or the purchasing power of our meat animals) out-bids poorer locals for the produce of their land.

While plantations growing fodder for livestock may enrich the plantation owners, we saw in the last chapter that they exact a tremendous cost from the host country as a whole. While, in Europe, the manure presents a formidable pollution problem. And, of course, welfare standards in such rearing systems are not high.

Most terrifyingly, the drive for cheap meat has brought us the horror of BSE. As we saw in chapter six, the emphasis on price competition, and the separation of farmers from the production of the food they fed their stock, were the forces behind this disease.

Industrial-scale meat production is taking off in Third World countries as well. Even when animals are ranged rather than kept in sheds, their numbers still pose problems, especially in tropical countries where soils are fragile. Cattle are big, hungry animals: if they are going to eat grass, they need a lot of it. Whole rainforests have been felled to accommodate cattle. Central America lost 40 per cent of its rainforest in just 25 years to make way for beef, Joni Seager reports in her book *Earth Follies*. Here in Britain, overgrazing has destroyed forests too: the mighty Caledonian pine forests, like the local farmers, have been erased by sheep. Once the trees have gone, erosion begins. Close-cropped pasture dries out more easily than a forest floor, and may turn to dust. This dusty soil is blown away or washes off in heavy rain. If trees and dense vegetation have gone, nothing checks the force of rainfall and flood. Staggeringly, it has been calculated that 85 per cent of all the soil lost by Canada, Australia, and the United States, is lost because of cattle farming.

Meat eating is spreading across the world as a sign of status and wealth. It is certainly a powerful way of co-opting large areas of land for the exclusive benefit of the rich. It seems hard to justify the oft-repeated claims that 'poor countries cannot feed themselves' when so much of their land is given over to feeding animals, at home and overseas. As Joni Seager reports: 'In Mexico, the amount of cropland devoted to feed and fodder for the livestock industry has climbed from 5 per cent in 1960 to 23 per cent in 1980, even though it is estimated that one-quarter of the Mexican population is chronically malnourished.'

In the US, half of all water consumed is used to grow crops that are fed to livestock; more than 50 percent of water pollution in the US can be linked to wastes from the livestock industry, including manure, eroded soil and synthetic pesticides. More than two-thirds of all US cropland is devoted to livestock.

Growing fodder for meat consumes not only land and water, but fossil fuels too: for cultivation, harvesting, distribution and fertiliser manufacture. The 500 calories of food energy in one pound of steak requires 20,000 calories of fossil fuel. It is far more efficient for us to eat the grain, than to feed it to livestock then eat the meat. In the end, for the same weight of protein on your plate, wheat, maize or soya is up to 20 times more energy-efficient.

The high rainfall in western Britain is soaked up by the grass which supports the meat and dairy farms in that area. But grass is far from the only plant which appreciates rain: peas and beans need plenty of moisture, and potatoes are thirstier still. Damp soil is essential for a lush growth of all the many delicious leafy crops: spinach, cabbage, chard and lettuce. The west country may be 'too wet for wheat', but oats, rye and barley are all rain-loving, nourishing grains. And there are other protein crops which would thrive without asking for any imported fodder: nuts such as hazel, walnut or sweet chestnut could yield equivalent or much higher quantities of protein from land, without the damage and expense caused by ploughing and fertiliser and pesticide applications.

GOOD FOR THE ENVIRONMENT IS GOOD FOR OUR HEALTH

Oddly enough, the produce of a balanced farm makes for a balanced diet. We certainly don't need to eat as much meat as we do – some of the healthiest people are those who eat no meat at all. Studies of different cultures where more whole foods and vegetables are eaten have found people do not have so many of the illnesses we worry about so much in northern Europe. These studies have been backed up by studies of groups – notably vegetarians – within our own culture.

Researchers have found again and again that vegetarians and other people eating a high proportion of fresh fruit and vegetable produce live longer, have less cancer, heart disease, bowel disease, diabetes, and other illnesses than those of us who eat more cooked meats, refined starch, sweet and processed foods. A fruit-and-vegetable based diet is also the easiest way to avoid and reverse obesity, which, alarmingly, is increasing quite rapidly in Britain. Although the health risks of being plump are sometimes overstated, severe obesity is not only dangerous, it is also uncomfortable and very miserable.

It certainly make biochemical sense that a diet with more vitamins, fibre, and essential fatty acids (the goodies) and less saturated fat and additives (the baddies) is going to be healthier. Specially protective foods may include the soya and the cabbage family, which seem to counter high oestrogen levels and may therefore protect against breast cancer; carrots and anything else yellow, dark green or red, which are high in anti-oxidants; and nuts and seeds which are rich in essential fatty acids.

Eating more vegetables also tends to lower the amount of fat you have room to fit in at each mealtime. Fat, in particular animal fat, is conclusively linked to heart disease and many cancers. And the fibre has the added benefit of speeding less desirable compounds through your body more quickly. A high fat, low-fibre diet, by contrast, means that food residues of a more toxic kind hang around longer in the bowel where cancer may start; and bowel cancer is a common cause of diet-related premature death.

OUR PRIORITIES

Good food, we have seen, need not be expensive, but sometimes we seem reluctant even to pay a fair price. Although we may know perfectly well that 70p for a whole cauliflower is a perfectly reasonable price, and a good deal better value than 99p for a small piece of soft, pre-cooked cauliflower in a lot of floury cheese sauce, ridiculously, sometimes we hesitate. You can't get half-a-pint of beer for 70p in most pubs.

John Dalby of the Soil Association bemoans this attitude, even while he catches himself at it: 'A lot of people are so used to cheap food. We have had such a culture of cheap food in this country, we are all conditioned to look for it, that even when we know what it really means. It is very difficult to pay a higher price. I find it myself! I find it really hard to pay 50p a lb for organic leeks when the ordinary ones are next to them at 25p.'

As we have seen, it is unfair that organic food should be priced so very much higher than conventional produce, or that free-range meat should cost so much more than the caged variety. The reasons are a combination of supermarket pricing policy and 'diseconomies of scale'. Nonetheless, compared to what many families spend on furniture, clothes, cars or holidays, the difference between buying 'ordinary' and buying high-quality and organic food is small. As a nation we have been devoting a smaller and smaller proportion of our income to food. For those of us who have a choice, this means we have been choosing other things instead of good food.

Steve Tidy, who grows organic vegetables on a smallholding in Hampshire, is amazed at how mean people can be when it comes to the food they give themselves: 'They want it at the cheapest possible price. They'll pay thousands of pounds for their car and holiday, but not for their food. They roll up in their £15,000 car, then won't buy my unsprayed strawberries because they can get them a few pence cheaper down the road. They worry more about what goes in their car than their own bodies.'

Dairy farmer Jeff Glyn Jones agrees. He blames the rise of BSE squarely on this 'cheap' food policy: 'As long as food is devalued in consumers' eyes it will be produced by the cheapest means possible. This situation originated from the cheap food policy; in order for a farmer to make a reasonable living he had to produce the food cheaper per unit. We have been trying since the war to cut corners and "make two blades of grass grow where one grew before".'

What crazy system of accounting drives us to shave the last ¼ of a penny off the price of a lettuce even if it means destroying landscapes and poisoning labourers – which we then find ourselves paying large amounts of cash to try and restore and support. What crazy system means that ¼ of a penny on the value of a company share is more worth having than clean air in the morning. What crazy system persuades us to buy pricy fancy food because ordinary food is so tasteless; to spend a fortune to roar off in an aeroplane and hire car on holiday somewhere 'still unspoiled' (by ring roads and industrial agriculture), and to shell out for taxes for health care, unemployment benefit, roadbuilding – so that someone else makes a profit?

Nation- and even EU-wide changes are needed to end the hidden subsidies to the industrial food system, and replace them with support for a food system which would really deliver good food, and to end the obscenity of 5 million people with an income so low they cannot feed themselves properly. In the meantime, happily, we can organise our own opt-out. As the next chapter shows, buying direct from a small, quality producer can give us access to real food at competitive prices and cuts out virtually all of the hidden costs – transport, packaging, pollution and poor health – of 'cheap' food. Local producers sell through local shops and some even deliver – an enormous boon to car-less households. The best way to ensure that more and more food is produced and marketed in this way, is to buy it in this way.

9

SATISFIED CUSTOMERS

Buying direct is an excellent way to get high-quality food, and at the same time it is a way of supporting producers of high quality food directly. When consumers are closely connected to growers, the growers can move much further towards producing the best crop for their climate, soil, resources and abilities. Farming to feed people is ecologically in a totally different league from farming to supply the food industry and the EU. Massive yields, cosmetic perfection, packaging and long-distance transport become unnecessary. Quality and variety take over. So, by seeking out good food, you protect the environment.

Direct selling never went away, of course: farmhouse cheeses, sacks of potatoes, Christmas turkeys and free-range eggs have always been available direct. But now more and more producers are concentrating their efforts on selling direct to consumers, because it is the best way for *them*. This in turn is giving consumers more and more opportunities to buy direct.

BOX SCHEMES

Mark Allen and his wife Rachel Harris, and their young son, receive a weekly box of vegetables from John and Ruth Daltry's organic farm 14 miles outside Leicester. In fact they also receive boxes for their neighbours, who collect them during the course of that evening. 'The veg are certainly much much tastier, they're fantastic. It's incredible the difference. And the value is superb. We did a price comparison of the boxes, and the small £3.50 one is about 11p more than buying the same in the market, and the bigger one is about 15p more. It is absolutely excellent value.'

'It's so different buying food when you know the people who have grown it,' says Mark. 'Ruth and John have organised days for us to visit, so we've been down to see the holding and see where everything comes from. You feel very much in touch with your supply of food. It's not as good as growing it yourself but it's the next best thing. Because it is almost all local, and goes right through the year, it helps you keep in touch with the seasons.' It means something to their little boy, too: 'We have a two-and-a-half year old who can be as awkward as any toddler about his food. But when we can tell him that is something that Ruth and John grew, it always helps.'

The benefits go beyond the food, too. 'Another spin-off for us is that we have got to know people in our street a lot better since they have joined the scheme and started coming round to collect their boxes.' The vegetable delivery has spread by word of mouth: 'People heard about it or saw the boxes arriving, so they wanted one too. It has turned out to be really popular. Overall the scheme has grown from 40 to about 150 [households]: Ruth and John have had to buy a trailer because they couldn't carry it all in the van.

'Getting these unusual vegetables, including some I have never seen before, makes you much more creative in your cooking. There you are with a vegetable you have no idea what to do with, so out come the recipe books. People also share recipes.

'We do do a lot of cooking and you need to on this sort of scheme. Some people have dropped out – and they tend to have the sort of hectic lives which means they buy ready-cooked meals. One person who left said to us, "I'm sorry, I've got a lifestyle problem". I could only agree!' Mark added, 'It does make an enormous difference that Ruth is so friendly. We were very keen to have organic vegetables but we never thought there would be so many benefits.'

Mark Allen is not the only satisfied box scheme customer. Such schemes are one of the most popular forms of 'direct marketing' by food producers selling to the public, rather than going through wholesalers or supermarkets. Vegetable and meat ordering, farm shops, pick-your-own and even help-grow-your-own schemes are all winning devotees.

People buying direct from the producers of their food are often very enthusiastic, both about the quality of the food – and about the way of buying it: 'My husband says its like having Christmas every week'; 'The quality is superb'; 'It's a sort of lucky bag, the kids rush to see what we've got'; 'They give such a good personal service'; 'There is no comparison with the taste, you feel sorry for people going to the supermarket'; 'Really, really good'.

There are sometimes drawbacks – too many swedes or tiny potatoes in the box, prices higher for meat products – but overall, it is small producers who are selling direct who are the ones who are thriving, so the customers must be happy. Schemes are growing and many even have waiting lists.

HUMANELY-REARED MEAT

Another customer delighted with buying direct is Claire Brown, who orders her meat regularly from Pam Finn of Naturally Yours. Finn has meat raised to her specifications on several nearby farms, as well as her own, where the breeds (of animal) have been chosen for flavour and the animals are kept in 'an extensive system where they can behave in a natural way and enjoy their life' as Finn describes it in the customers' newsletter. Claire Brown explains her reasons for buying from Pam Finn: 'My parents were always worried about how animals were raised. My father was a Quaker and felt strongly that it was a moral issue. They did not object to eating meat as such, but would only ever buy meat when they knew it had been kindly raised. Very close second as a reason came the fact that both my parents were very interested in food and my mother was a first rate cook, and meat which has been kindly produced is just much nicer than meat which has been rottenly produced.

'When my father died I went through his papers and there was a newspaper article about Naturally Yours, which he had cut out and marked "send to Claire", so I tried them and now I use them all the time. As well as excellent meat, there is an excellent personal service.

'I know they rear their animals humanely because a friend of mine who has farmed herself visited, and she really cared for her animals. When I'm out I always say I'm a vegetarian so I won't be confronted with something I'm not happy about, but if people who cared about animals gave up eating meat altogether it would leave the field clear for those who didn't care at all!'

People with children value the 'good food habit' particularly highly. Ann English, who buys all her meat from Pam Finn says: 'We have two small boys, and we like to think that they are getting food of as good a quality as possible. We know Pam's meat has not been pumped full of hormones and additives and other unnatural things to enhance the growth. The flavour is so much better, there's no comparison. And I do want the boys to grow up in the right way of eating, not willing just to accept any old rubbish.' Although the meat from Naturally

Sow and piglets, Ragman's Lane

Yours is more expensive than the supermarket 'you don't have to eat meat every night' as Ann English says. 'I don't buy the top of the range stuff, except for a treat. We get mostly things like mince and sausage, things for children, and stewing meat.'

SATISFIED FARMERS

Pam Finn laughs when you ask why she sells direct to customers rather than through a supermarket or butchers' shop. 'Oh we couldn't produce enough to be involved in a large set-up like that. And the way we raise meat means there is variation, we can't provide what they call portion control: everything the same size every time. That isn't a problem for our customers, though. We really enjoy the personal side of the work – it is nice to think we have become so friendly with people like Claire, just through the business.'

For the Finns there was never any question of an intensive system for the animals: 'We have always kept animals the way we do (with the emphasis on welfare and a natural life) because that's how we thought people did it – that's how out of date we were! Then when we found out what they *were* doing: well – my God! Never on your life!'

Because producers who take the trouble to raise their plants or animals carefully are at a commercial disadvantage if they then have to sell their produce into the main commercial stream, farmers who take care of their stock, like good vegetable growers, value interested customers who come directly to them.

Like Pam Finn, beef and pork producers Richard and Rosamund Young now depend on direct sales to customers to ensure the welfare of their animals. They began selling direct in 1980. Many of their customers have come through word of mouth. As they told a reporter from the *Telegraph*: 'We were rearing animals carefully to a tight set of welfare standards and we were always worried about how the animals were treated once they left us. When would they next be fed or watered? Might they be exported abroad? I think people like buying from us because they can see for themselves, at first hand, exactly how we rear our animals.'

The direct link between producer and consumer benefits both sides. It enables high quality production to make a living for the producer while still being affordable to the consumer. And it gives a great deal of pleasure to both sides. Just as Mark Allen and his wife found any number of advantages from buying directly, John and Ruth Daltry, who grow the vegetables, have found numerous advantages on their side of the relationship. The Daltrys supply a weekly box of whatever is good from their holding, supplemented with one or two items bought in if necessary. (There are very few soils and situations on which you can grow absolutely anything, and smaller holdings may not have space and labour enough for bulky field crops such as potatoes.)

As Ruth Daltry explains: 'We have sold in all kinds of ways: to a local wholefood shop; into wholesale and organic wholesale markets; to an organic co-op, packing for supermarkets, and we certainly like boxes the best. The logistics are just so much better, to sell direct. It is picked on Thursday and in people's kitchens on Thursday evening – and obviously, the better condition your customers get their vegetables in, the better they like them, so the better it is for us.

'It makes so much more sense from our point of view. We can pick our lettuces when they're ready. A supermarket needs produce at a particular time and if something is not ready that's it, you have lost the sale. We lost our peas one year. They weren't ready the week they were wanted and that was it. It was no use trying to get them to take them later. By contrast, our customers in Leicester are delighted to have peas whenever they're ready.

'And there is so much less waste. The supermarkets insist on tremendous grade-outs. We have to grade very fussily for the co-op packers and they still grade it again. Our customers get much better value as there is no wastage, so we don't need to put the same kind of mark-up. And we get a much better price. It's very much worth having this outlet. The pigs used to get all the delicious but misshapen tomatoes and cucumbers, they're feeling very hard done by nowadays!'

Growing for people's entire vegetable needs has made Ruth and John's work more satisfying. 'We have had to greatly expand the range of what we grow, which really suits our personalities, as we love to try new things. It is much more interesting than a few solid fields with just one crop in them. We do mixed salad bags, we are growing mizuna and pak choi, kohl rabi and fennel. It is horticulturally much better to grow a wide range of vegetables, and much more fun!'

CONSUMERS ARE A FARM'S BEST FRIEND

There are all kinds of ways in which consumers can link with producers. Many will sell direct from the farm, dairy or bakery, or have a dedicated shop. Others will sell through established local outlets: a stall in a town market, or a regular supply to a market trader or local shops. Other producers have opted to deliver direct to customers' homes, or via pick-up points, so that consumers are grouping together to receive the kind of food they want. Consumers can also take a more active role by seeking out suppliers and setting up 'buyers groups', making it worthwhile for the producer to sell and even deliver directly to them, without a middleman, at a keen price.

The joy of a direct connection between producers and consumers is that so often they want the same things – things that supermarkets and big wholesalers may not be able to, or wish to, cope with. The ideals of many consumers and producers coincide: small scale and top, often organic quality; information and feedback; freshness, variety, and a non-exploitative price for both parties. But these may be exactly the opposite of what is sought by the middlemen: supermarket buyers and wholesalers. Their profit lies entirely in the gap between the price to the farmer and the price to the consumer: they make their money by buying cheap and selling expensive.

WHO WANTS TO EAT A MONOCULTURE ANYWAY?

There are important agricultural differences too, between growing for a supermarket and growing for individuals. One example of the way producers' and consumers' needs mesh closely together – leaving big operations out in the cold – is with variety. Natural systems contain a wide range of species side by side, all occupying their 'niche'. A healthy natural farm system works in the same way. Different crops take different nutrients from the soil. Some have deep roots and some have shallow ones. Onions and garlic may deter pests which attack carrots or fruit trees; salad greens may disguise the shape of cabbages from the pigeons; hens can eat aphids and snails, and their manure is a fertiliser. Rotations and mixtures of crops prevent the spread of a pest 'epidemic' right across a farm – the kind of epidemics that can sweep through conventional farms with huge acreages down to a single crop – or through sheds packed with a single animal species, and which then have to be drenched with pesticides and antibiotics.

Organic systems, in particular, work best if each piece of land is used for a different crop or animal each season (rotation), which obviously requires a range of crops to be grown. And if one crop does fall foul of weather conditions or pest attack, the more other crops there are on the same farm, the less likely this is to mean disaster to the farmers. And as Ruth Daltry pointed out, it is also less boring!

Large buyers like supermarkets don't want to buy like this. They don't want a lorry with 17 sacks of potatoes, three crates of lettuce and five of sweetcorn, and a few trays of eggs: they want one lorry filled to the roof with one uniform crop, so that every one of their stores from Gravesend to Galloway can carry 'Organic sweetcorn, two for £1.49' at the same time. Small buyers like families, on the other hand, *don't* want a lorryload or even a boxful of sweetcorn and nothing but sweetcorn. They want a mixture of potatoes, lettuces and sweetcorn, eggs and everything else: a healthy mixed diet pretty closely matching a healthy mixed cropping pattern. Just what the grower wants to sell. It suits both sides.

The reason organic food is scarce and expensive in ordinary shops is *not* that it is difficult or expensive to grow. It is difficult and expensive to sell through shops. Many growers find it is easier and cheaper to sell direct to the consumer.

Ordinary people are reliable customers, too. Although supermarkets – and 'the market' at large – may be fickle and changeable, the people who shop in them have predictable habits. They aren't generally anxious to be in front of this week's food fashion, and they won't (as the big stores do) suddenly refuse to buy potatoes because a shipload of Egyptian ones has docked at Tynemouth costing a quarter of a penny less per kilo.

Not will they reject cucumbers because they are curly. Dave Burlingham, who grows for the Ayrshire Organic Growers scheme, values this: 'The shareholders are interested in quality and taste, and the fact that the food is organic. They're not interested in cosmetics'.

Customers can pay a better price than a wholesaler or supermarket, as there are no middlemen to support. As Rob Keene, who has a farm shop on his big vegetable farm outside Gloucester points out: 'The prices we earn in the shop are just not comparable to wholesalers. We take stuff to the wholesale market if the only alternative is to dump it!'

An established, regular market is equally important to growers, and, as we have seen, this is exactly what the big market does not offer. Tony Edwards was one of the Herefordshire Green Growers who was disenchanted with selling to the erratic and unreliable supermarkets. Like his co-members, he is delighted with the growing list of customers taking a vegetable box through their marketing co-op, OMC, each week. He told BBC Radio 4's *Food Programme*: 'I can grow with confidence, knowing what we grow is going to be sold through the year. I can grow a wider range and know it's appreciated. It makes work more interesting and spreads the load. Over the last couple of years I've definitely felt much more job satisfaction.'

His colleague Simon Brenman also found a world of difference between dealing with a group of people with a personal commitment and the purely market transactions. He used to stand in for the co-op's marketing manager when he was away, and dreaded dealing with the supermarkets: 'Supermarket buyers really look out for the weak point: they knew when our chief marketer was away and they really drove down the prices and gave me a hard time. The co-ops on the other hand knew to give me the orders a day early when I was there on my own'.

Green Growers and their partners in OMC, Organic Growers West Wales, sell their produce into semi-direct box schemes in Birmingham, Manchester and Sheffield. They have gone from strength to strength since they discovered the benefits of selling direct to consumers, rather than to supermarkets. By 1996, only 10 per cent of their produce was going to supermarkets, with most going to box schemes. Profits are up 40 per cent, despite the fact that their customers pay less for a better choice of vegetables than they would get in the supermarket.

Organic farming inspector Mike Michaud agrees that customers buying direct have enabled their small organic producers to flourish at a time when other small producers have been closing down. 'All the most successful organic producers I see do at least some of their marketing locally, through a box, or through the weekly town market. Meat producers too, mostly selling frozen meat. More and more people are doing it.'

One more conventional body which has recognised the potential value to farmers, in particular small farmers, of selling direct is Devon County Council. As they observe, 'small farms are becoming increasingly un-economic and the average age of farmers in Devon is high, reflecting the lack of opportunities for young people'. Research commissioned by the council suggested small farm incomes could rise by as much as 30 per cent if a 'diversified sustainable agricultural strategy' was employed: for example, adding in a small horticulture enterprise in the most suitable part of an all-dairy farm.

In the Council's view, the key to this is customers – *local* customers. As the forces of centralisation, globalisation and subsidised infrastructure advance, so Devon's farmers have been left on the periphery. But Devon's farmers are not remote from Devon's consumers. By promoting marketing of high-quality produce direct to people in Devon, the council hopes to make farmers less vulnerable to the cold winds of change. By forming a 'Food and Land Links Trust' the council aims 'to make the local economy less vulnerable to national and European changes in agriculture, by developing stable local markets less reliant on subsidised markets and large scale infrastructural improvements'.

Devon Council are almost certainly thinking along the right lines. For her MSc in sustainable agriculture at Wye College, Arzeena Hamir interviewed 32 growers who were selling vegetables direct to the public via weekly boxes, and the advantage most often cited was 'direct contact with the customers'. 'There were sound commercial reasons for this,' says Hamir. 'It meant growers knew what customers wanted.' The reduced wastage and better returns that growers were able to make from selling direct was vital to many businesses, she found. 'Quite a few told me that if it hadn't been for selling direct, they might well have gone under.' Growers also told Hamir they appreciated the steadier cash flow and greater market security.

THE JOY OF BOXES

The arrangement that suits many growers best of all is the vegetable box scheme. The growers harvest several 'households'-worth' of produce each week, enough to feed all the customers, selecting from what is available from their range of different crops. Some basics are guaranteed: perhaps, potatoes, carrots, onions and some greens each week, but the decision on what else goes in week by week comes from the grower. With this system there is the absolute minimum of waste, and it is far less time-consuming for the grower (or for the consumer group, in consumer-organised schemes) than filling individual orders. Instead of having to write down and read through 60 people's orders, hoping that everyone won't want the same thing and enough people will ask for French beans, the vegetables are simply harvested and divided between the boxes.

When Tim and Jan Deane first thought of selling the vegetables from their small Devon holding this way, they weren't sure how it would go down with customers. 'We did wonder if people would cope, but it seems lot of people actually find it easier, not having to stand there and decide in the shop, week after week.' Their customers do have the right to have a couple of 'absolute dislikes' registered – more of everything else in return for no green peppers, for instance – but Jan won't let customers get pickier than that. And they have a very long waiting list, so clearly people are happy.

People receiving the weekly box from the Perry Court biodynamic garden in Kent also enjoy their boxes: 'We have been educating ourselves. At first it took a bit to get used to: cooking with what you've got when you've got used to buying what you want. But you know I really appreciate not having to just stand there and *decide*, week after week. Its very nice, really nice.'

Janet Maresh, whose weekly box comes through Limited Resources in Manchester, agrees. 'It's like a lucky bag, really. We have had to start looking up recipes or using our imagination. Now we have had some new dishes on the table, and we're eating vegetables we'd never even tried before: kohl rabi, artichoke, celeriac. You've got to change your attitude. Some things you do miss, you are used to having tomatoes all year round, now we only get them when they're in season. But I always used to look forward to the English strawberries as a treat: and you start to look forward to the other things like tomatoes, too.'

When Arzeena Hamir was doing her research she also spoke to customers, and they confirmed that they found vegetable boxes convenient rather than troublesome. 'Convenience was actually the second most common reason cited for getting a box – after the *most* common reason, which was simply the access to organic vegetables in useful quantities. Ten per cent did actually say they bought this way because it was *not* the supermarket!'

Selling through boxes is much more in tune with what happens on the farm, which means that it is cheaper. There is minimal wastage – all sound produce can be used, and nothing is picked unless it is already paid for – thus prices can fall. The grower's income is also more stable and predictable, which is worth more to many small businesses than high but unpredictable profits. Both grower and consumer are freed from the tyranny of market prices which can make crops suddenly very pricey, or so cheap they don't cover the grower's costs. It's all much more reasonable.

Some schemes do take note of market prices, item by item, in order to assure customers that they are getting value for money. Jan Deane is one who believes that this is ultimately unnecessary, as she told Judy Steele: 'When we have a glut of aubergines there might be three in a box. Would someone go out and buy three aubergines for 89p a lb? Do we have any right to charge them £3, even in our heads?' In January, Jan Deane points out, when the box has the conventionally cheaper carrots, onions, leeks, cabbage and potatoes, 'it still adds up to as much food value in the belly' as summer produce, which is more perishable, and has a higher price on the open market.

What is important, after all, is that her customers eat well and are paying an affordable amount week by week. Overall the Deane's customers, like those on most box schemes, do get good value. A big £7 box can provide a vegetarian family with a large proportion of their food needs for the week. Some of their customers are on very low incomes and still consider this the best way to buy their vegetables.

A Commitment to Healthy Eating

It isn't immediately obvious that getting vegetables delivered once a week in a box would make a difference to a family's eating habits compared to the days of going to Sainsbury's. But it seems to. Jan Deane comments: 'Some people say they now eat more vegetables than they did before. They have risen to the challenge, and they consider this a plus of the scheme as it has done something positive for their health. It isn't part of the sell but it is mentioned to us often enough.'

Researcher Emma Delow, who canvassed the views of some of the Deanes' customers and members of two other direct buying schemes in Devon, found that 74 per cent of the adults and 40 per cent of the children in the households she surveyed were eating more vegetables now they had a box delivery. Motivation about healthy eating in general seemed to rise, with people making more effort to avoid processed foods, and buying more wholefoods.

Limited Resources customer Margaret Biddle has been able to stop going to the supermarket every week now that she gets a weekly box of organic vegetables. 'I would say when you're in Tesco you are being urged to buy rubbish you don't really need, that costs a lot of money. I find by not going to Tesco's we don't get all that any more. We get a bar of chocolate once a week as a treat. We're not buying all that packaged stuff'.

Connecting your eating with the produce from local farms has something else to offer your health: food in season. Some foods are difficult to supply in Britain all year round without either importing them from far away, in which case they need spraying or fumigating to

.survive storage for a long journey; they are grown in conditions they don't really like, which tends to make them vulnerable to disease – and liable to be sprayed. Choosing food out-of-season leads to all sorts of unwanted and unhealthy processes.

For instance, lettuces grown in a greenhouse in winter are prone to fungus – hence the frequency with which they break fungicide safety limits. Box scheme growers can explain this to customers, and grow alternatives like sugarloaf chicory: prolific, crispy and sweet, with just enough bitterness for taste; dainty mizuna; spicy mustards. You might never choose such unfamiliar leaves from a shop, but if they are in your box, you eat them – and discover how delicious they are.

REAL MEAT IN A REALISTIC MENU

Just as vegetable and fruit growers like to supply everything that is edible from the farms, without unnecessary waste, meat farmers want to sell every cut of meat from the carcasses of their animals. Organic farmers in particular have a problem here: the supermarkets' idea of meat is a limited range of cuts anyway, but an organic farmer may find it hard to get supermarkets to buy much more than lamb chops and beef steak. When was the last time you saw organic lambs' heart or organic sausages in a supermarket?

Some organic and non-intensive meat farms sell direct to their customers and these farms are able to match what goes into the shop with what comes off the animals. Obviously, it makes sense to the farm to sell all their produce, but it makes just as much sense to customers too. Just because you want to eat organic meat, doesn't mean you want, or can afford, sirloin steak or lamb cutlets every time. So cheap cuts are there: belly pork, stewing lamb, hearts, liver, kidneys, braising steak and mince.

'IF YOU LIKE THAT, I'LL PLANT MORE NEXT YEAR ...'

Growers will put flavour first if they know the people tasting the produce. George Glide in Herefordshire grows potatoes 'for taste rather than yield'. They also adapt to suit local tastes and even individual requests. The subscribers to Ayrshire Organic Growers are invited to meet the growers at a garden party in the summer and at a more formal meeting in the winter, when the planning of next years' crops takes place. Subscriber Marcelle Edwards observes: 'We all meet twice a year and discuss what they are growing, and they're very amenable. If we say, "oh there's too many turnips", immediately there are less turnips. They listen. This year we had a lot of nice things like beans and mange tout peas – because of us asking'.

Bart Ives is very popular among his customers because of the fascinating, delicious varieties he grows. Ives grows lots of 'unusual' vegetables: Pink fir apple potatoes for salads, Edsall blue for roasting ('A superb potato. I could have sold ten times as many'), Samba, which store so well, improving to a nutty flavour as they are kept, little round crystal apple cucumbers ('so popular and very prolific – and ideal for one person!') oriental leaf vegetables for salads, stripy beetroot, sculptural romanescu broccoli.

And yes, he does do individual requests: 'A customer came up to me at my stall on the market and gave me some seeds she wanted me to grow. She had saved them from a squash she really liked. They're really easy, you just bung a bit of dung on the ground, so I'll grow them for her next season.' This is serious consumer power! When the squash plants flourish and bear fruit on Bart Ives' Sussex smallholding, not only will his customer be assured of her favourite squashes, she and Bart will be able to share this favourite with his other customers. 'Sometimes they ask me to grow something in particular, maybe mizuna (a lacy Japanese salad leaf) or rocket, and I can get them a crop in about three weeks, so it's no trouble.' The sense of shared enjoyment is irresistible.

And of course, if there's anything wrong with the produce, the grower can hear about it in person. With a very personal reputation to maintain, producers are extremely anxious to please. There may well be a good reason for the problem – part of the joy of direct buying is the two-way education process. Jan and Tim Deane send out a newsletter explaining when bad weather has delayed the sweetcorn or badgers have destroyed the carrots.

Ruth Daltry's customers share their views with her, too. 'They certainly tell us what they think. At the end of May, June, we had to buy some stuff in and it was really not very good, and my goodness we got it back in our faces!' she cheerfully recalls. 'We had to explain that they were lucky to get even that; at the time prices were sky-high. It was such a cold spring last year. It is an education process, definitely.'

A SHARE IN THE ENTERPRISE

One of the most powerful ways consumers can contribute to their own food supply is to pool their resources – literally – at the start of the growing season.

Plants and animals take time to grow. Winter cabbages start life in early summer. October's pumpkins were probably sown in May. The seeds were probably paid for in March. August's barbecuing steak has been chomping grass and silage for longer still. Customers who buy direct at least pay up more quickly than the wholesaler or supermarket who, like most big businesses, sit on bills for months, as any small business can tell you.

But even so, the lead times are long and the margins narrow. Getting an overdraft is perilous. Jan Deane, who as well as running her own box scheme advises other organic producers, points out: 'It would be very hard to service much of a loan from growing vegetables unless it was on a very large scale. Interest charges do contribute to growers giving up. If the bank forecloses on the loan, you can lose the land too.'

When operating expenses and living expenses are added up, the money a grower needs to have in hand to get through the season will be several thousand pounds. This is a daunting sum for one person or a family. However, divided between, say, 70 families, it is within the reach of many.

'Having payments up front has got to be good news. For one thing you are getting the money at the beginning of the season when the expenses are. That is when you are using your tractor and it is going to break down; even seeds cost a lot. On a small farm like ours we can spend £1,000 on seeds. Better still, you avoid having to deal with the banks, and they have so much power.'

Up-front financing can make fresh, ecologically-grown food available in places where it wouldn't otherwise have been. It could almost be seen as a kind of private collective garden or farm. For example, investment by consumers has secured – and transformed – Dave Burlingham's vegetable holding at Sundrum, in Ayr, mentioned above. 'I was growing vegetables and had built up a round in my van. But you never know what people are going to want, they buy different things each week, and you are left with unsold stuff each time.' Dave Burlingham realised that he could not make a living that way, and had more or less decided to go back to working as an electrician.

The garden, and the organic vegetable supply, was saved, however, when he and his wife got together with two other growers and set up a subscription farming system. They sought out local households who might be interested in buying organic vegetables regularly. These customers agreed to pay £180 in advance for a year's supply of vegetables.

'Now there is no insecurity. Everything I grow has a home to go to, and it doesn't have to be straight or of a uniform size.' No wastage means good value, too: although Dave only guarantees £170 worth of vegetables, so far each year the shop value of what subscribers received has been more like £250. Customers also consider the quality to be first-rate, and the scheme is growing. Dave and his colleagues recognise that £180 is a lot to find at a time for poorer households, so there is an option to pay in three instalments.

Many farms have been rescued this way, and gone on to become thriving, popular subscription systems. The approach has taken off in several countries, including the USA, where it has the rather worthy-sounding title of 'community supported agriculture'.

Robin van En of Indian Line Farm in the US, has leased a part of her farm to a community group which employs a gardener to grow their vegetables for them on biodynamic principles. She loves to tell the story, repeated in her local *County Voice* magazine, of the day she was stopped by a local farmer with her cart laden with 12'' lettuces. 'He called out "how much do you get for a head?" I hollered back that it was already paid for – that *all* our vegetables already had buyers. His mouth dropped open and he stood in amazement.'

On the basis of mutual trust, some American CSAs have developed to a stage where members themselves decide what they can afford to pay. When the membership gets together, the predicted budget for the year is presented and members write down on a slip of paper how much they think they can afford that year. The sums on the slips are totalled up, and if there is a shortfall, members are asked to put in another bid and the process is repeated.

THE SORROWS AND JOYS OF LIFE

Subscribers can contribute much more than money, too. At Ayrshire Organic Growers, customers spend time helping in the vegetable garden, some on a regular basis and in return for their share. Others contribute their own particular forms of expertise: accountancy, water engineering (for irrigation) and simple personal support. Some members, like Marcelle Edwards, have become personal friends and feel genuine concern for their growers: she commented that she felt they ought to be earning more for such a good service. Not least because the quality of the service can be so high, customers have an interest in the business staying afloat: as Marcelle Edwards said: 'If Dave and Eileen gave up I'd be devastated'.

In Japan, this kind of partnership between consumers and farmers has been fundamental to the organic farming movement for at least 20 years. In 1978 the Japan Organic Agriculture Association issued a document offering guidelines to the principles and practice of this partnership. The declaration emphasised the virtues of mutual trust and assistance: farmers would grow for the consumers' needs: (quality, safety, freshness, taste) rather than the artificial, cosmetic demand of the market (uniformity, durability etc). In return the consumer would guarantee a market and a fair price, and take the rough with the smooth.

This philosophy recognises the support that customers can give to growers by sharing in their risks. It is hard enough to find thousands of pounds to see you through the season until the harvest is sold: but supposing there is blight, hurricane, flood, June frost – or invading goats!

Growing a wide range of crops for a direct-to-consumer scheme – eggs in a variety of baskets – certainly lessens the impact of one particular crop failure. For instance, in 1994, like many other growers, Dave Burlingham suffered blight on his potatoes. But this has not wiped out his business: 'Our potato crop was an absolute disaster! But the brassicas have been super, with 15lb January kings and sprouts like cabbages'. Dave agrees to supply staples (he had to buy in replacement potatoes), but otherwise the customers get what's available: 'If the strawberries fail they don't get strawberries.' But with 50 varieties of vegetable and a soft and top fruit orchard at their service, subscribers always get plenty.

Ayr customers have taken a small step further, too: they agree by contract to accept the first £10, at any rate, of loss of harvest below the £180 they have paid. Thus, they accept that they have been guaranteed only £170 worth of vegetables though they pay £180. Though perhaps more of a token than anything, it is psychologically very important; as similar schemes in Japan describe it, 'sharing the joys and sorrows of life'.

STARTING UP

The *transition* to ecological farming can be a particularly difficult time for a farm, whether or not an organic symbol is being sought. Years of chemical agriculture may have used up most of the organic matter – dead leaves, worm casts, manure, insect droppings and remains, living fungi and bacteria – which naturally gives soil its fertility. The soil has to be rebuilt, so to begin with yields will be lower than on a mature organic farm, and lower than they were with artificial fertiliser. At the same time, pests and diseases will still be around, as poisons are no longer applied but the natural balance of pest predators is still building up. The 'conversion period' varies for different countries and different aspects of farming. In the UK it is two years before the farm can sell produce as organic, at the 'premium' prices that this allows. And of course the grower will be struggling with a new way of farming, so will be most vulnerable to making mistakes.

Commonly, large farms convert to organic methods part by part, but with a small operation it may be too much trouble to sell different categories of produce at the same time. At this stage support from consumers is doubly important, but hard to offer through long-distance marketing. 'In conversion' grade produce is available, but often gets lost among all the other labels and certification schemes; it is a category that has never really taken off.

A more personal sort of support can be more convincing to consumers and farmers alike. For instance, people who buy produce or eat at the cafe at Ruskin Mill in Gloucestershire are supporting the conversion to organic of part of a neighbouring farm. The fact that the customers were there was one reason that the farmer got interested in the first place.

As Ruskin Mill's Duncan McCanlis explains: 'A local farmer became interested in what we do here (there is already an organic vegetable holding on site) and wanted to put two acres of his farm under organic. We said, "yes we'll buy from you". He now has a guaranteed market for those fields, which in effect covers his risk. Selling produce described as 'in transition' and explaining who is growing it and how, has a powerful educational role helping people to understand what the farmer has to go through.'

LINKING UP

Contact with a farm is a contact valued by many: it is enjoyable, satisfying and educational. As Janet Maresh who receives a weekly box through the Limited Resources co-op says: 'The kids are interested in what comes in. We compare one week's carrots with another, and the children are interested in organic gardening now. I bought some slug pellets for the allotment and one of them said, "Limited Resources are better than us now because we're not organic". We were talking about visiting the farms. I would really like to know how they deal with slugs! It's lovely to have that direct contact.'

Japanese consumers who have built up a relationship with their provider of 'safe food' over the years treasure this relationship. As Japanese environmentalist Koyu Furusawa reports in his contribution to the book *A Future for the Land*: 'The most striking aspect of the outlook of some ... co-op members is the importance attached to the relationship between producer and consumer. The relationship is sometimes spoken of with reverence and considered far more important than the mere pursuit of safe food to consume.' He adds that the consumers often make a point of thinking about the farm, the farmer, and the way the food grew when they eat it.

Getting in touch with the source of our own life, the earth, by knowing, visiting and even helping in the place were our food comes from can be very enriching – and enjoyable. It can be a special treat for people living in towns. Dave Alkist and a friend are, like Mark Allen, subscribers to the Daltry's box scheme, and every so often they get together and put in a day's work in Ruth and John's fields: mending fences, weeding, planting – and enjoying themselves. 'We really enjoy it, working together. And I get a real buzz out of putting something on the table and saying, 'I planted that!'

For her part, Ruth Daltry is a friendly, outgoing woman who appreciates the social side of direct selling almost as much as the horticultural and business advantages. Selling locally has brought some of the social contact of city life out to the farm. 'We get to see our customers at 4.30 or 5 when they are just finishing work, so we hear about their day. We know what people like from the delight when people see the boxes. I remember dropping off a box and when the customer looked in the box and exclaimed "Oh – strawberries".' He was really thrilled. We get so much of that. It is a lovely credit to us when people are so keen.'

In Leicester members of the local exchange trading system (LETS) can work on the farm to earn local currency (called Leaves in Leicester). In return, the Daltrys sell some of their produce for Leaves, which customers have either earned by working on the farm, or by doing other jobs for members of Leicester LETS.

When they initially made contact with what is mainly a young and urban group like LETS, Ruth and John Daltry were not sure what they would find, but they have been delighted: 'The organic movement is a bit like a big family, and now we feel we are in the LETS family too. When we went along to the first LETS meeting we thought, well we're old stick in the muds. And when we saw the people there we nearly died! My goodness! But we were in the family really quickly!

'We had an open day here for Henry Doubleday (the organic gardening research association) and we hired some people on LETS to do catering and cooking and farm walks, and when they were finished with cooking they went out and spent the afternoon weeding. Then we all had a party tea together afterwards. Really we wish they were all a bit nearer.'

It is easy to see the mutual benefits of such a lively, friendly relationship. The people in the city of Leicester get the chance to work in the healthy surroundings of an organic farm, to learn about agriculture and enjoy the satisfaction of sharing in food production. The farm gets satisfied customers who become better informed, the more time they spend on the farm. The farmers also gain some of the social contact people enjoy in towns, without suffering urban stress.

The latter has been cited as a benefit of the close-knit farmer-consumer groups which have grown up in Japan. According to Koyu Furusawa, the close involvement and support for Japanese organic growers backs them up when they face hostility from neighbouring farmers practising conventional chemical agriculture. Furusawa also suggests that the consumers' hair-raising tales of city life also help the farmers to be more contented with their rural lot, away from the bright lights. They get more satisfaction from contributing to the wellbeing of customers and 'overcome the common tendency to downgrade their occupation'.

A number of thriving farmer consumer groups, or *Teikei* (partnerships) have grown up in Japan in which these ideals are lived out. The groups value the 'farmer's face on the vegetables'.

Many people who enjoy gardening recognise the meditative, therapeutic qualities of working with the soil and with plants. It is sometimes suggested to people specifically *for* its therapeutic powers. A north London doctor who has been helping refugees who are the victims of torture by finding them allotments on which they can grow vegetables together, says: 'I do believe that if you look after the soil, it looks after you, not just physically but spiritually as well'

Grower George Glide believes that connecting box scheme

customers to his farm will bring similar benefits. 'It's not just about growing and feeding people physically. It's a lot to do with people's need for centring and grounding. People know they need to get away from the noise and vibrations in the city, and the turmoil and confusion. Tim and Jan [Deane]'s newsletter is quite reflective: it talks about the crops, it helps connect people. People need contact with the land, it's real, it's an education in a way.'

And he agrees that it's good for the growers. 'Communication is a dimension so often missing for growers. It is easy to get bogged down in the day-to-day running. But if people come in it becomes more real to the grower. It is important to me personally, spiritually, to have other people know what is going on.' Horticulture student Jeremy Taylor comments that when volunteering on organic farms 'I met loads of moody growers' but those who are selling direct to the public seemed 'fantastic people, really warm and friendly'. Although, of course, the friendlier people are likelier to do better, Taylor is sure that the pleasures of selling direct have made growers happier. 'I have surveyed growers who sell direct and they all rate increased job satisfaction from contact with customers as a great boon'.

Growers contacted for information never seemed to have difficulty suggesting the names of regular customers to interview about the service – and the customers in turn spoke with real affection about 'their' producers. First-name terms are the norm. How different from the relationship one builds up with a chiller cabinet in a supermarket.

Warmth towards their customers is evident in the relationship between Tim and Jan Deane and their customers. 'I carry a lot of information about customers in my head. For instance, if I know someone is living alone I won't give them a huge marrow – maybe they'll get more of the treats. If I know a family has three children I will give them five sweetcorn even if everyone else is getting four. And I think, in a scheme like this, a kind of "taking according to your needs" is fine. People are buying a share of the harvest, and they are all getting good value, and getting a good service. It's more than just veg.'

Indeed, for some people it is a lifeline. 'There are some people, ME sufferers, one with MS, some with cancer, who feel organic veg are an essential part of their health care. Anyone who makes that known to us we will try very hard to squeeze in despite the waiting list – how can you say no?'

'One housebound customer who could not come to the Exeter pick-up point was desperate to get our veg, so we found another customer who was willing to deliver to them, by asking in the newsletter.

'Another customer who moved away felt so dependent on our boxes that she was sending a mini-cab to collect her box. Once Tim was late with the delivery and found the taxi there with its meter ticking away. We were knocked out that she felt it was so important – and she was on quite a low income too – so we had to squeeze her onto the round somehow.'

Even in slightly larger-scale systems of direct buying which have started up in some big cities, personal contact remains very important. As Janet Maresh from Manchester points out: 'There is a dialogue and you can have more confidence in what you buy. It gives you confidence and it gives you control. You can find out about things. If you don't like something you can ring the co-op and tell them.

'I have my nice half hour when Troy phones me once a week and we chat away about what I might buy – he says they've got a new line of something or another. It's value added. Everyone laughs in the office. It's absolutely brilliant. It beats Tesco's any day.'

One of Jan Deane's customers told resaearcher Emma Delow: 'That personal thing seems to make each vegetable more valuable and significant.' Delow adds: 'I think people were getting all sorts of benefits from belonging to schemes. They were sometimes quite ecstatic about the quality of the produce, and they were eating better, and their children were. They were being more adventurous with food and cooking. They had all the psychological benefits of the pleasure and interest, and the peace of mind of knowing where their food came from. That was very important to people.'

10

SHOPPING TO SAVE THE WORLD

The Pipers Farm butchers' shop in Exeter doesn't look out of the ordinary. People shop there because the meat is above average quality, 'traditionally reared' but affordable, and the shop is friendly and convenient.

But Pipers is no ordinary butchers. Every time you come here to buy a slice of belly pork or lamb shoulder stuffed with rosemary and garlic, you are helping to protect the rural community and the landscape; you are supporting family farms using small-scale traditional techniques, and sparing the animals and the environment the effects of intensive meat rearing. Peter and Henrietta Greig who run Pipers Farm supervise every slice of meat they sell from birth (or hatching) to the shop counter. It all comes from just seven farms in the surrounding Devon countryside. It is all raised to high welfare standards and on an extensive regime with no bulk imported feeds, growth promoters, feed antibiotics or water in the meat.

As Peter Greig explains: 'We want to make the chain as short as possible and control our destiny, with no middlemen or politicians interfering with the process. We feed our stock absolutely additive-free diets. Chickens are in deep litter in natural light; they can scratch and they grow slowly. They are killed on the farm so there is absolutely no stress. These things really matter. There is no point in producing an organic chicken if you kill it in a factory.'

By working directly with local farmers, Greig ensures that neither live animals nor carcass meat make long, unnecessary journeys. And he can ensure by personal contact that the producers get a fair deal that suits both sides. Thus he is supporting, and allowing his Exeter customers to support, the kind of small family farm and good husbandry that is otherwise rapidly vanishing from the countryside.

'We wanted to live and work in a farming community. We wanted to be in an area where there were still small family farms. In many areas these have been completely wiped out, but fortunately not here in south Devon. The mosaic of small farms is the framework for what we do. Seven different small farms running specified dedicated businesses, like free range turkeys or pigs or poultry. The whole system is entirely controlled by us locally, which is very important from the production point of view.

'I think it works very well for the farmers. The enterprises bring in extra income and on these sort of farms there are always people there: for instance the wife runs it, or the younger generation. And it is not heavily capitalised. Traditional small-scale rearing uses traditional farm buildings which are otherwise redundant.

'We have had a brilliant response from the farmers we work with. They are very good at this sort of thing, they have the skills. One of our neighbours is producing chickens for us: she grew up doing chickens. And the farms supplying us are the sort of farms that make our marvellous countryside. If they keep going then village schools and post offices will keep going, the hedges will be kept up – all those things that agribusiness has no time for at all.

'The beauty of it is that the way we do it, we can increase volume significantly without compromising our principles. We simply multiply up the small-scale farm enterprises. That means, for instance, that though we sell a large number of turkeys, there are never more than 50 in a flock.'

When Pipers Farm began, sales were by farm gate and delivery. But since most customers lived in the town – Exeter – this was not the most time or energy-efficient way to sell. 'When a butcher's shop closed and became available in the part of Exeter where we already had customers, in a parade with a greengrocers, a baker, a wholefood shop, a fish shop, a chemist, a post office – everything – we took it. We have been delighted with the move.'

Greig sells at reasonable prices, and for obvious reasons, sells as many cuts as possible: luxury and budget. Because the money goes direct to the producers they get a better price without customers facing extortionate prices. 'If prices go up in our shop it is because production costs have risen. If prices go up in Tesco's that increase does not go to the farm gate. A far greater proportion of the price paid to us by customers is reflected at the farm gate and is going into the local farming community. Yet supermarkets are convincing people of all sorts of things by liberal use of words like "fresh" and "country" and "natural".'

Peter Greig knows only too well what these words hide. 'My father was a pioneer of broiler systems, so I've got a very close interest. How much factory farming does the public ever see? Most consumers do not get a chance to see how their food is produced. An awful lot of people are completely hoodwinked without knowing it. They would be so disillusioned to see inside an agribusiness, with 200 horsepower tractors and two people working on 200 acres, one shed with 100,000 chickens being fed a cocktail of antibiotics. Meat is not cheap in the supermarket, for what it is and the way it is produced: it's bloody expensive. Our products will stand comparison alongside absolutely any others as value for money. And we are not selling water and we are not selling antibiotics. And in some cases our prices are a lot less than the supermarkets.

'I really do feel that proper husbandry is what the majority of family farms want to do. Unfortunately the new agribusinesses have each obliterated six or seven family farms to make one massive business. If I went to the farm manager of one of these he'd probably laugh at our set-up.' But for Greig, running a family farm is 'a wonderful way of life. It is hard in many ways: probably the *Country Living* readers who, for the best of reasons, do want to see this way of life preserved, have no idea just how hard it is. It has to become viable, there has to be a market for it, for it to survive.'

Chapter six described the loneliness, unemployment and poverty that rural communities face as jobs are lost. Shops like Pipers Farm butchers give people an incomparable chance to support farmers and their employees in the way they want to be supported – in return for good food.

THE LOOK OF THE LAND

As Peter Greig points out, farming families and the buildings they occupy are an integral part of the landscape. As agriculture changes, the building and landscape changes. And if some recent structures are ugly, perhaps that is not just an unfortunate coincidence. It may mean something ugly is happening inside.

In her book *The Farm* written for the National Trust, architectural historian Gillian Darley writes: 'Farm buildings and the farmhouse itself are functional structures, and their beauty arises from the natural wisdom that governed their construction ... As we notice the pinpricks of bright white farmsteads on the green hillsides of the Lake District or the stark black weather-boarding of an Essex barn against the brown, green and gold of its surroundings, the connection between buildings and the setting is entirely harmonious and logical.' But modern farms strike a very different note: 'Heavy capital costs require ... high yields obtained by intensive methods ... All this has led to a form of agriculture in which specialisation tends to make each process increasingly isolated from the next. The new buildings reflect that fact.'

Americans have grasped more quickly than we have that their agricultural landscape and culture is about to disappear unless it is supported directly, and unless people take an interest in properly produced food and make links with farmers. In the US in 1988 180 farms *per day* were closing. Apprehension about the catastrophic changes this would wreak on the American landscape has been one of the reasons that US consumers have actively sought out ways to support farmers to go on farming in their communities. Not only do they want authentically fresh and, usually, organic produce, they want the farm to remain, and not to be replaced by a golf course or a housing development.

Similar threats face our countryside and culture. The government's answer to this is 'diversify'. This can mean farm shops and on-farm processing (if the other government regulations allow it) but it can also mean war games courses and off-road scrambler car training. Many people would prefer to support the Pipers Farm approach: to support farmers farming within the traditional buildings and family structures, and at the same time have a good chat, ensure animal welfare and a safe environment, avoid the health worries of eating intensively farmed meat, and have a delicious meal at the end of it – all without spending a fortune.

THE GROWER IS THE SYMBOL

The rapid growth of information, labelling and certification of food shows that we do want to know about our food. But as Tim Lang says, no label can tell you as much as a visit to the farm or factory. Mainstream marketing of agricultural produce, especially of meat and poultry products, is designed to take our minds off how the food is really produced and to replace this reality with a picture of something more palatable. Producers who sell direct can practise no such deception.

The very attitude that a producer has to visitors will tell you a great deal of what you want to know before you even get there. The supermarket which sent a press-release to food writer Frances Bissell, boasting of their super-cheap chicken at 39p per lb, sent, by the same post, promotional material about its traditional free range chicken with an invitation to visit the farm. When Bissel asked if she could visit both farms, the request was turned down.

The proprietors of the Russell's Farm stall in Newmarket, Cambridgeshire, sell their poultry ('those are farmyard ducks, completely free range'), pork and lamb, with a very different attitude. 'You're welcome to come and look round the farm, any time you like!' they say to customers. Customers of Longwood Farm in Suffolk visit often enough to know the boar by name, and ask after him when they buy the delicious Longwood Farm sausages and bacon. Ann English, one of Pam Finn's customers, took her young sons to Ely to visit the farm and the animals. 'It was a wonderful experience: it's very nice to go and see the animals, but in a way the important thing is that you know you can – that they are so open and welcoming. Then you know they are real people, doing the right thing, with nothing to hide.'

When you buy from an identifiable producer, neither you nor the producer has to rely on certification by outside parties to reassure you that high standards are being met. Visiting is the most direct route of course, but buyers' groups can also rely on one of their own number – rather than a distant, expensive and possibly rigid scheme – to see that all is well. Ann English's friends buy through her; they know Ann and trust her judgement (and love the meat!); and Ann knows Pam, and trusts her.

Buying direct means you are also in a position to find out a good deal more than a label could ever tell you. As I mentioned in chapter five, labels like 'Freedom Foods' or assorted descriptions like 'traditional', 'natural', 'country' and 'farm fresh' have come in for a lot of criticism. Visiting a 'Freedom Foods' farm might be an eye-opener for many; you might not be expecting to find sows confined in farrowing crates or chickens at 15 birds to the square metre; visiting a 'farm fresh eggs' battery shed would very possibly put you off for good.

But as long as the personal contact remains central to a system, you can also trust more formal set-ups to be your eyes. Customers of Limited Resources co-op in Manchester trust the people at the co-op to assure their food sources. 'Free range eggs in the supermarket might be produced as a sideline by a battery outfit, whereas they had visited the farm ours came from, and inspected it, and seen all the hens running about happily,' explains Janet Maresh. She also welcomes the detailed information she receives through personal contact: 'Usually you don't know which motorway your food has been growing next to, but I can ask, I can find out. We also know they're looking out for the wages and conditions of the workers, and they will check who is making the money.'

Some producers find that their personal relationship with customers enables them to dispense with expensive outside certification, such as 'organic' or 'Freedom Food' altogether. Some producers (it may be the same people) also have their own personal standards which they feel are *higher* than any certification scheme: refusing to transport animals for slaughter, for instance, or growing traditional varieties or breeds. Producers like this want their produce to be recognised and bought for its particular virtues, and by far the easiest way to communicate those standards is through direct contact with consumers.

As Peter Grieg says: 'We are Pipers Farm, we have to build a strong image as Pipers Farm. The words organic and free range have been abused and misrepresented so much we don't want anything to do with them.' Their strong local reputation means customers do not feel the need for a 'third party' to certify the farm. This not only saves the farm money, it also gives them the freedom to make their own decisions. 'We do not have an organic symbol, I don't really agree with organic farming as a philosophy, though we probably would count as organic. But I don't want that straitjacket. I would not want to block out any avenue science might offer.'

This kind of approach allows growers to use their own judgement. For instance, if there isn't a good supply of registered organic hay for the animals or registered organic manure for the vegetables, but there is some perfectly good stuff which is not symbol organic, producers can make a decision, tell customers about the way the decisions are made, listen to objections, answer questions – and then choose the best route for the people concerned. An independent inspector who depends on the farm neither for food nor a livelihood, need not interfere. As one grower put it: 'The grower is the symbol'.

'Secondary' businesses like shops and bakeries may find symbol registration particularly cumbersome and expensive. Anyone selling a product and describing it as 'organic' is legally required to be registered as an organic symbol holder with a recognised certification organisation. Symbol holders often have to have dedicated areas in the premises for storing and handling organic produce, and always have to keep detailed records.

Supermarkets get round this by selling organic produce in 'pre-packs', leaving the packaging company to register and pay for the symbol. But this is hardly an ecological or economical solution. Small, personal businesses can deal with this another way: they can just tell customers where something came from and how it was made. At Boat House Farm in Sussex, wheat is grown and milled to flour under a symbol, and so it can legally be called 'organic' and sold to organic bakeries. But there is no organic bakery nearby, and Boat House Farm wants to sell its own bread. So they have their flour baked by a local baker, who has no symbol, and they sell the bread in the farm shop. It is not described as 'organic' because legally, it cannot be. But the customers know what flour is used and which baker has baked it, and they have no problem with the arrangement. This is quite a common practice, but can only work through personal contact.

Not only does the communication and trust between producer and consumer lead to a better service and a better standard of living for both, but that trust and communication is in itself valuable. Some believe that because symbol schemes might replace this relationship, symbols themselves should be avoided. This school of thought sees the organic symbol as just another way to keep consumers and growers apart, with both sides giving up responsibility to a third party. This is the view of the Japanese Organic Agriculture Association. Organic farmers in Japan have always marketed direct to consumers. In the absence of an official certification system for organic farming, identification of the farm of origin enabled consumers to check for themselves, or have more confidence that the farmer had nothing to hide.

The JOAA believes that the 'organic' relationship between farmers and consumers is as fundamental to organic farming as the use of composts and manures. Recently a 'symbol scheme' for organic farming was set up by the Japanese government, and was bitterly resisted by the Japan Organic Agriculture Association who saw it as diluting the personal and mutual nature of consumer-grower relations. The JOAA rejected the idea of inspectors and certification as unnecessary within a relationship of mutual trust and dependence, based on traditional Japanese preparedness for co-operative effort, mutual assistance and 'plain hard work'. So far, direct links between Japanese organic growers and their customers remain the rule.

Many of the box schemes run by symbol-holding vegetable producers in Britain are also finding themselves distributing 'non-symbol organic' produce alongside their own, to meet the demand they have sparked off for locally produced food. According to the Soil Association's Eric Booth: 'People find that once a delivery has been established, it is an obvious thing to add in other locally produced food like eggs and bread. These will be organic too, as that tends to be a selling point for the round, but the growers by no means all have symbols.'

THE (VERY) ACTIVE CONSUMER

By buying direct from producers, consumers can become much more active in encouraging, supporting and participating in the kind of food production they want to see happen. Sometimes the initiative even begins with the consumers. For instance, when members of a Kent subscription scheme for biodynamically-grown (a sort of super-organic) vegetables found out that the farmer who supplied their vegetables was not going to be able to continue, they decided to organise the vegetable growing for themselves. They put their heads, their money, and some of their time and energy together, and hired a field on the same farm, Perry Court, and a gardener to help them grow the vegetables themselves.

When Debbie Bennett realised that a fully-organic diet was the best way to calm her daughter's exhausting, hyperactive behaviour, she had real difficulties finding the food she needed at the greengrocers in the supermarket. She had to be sure that nothing she fed her daughter had been sprayed. Talking to her friends she found many of them felt the same: that organic food was just not easily enough available in the south London suburb where they lived. They tried to persuade the greengrocer to stock organic produce, but he insisted there wasn't a market for it. 'So we realised we were going to have to organise it for ourselves.'

Debbie organised a buyers' co-op. The co-op buys organic wholefoods from a wholesaler, and organic fruit and vegetables from Sunnyfields Farm, near Southampton. Every week a van travels from the farm to London to sell produce: the van was already passing through Carshalton where Debbie lives, so no extra transport was involved. She sends an order to Sunnyfields and the farm fills most of it direct, topping up with organic produce bought wholesale. Debbie and a rota of fellow co-op members pack the orders for collection.

As the co-op expanded, another 'branch' was set up in nearby Epsom Downs. And as people began to eat high-quality and organic vegetables and dried goods regularly, they began to wonder about their meat and milk. So Debbie and her colleague Jeanette Smith in Epsom Downs have tied in with (different) dairy and meat producers in the country south of London, either organic or conservation-grade free range. Like the members at Perry Court, the co-op's demand has also brought a small new supply of high-quality produce into being. When local smallholder Bill Whitfield heard that Debbie was buying organic free-range eggs he told her, 'I can do those for you'.

Bill Whitfield's traditional, cottager's approach to stock rearing has brought him on the wrong side of 'the inspectors' often enough to bring him near ruin. The centuries' old food for pigs – domestic food scraps, or 'swill' – was outlawed, perhaps because on an industrial scale all kinds of horrors might have found their way in. Bill's enterprise is not industrial, and small enough for him to know what the pigs were eating, but it was closed down anyway. However, he still kept hens on a totally free-range system. When Debbie's customers started ordering more eggs than Bill Whitfield could supply there was a problem: Bill was so broke he could not afford to buy in more hens. So the pooled resources of the co-op's membership fees were invested in 50 more hens, to boost the supply.

Bill Whitfield has also revived his pig-fertilised polytunnels and begun growing sweet, sweet cherry tomatoes and tender greens for the co-op. Picked at eight in the morning and collected by the members in time for lunch. One enterprising member of the co-op bakes cakes to order, using the organic ingredients sold through the co-op. Others contribute the surplus produce from their allotments or gardens, and the Permaculture garden of the local environment centre sells them fresh herbs.

In inner-city Birmingham, the Sandwell food co-ops, a network of 31 consumer co-ops and other outlets who buy together, grew dissatisfied with the quality of fresh produce they could get from wholesalers. 'Supermarkets buy up almost all the grade A stuff, and much of what you buy has been stored or chilled: but it doesn't have to say so. So we have no control over the quality and freshness of the produce,' co-ops co-ordinator Linda Gomilla explained. So the Sandwell co-ops have taken very direct action. They have bought fruit trees which have been planted in community orchards: local residents will take what they want and sell any surplus back into the co-op fruit supply.

Such is the support for the co-op initiative that people who already own fruit trees and bushes are giving their surplus to the co-op to boost the local supply of fresh produce. Further plans include conversion of disused land, including former allotment sites, into a 'patchwork' of market gardens, to be worked by co-op members and other groups in the community, such as people with special educational needs who can receive practical training as they grow food.

Consumers like Debbie Bennett, the Perry Court group and the Sandwell Co-ops have decided that they don't just have to get what they're given. Instead of waiting passively to be served by supermarkets and multinational companies who all say, 'we are only supplying what the consumer demands', these consumers have taken an active part in creating what they really want.

As with co-operation between consumers and growers, co-operation between consumers and consumers also leads to social contact and bonds of friendship. Bath Local Organic Buyers (BLOB) take bulk deliveries of produce from Radford Mill farm in groups of 12 or so households at a time, units known as *hans* after similar groups in Japan. These *hans* are then responsibile for sharing out the orders for the members to collect. One of BLOB's founders, Tim Baines, says that in some *hans* this has become 'quite a social event'. 'A lot of them do the packing together. They come round and have a cup of tea and get stuck in. It's a Friday evening and some people seem to have a pretty good party when everyone comes to collect. It's really nice, they're getting together and chatting away, all the kids running around and wrecking the place! I must admit it overawed me slightly but some people are natural hosts!'

In Japan, consumer co-ops buying direct from the farm have gathered so much enthusiasm and strength that they are now a major force in Japanese agriculture and environmental politics. Over 600 consumer co-operatives in Japan between them run 2,400 food stores, with women members also receiving deliveries direct in small groups or *hans*. Co-ops set their own food safety standards, often much stricter than those of the government, and buy food direct from farmers or processors. If they can't find a product which meets their requirement, they may set up production themselves: one group, *Radish Boya*, has a free-range pig unit; another, *Seikatsu*, a milk processing factory.

The link with the land is strong, with members making frequent visits to 'their' farms for demonstrations of production, or for harvest festivals. Members have developed strong links with each other and work together too: on a local level, they get together to cook, or to share childcare. On a national level these (almost entirely female) groups campaign vigorously against environmental damage, commercial agriculture and unfettered free trade.

DELIVERIES

Some of the most enthusiastic customers of vegetable deliveries are those who have no car. Food shopping, particularly for a large family, is one reason many people feel they need a car. If the heavy items are delivered, it is much easier to manage without one, saving hundreds or even thousands of pounds per year. To households which don't have the option of driving, deliveries are a godsend.

And the environment benefits too; one van delivering to 50 addresses in the same area adds up to a fraction of the vehicle miles of 50 households all taking the car out and driving to the supermarket on the ring road. Many schemes cut back on transport further by dropping off 10 or 12 households' deliveries at a time, usually in walking or cycling range of the group. Some urban schemes, notably Manchester's Limited Resources, even deliver by bicycle-and-trailer. A remarkable amount of vegetables can be towed behind a bicycle, but technology is not standing still. A four-wheeled cycle which can carry a quarter of a tonne has been designed for the Manchester-based Brox Corporation, and is being tried out for food deliveries. Goodbye to parking problems and road fund licences!

A delivery service is an enormous boon to a community, particularly for low-income, elderly or disabled people who frequently have no access to a car. They need good local shops and delivery rounds but the industrial-style retailing of the out-of-town supermarket has eroded both of these resources. The undercutting of milk deliveries by the supermarkets has led richer families to abandon the milkman; rounds have closed as a result, a terrible disservice to those families who now have to carry all their milk home. Similarly, Jan Deane finds that the delivery is an important attraction to many of her customers, especially the elderly ones. Busy parents also appreciate the service. And there is a nice personal feel about it which people enjoy. Rita O'Neill joined the Exmouth Farm Link vegetable scheme because: 'I wanted to go back to the old-world feel of a delivery man. I would join a meat or dairy delivery too if I was satisfied with the price. My dad's first job was a delivery boy and that's how he met my mum. She was in service at the big house and dad used to come on his bike, with the big box on the front, bringing vegetables for the house and boyfriends for my mother!'

The weekly delivery from Limited Resources has enabled Margaret Biddle to do her shopping without the car, too, though she does have one. She has now returned her custom to the small, local shops in her immediate neighbourhood, which will benefit those of her neighbours who cannot get further afield: 'We used to have a small supermarket in the same parade as local shops, so we used to get some things at the supermarket but other things, like bread and fruit and veg, from the local shops. Some of them are very nice, like the cheese shop, and I think it's a good thing to support the local economy.

'Then they closed the small supermarket and opened a bigger one about a mile and a half away. So now if you wanted to shop at both you would have to make two separate journeys, and no one's going to do that, so I found I was getting everything at the supermarket. And I don't particularly enjoy supermarket shopping. I thought it would be a good thing to try to cut the supermarket out. Now I have the delivery I can go to the village on Saturday and get treats at the cake shop, go the cheese shop – it's really enjoyable.'

LOVELY LOCAL SHOPS

Small shops have a great deal to offer to all of us, whether we are in a direct delivery scheme or not. But as we saw in chapter five, the small shop has been vanishing fast. Where supermarket competition has not closed shops down altogether, as their turnover declines so does the freshness, quality and range of goods. Chapter eight showed that the poorer the customers, the dearer the goods, and, in particular, the dearer and poorer the range of healthy foods and fresh fruit and vegetables. And speciality services, such as knowledgeable fishmongers, and personal connections, disappear.

As well as supporting the local community, shopping in small shops is often much more enjoyable. You are greeted, your children fussed over, you joke about winning the lottery or the awful weather. Anyone interested in where their food came from, how it was produced, is much more likely to get a detailed answer from an independent shopkeeper than the duty manager of the supermarket.

Small greengrocers and butchers often sell produce from local farms as well as from wholesalers. Local shops may well sell milk from a named local dairy, whereas the supermarket in the same town will sell 'Trolleyco' milk, which has almost certainly been from farm to packing plant, packing plant to warehouse, then warehouse to supermarket. A survey by the Green Party of town centre shops and market traders in Ludlow showed that almost half of the shops sold at least 70 per cent local produce, and only one in five shops sold nothing local at all. No supermarket, whatever its claims to 'local sourcing' can match that.

As well as fewer food miles, local produce will certainly mean freshness: these go together. It also means you can get information. A retailer you know and trust can be your contact at the farm, can be your eyes and your certification. 'Local strawberries' 'Local farm chickens', 'local rabbit' and 'local pork' may or may not have been grown or reared according to high standards. But you can ask.

In his greengrocer's shop in the smart town of Alderley Edge in Cheshire, Bernard Harrison is proud to sell wholesome, 'naturally grown' vegetables from a nearby smallholding. He explains what this means: 'To put an "organic" sign on the vegetables, the land has got to be lain by, you can use only manure from cows which have had no additives in their feed and so forth. It's a long drawn out job. But I know exactly where the food comes from, and it is grown in a completely natural way, often on land which had been pasture for a number of years, so it's as natural as you can get.'

'We take quite a lot from local growers, especially in the summer. At the moment it's mainly January King and Savoy cabbages, sprouts and carrots; in the summer we get peas, broad beans and runner beans. The small growers round here don't like to sell to the wholesalers any more, they are fed up with getting ripped off on price. They want to sell to us.

'Of course vegetables from a small holding are better, and they will be picked by hand, to order. I get on the phone to Arthur Jepson for some cabbages, and he is down there in the field at 6am picking them for me.'

In parts of the country where holdings are larger, shops may find it harder to get their produce locally. A greengrocer in Pangbourne, in rural Berkshire, lamented: 'We'd love to sell local produce, but we can't get it. The growers round here aren't interested in selling anything smaller than a lorryload. We have even ended up going and picking at the pick-your-own to bring our customers fresh produce. But most of our stock comes from the wholesalers in Slough.

Spitalfields Farmers' Market

Probably some of it goes all the way down the motorway from round here, then we have to go all the way down the motorway ourselves every morning to bring it back again. It's crazy.'

The one other local line he does buy is organic green beans, from a woman with a very small local holding – though he doesn't label them as organic, 'because people will think they are too expensive'. Greengrocers like this one probably won't have access to more of a range of fresh local vegetables until smaller local growers have started up through box schemes, and become successful enough to have a surplus to sell.

Small shops in rural areas are even more of a lifeline than those in the cities. As Post Offices have been 'rationalised' out of existence, and the richer members of the community take their custom to far-flung supermarkets, more and more of these stores have closed. In 1996, the government announced plans to cut the business rate for village shops in isolated areas by 50 per cent, even allowing councils to waive the business rate altogether, in an attempt to boost viability. The National Food Alliance warned that although this relief was welcome, supermarket shopping was probably a greater threat to these shops than the business rate.

Some communities are fighting back, however, and opening their own shops. This is not just so that there is somewhere to get milk and bread without waiting for the bus to town (which might not come by again till Tuesday), but also to provide a nerve centre, a meeting point, for the village. These little shops offer a good outlet for local produce. The community shop in Tallaton, East Devon, sells jams, cakes and vegetables produced locally. The more customers ask for this kind of thing, the more support there will be for local producers who want to support themselves – and even employ others – in small-scale production.

MARKETS

Along with the beaches, restaurants and flamboyant local dancing, one of the commonest images in any holiday brochure is of a street market: colourful, crowded, lively – and distinctively local. Markets are great fun.

All this is true of our own markets too. Markets are an excellent place to get vegetables in season. You can be certain much of the produce will be from this country. As south London resident Ann

English says: 'I love to buy vegetables from the street markets here. You find the natural rhythm of the seasons there. When there is a glut of something, it's the time to eat that. It's nice to go through the natural rhythm with the vegetables and the seasons.'

Outside the big cities, markets are good places to find truly local produce. Although there are precious few food shops left in Newmarket (they're out on the bypass), the market itself is still very lively. Beside the cheap screwdrivers and socket sets, and the leggings for £1.99, you find local produce: fish from Lowestoft, local honey. Newmarket is on the fringe of fen country and fenland vegetables feature prominently: the celery with the dirt still on; 'dirty' carrots too. The young woman confirmed that her customers bought these 'because they say they last longer'. Some stallholders were selling their own produce, or produce from neighbours: 'local coxes, 10lb' in carrier bags.

The produce is fresh: 'The growers ring you up and say what they've got. It was all picked yesterday.' Another joy is the meat stall run by Russell's poultry, mentioned above. The meat is all at extremely keen prices. ('We sell to Harrods, but you'd probably pay double there.')

FRESH FOOD FOR EVERYONE

In the US, a top Californian restaurateur, Alice Waters, decided to go out and actively recruit growers who could supply her with organic produce within hours of harvest. This kind of insistence on top quality and absolute freshness has been one of the driving forces behind a national boom in organic growing, and selling of produce on a small local scale. Now many US towns have farmers' markets where growers come in to sell their produce – markets enjoyed as much for their 'country ' atmosphere as for the high quality produce. There are now 2,000 farmers' markets in the US, in both larger urban centres and smaller, more rural towns. Some city authorities have encouraged them in run-down city centres in order to bring back the shoppers – and the vitality – that have deserted town centres for malls and superstores on the peripheries.

As one impressed British shopper put it: 'The produce is really peerless, and small growers can build up great reputations on the back of flavour and quality, which people here value highly. When you see green, yellow, orange, plain and striped tomatoes in all sorts of shapes and sizes with incredibly different tastes it puts our hot house red same-sized variety to shame.'

People buy direct from farmers in the US is because they recognise that this produce is both fresher and cheaper than anything available in the supermarkets. They also feel good about buying direct from small farmers; the markets certify that all produce is being sold by the people who 'grew raised baked or caught' it and the farming community is very important to Americans. But as well as all that, people like to shop in farmers' markets because it's fun – or 'friendlier, happier, more sociable and more personal' than supermarkets, according to research from the University of California, a state where farmers' markets have proved particularly successful.

Probably the best-established farmers' market in Britain is the Spitalfields organic market in the City of London. At Spitalfields there is a fair range of stalls: several selling fruit and vegetables, plus bakery, juices and wines, dairy produce and meat, so it is possible to do a pretty comprehensive shop there. Like some of the livelier US farmers' markets, Spitalfields has crafts, hot snacks and children's entertainment as well as food: it can be an outing as well as a food-shopping trip to go there.

Other markets have been set up, such as that in Altrincham, on the edge of Manchester. However, it can be difficult for producers to make the long journey into a big city and, as Julie Alderson found, even a pitch fee of £25 can be off-putting to small organic growers. Alderson has found it hard to sell the 'farmers' market' idea to the local authority. 'It can be quite difficult to persuade councils about how a farmers' market could be run: that it should be attractive and distinctive, with a kind of 'country' flavour. Really they do seem to have a dreadful lack of imagination and vision.'

Some local authorities charge as much as £50 for a pitch fee in a regular town market, and getting a licence is also difficult in some places. This is simply prohibitive for many small growers. It seems inexcusable that local authorities in Britain, who are charged with the responsibility of encouraging the local economy, and now, under Agenda 21, of promoting sustainable development, should make life so difficult for one of the most valuable and sustainable of all endeavours.

In France, one of the important factors in their relatively flourishing local food markets (there are 6,000 weekly markets in France and Parisians buy 15 per cent of their food from markets) is said to be priority given to producer-owned stalls in local markets. This is a policy which could boost both local shopping and local growing here. As mentioned in chapter seven, the traditional, small-scale producers of central and southern France are facing tremendous difficulties from the commercial, industrial-scale squeeze. Street markets are one of the main outlets in which they can sell direct to their customers, with all the advantages that brings for both sides. French markets are a major outlet for regional specialities.

The authorities in the US have supported farmers' markets in a different way. Farmers' markets are often sited in run-down urban areas in order to bring vitality and access to good food to the neighbourhood. Around 20 states offer coupons to families eligible for food stamps, to spend on fresh produce at these markets, thus enabling poorer households and local farmers to support each other. Politicians, lobby groups and the media are all keen to lend support to farmers' markets in the US, according to researcher Harriet Festing, 'since they are associated with preserving the countryside, supporting traditional communities and values, and revitalising town centres.' This consciousness has been sadly lacking here to date, but things may just be beginning to change.

In Britain, it isn't just local authorities who are holding things up. Like Julie Alderson, Dirk Bauer of Busses Farm in Sussex felt so much was wrong with supermarket shopping that he too wanted to set up a market where consumers could meet growers and make closer connections with the sources of their food. 'We have all become so dull shopping, we don't talk to each other,' he says. 'You go into the supermarket and ask what is this cheese and they say the cheese is yellow in colour, that's all I can tell you about it. There is no relationship between the people selling and the people buying.'

Bauer and some colleagues devised a plan for a market in the centre of East Grinstead, which was remarkably similar to the concept of farmers' markets in the US, though at one time they were unaware of the American model. 'Safeway and Sainsbury have moved out of the town, so we wanted to pull organic producers together into a marketplace. The intention was to have various stalls in a semi-open situation: vegetables, meat, eggs, health products, artisans, and an information centre. Every week something would be happening: sheep shearing, calves to look at, wood craft, with somewhere for children to play and a place to have real coffee and some good quiche or something. But when we tried to set up our market, the people who had leased the space could not rent it out to us, because Sainsbury's owned the site and had said under no circumstances should anything to do with food be allowed on the site.'

Some rural local authorities have been persuaded by regional food enthusiasts to consider adopting a more permissive attitude to farmers' markets, so with luck some may spring up offering truly local produce direct from growers. Any which do will be well worth a visit, both to encourage the idea and because they should be a very enjoyable way of getting high-quality, fresh food.

How many of us are able to combine the weekly vegetable shop with a party? Yet it isn't such an odd idea. 'In Italy in the market, people will happily spend half the day shopping, talking about the quality of what's there, what to do with it, how is the grower's family,' says Julie Alderson. 'Sainsbury's is a nightmare by contrast, we shuffle around in deadly silence, grab our food, the members of staff know nothing about the food and don't care about you and you don't care about them. It's a factory shop.'

NEW HABITS

Buying actively and as directly as possible does not solve every shopping problem you will ever face, but it is certainly a wonderful way of getting good food in a responsible way. The joy of it is that you become much more powerful as a consumer. We do not have to remain, to quote the US journalist Anna Maria Caldara: 'tragic figures, whose money supports the far-away agribusinesses, but who have no knowledge of how their food is being grown'.

Consumer power can be exercised every day. Even the most mundane shopping trip involves choices: pink veal or Dutch white veal? Do we like veal crates? No. So we'll buy the pink. New Zealand apples or English? Do we approve of shipping apples 10,000 miles and chilling them for 4 months? No, so we'll buy the English ones. Ready-made cauliflower cheese or a cauliflower and some cheese? Do we want our children to get more vitamins tonight? Yes, so we'll buy the cauliflower. Bread baked in the bakery here or somewhere away up a motorway? It only took one sack to deliver the flour – how many lorries to deliver the loaves? Where would you rather see jobs, here or there?

Just as important as making choices is asking for information. Where are these tomatoes from? Which farm supplied the beef? Local rabbit? – well it's a bit unfamiliar, so ask the butcher. Was it a wild one, shot near here? Or farmed? How do I cook it? Did these aubergines come by aeroplane? What do these pumpkins taste like? Why aren't any of these plums local? Who bakes the blackcurrant pies? What is in the sausages? Are the hens really free range? Have you seen them? Is there any chance of getting in organic potatoes?

Asking question not only makes your views plain – it's a good way to learn and understand more about the food you eat, too.

THE FUTURE

Already at the time of writing, vegetable boxes are in such demand in some places that there are waiting lists, with collective schemes actively looking for more growers to swell the supplies. Some of us wanting to join a local scheme might have to be a bit patient, waiting for growers to believe we really want their lovely stuff, and that they should grow for us not the supermarkets. There are would-be growers without access to land, too, and there are initiatives such as proposed land trusts, and share-farming schemes, to make land available to growers in return for affordable rents, labour or a share in the produce, rather than capital.

Quality meat producers are actively exploring ways to sell their product in an identifiable way: once again, brisk demand at farm shops and for direct home delivery will play an essential role in persuading producers to open up to the public. The more local people who buy from any one farm, the less far that farm has to cast its net. It seems crazy that there are people in Kent buying meat from Pam Finn in Ely, when there are farms in Kent and customers in Cambridgeshire. We can certainly make that change, and shorten everyone's journeys.

As Simon Brenman put it: 'As box schemes and organic growing pick up, we should draw back in, so instead of going to 80 families in 80 streets , it's 40 streets with 2 families, 10 streets with 8 families, and finally the whole street of 80 families. The veg round will become like a milk round, that is the target, with 80 per cent of houses all supplied on one round. That way it will be fresher, cheaper, and more environmentally sound.'

THE REACTION OF THE MARKET

As consumers' priorities and habits change, the 'big' market will of course try to follow them. Supermarkets are already trying to change their image by introducing, for example, some degree of regional sourcing. Pressure to change has come from groups like the SAFE Alliance with its well-publicised 'food miles' campaign. One chain, Sainsbury's, has gone so far as to propose a true 'local sourcing' experiment in one county, and they have also taken a small step in the footsteps of the American supermarket chains, by introducing stands selling produce from a local farm into a few of their giant hypermarket stores.

US supermarkets, stung by the runaway success of farmers' markets there, have tried to copy them: 'The supermarkets have mimicked farmers markets by running their own stalls outside, or by creating a market atmosphere inside their stores. Wegman's supermarket chain in NY state have created a mouth-watering display of fresh produce and deli items among the chalk boards and features of local produce,' writes Harriet Festing, in her report on direct marketing in the USA.

In the Sainsbury's initiative, a small number of 'Savacentres' (hypermarket stores including a larger-than-superstore Sainsbury's, plus a clothing chain) have a stall selling, for example, potatoes, carrots and mushrooms from a named local farm – with separate signs written by the farmer. 'It has gone very well,' comments spokeswoman Julie Shrimpton, though she adds that they still bring in most of the potatoes and so forth from central depots, as usual. 'We couldn't source enough locally,' she explains. This is the situation in the US too, says Festing.

There has been another attempt by some of the other big supermarket chains to provide regionally distinctive produce, Somerset farmer John Armitage reports: 'They started to sell our meat as 'West Country' lamb, but the scheme crashed after only six weeks. They had put together an unfeasible set of assurance standards, including things like restrictions on use of barbed wire on the farms, which would have been extremely expensive to implement – imagine going round replacing all your fencing! But the main reason was that they were selling it at double the price of ordinary lamb, they did not tell us what the price in the shops was going to be.' This 'luxury niche' approach is very similar to the fate meted out to organic produce, as Atkinson realises: 'I have every sympathy with the organic crowd,' he says.

The pity of it is that this high pricing prevented ordinary consumers, including those in the West Country and those with happy memories of holidays there, from buying meat which might have meant a bit more to them. 'I think that consumers do favour the kind of farming of the small farms in the Family Farms Association, that we have a favour with the public which we should be able to trade on. We don't use chemicals except fertiliser, the pasture is permanent pasture, we don't need to use huge prairies, we use small fields and rough moorland.'

Whatever new initiatives the big retail chains try, the majority of the produce on the shelves of these stores will be the produce of industrial agriculture and processing for a long time to come. To enable truly individualised, local produce to dominate in their stores would require a radical alteration in the way supermarkets run – and the way they make their money.

Even where there are some concessions to regional sourcing for a few fresh products such as milk, this is all still centrally controlled from the national head office, giving local store managers no opportunity to build up personal contacts with local suppliers and thus to learn more about the produce they sell. A 1995 Compassion in World Farming survey found that one in four local supermarket managers did not know the difference between so-called 'farm fresh' or 'country fresh' (i.e. battery-produced) eggs, and free-range eggs, and one in three were unaware that 'farm fresh' actually meant battery produced. As Dirk Bauer said, they can just about tell you the colour of the product you are buying. Currently, most of the supermarket chains reply to questions on food miles and regional sourcing not from their buying department, but from the 'environment' department – which, more often than not, is itself a branch of public relations. These concerns are not yet central to supermarkets' operations.

There will doubtless be other initiatives, and the more consumers who decide to buy food directly for local sourcing, personal contact, assurance and quality, the harder supermarkets and other retailers will have to run to keep up, which is no bad thing. Genuine moves towards sourcing produce locally, with individual store managers able to respond independently to local suppliers would, in particular, be very welcome.

This might become easier if British producers were more inclined to emulate the small, and often part-time craft producers in the French countryside. They band together in co-ops, so that even the smallest producer can supply the local supermarket. However, the immediacy and the genuine mutual interest in direct buying/selling relationships could never be achieved by a big store. The way supermarkets make their money is by bulk handling, few staff and many packages, bar coding, computerised tills, and no one standing around chatting, still less actually telling you something about your food. It is always going to be a different experience.

The supermarkets have their own vision of personalised shopping to offer us: personal attention in the form of our own computer file. Loyalty cards may look like a kind of high-tech Green Shield Stamps, but they are a lot sneakier than that. The same swipe that tots up your loyalty points also logs all your purchases into your own computer file, so the store can target their 'personalised' marketing promotions. Although such marketing is 'still very much at the Noddy stage', according to marketing journalist Alan Mitchell, 'they already know if you are getting drunk on gin each week'. It has all the loneliness of anonymous shopping, with none of the privacy.

On a smaller scale, various 'entrepreneurs' have tried to cash in on the success of local box schemes by setting up nationwide systems to bring produce, organic vegetables in particular, direct to customers' doors. They buy in from either wholesalers, or large suppliers who may be remote from the customer, so in fact they offer few 'food miles' advantages over supermarkets. They are also, inevitably, more pricey than genuine local box schemes, and because they centre on a 'middle man' the prices paid to the growers are correspondingly as low as prices to consumers are high; most of the benefits to producer, consumer and the wider society of a local farm link are lost. However, for people without a local box scheme in their area, they are really the only way of buying a reasonable range of organic vegetables: and of course the delivery is a great boon to many and helps some to cut out trips to the supermarket.

A less overtly commercial initiative for bringing organic produce to people's doors, with some consumer investment and input, was the Creative Consumer Co-op. It was a kind of consumer-owned supermarket system, complete with a national packing shed (its distribution centre) and separate retail outlets in people's houses (where the vegetables were packed into individual orders and collected). However, without any local focus, the people interested in participating were all too far from each other and the growers had no personal or geographical links with the consumers. As a result the scheme collapsed.

So far, many of the successful 'direct' initiatives have come from producers themselves. If consumers take more of an interest in buying direct, then there will almost certainly be more opportunities for us to do so: more farm shops, more box schemes, more identifiable produce in shops and street markets. Farmers and producers might even get together to run collective farm shops like the ones operated so successfully in France. In these, local vegetables, cheese, wine, sausages, fruit and so forth are enticingly displayed, along with photographs of the farms and the animals. Farmers take turns to serve behind the counter, and customers have a guarantee, administered under a voluntary charter, that all the produce is indeed locally produced and processed.

Some people in the organic movement worry that as more and more organic food is available they will run out of people willing to pay over the odds for it. As we have seen, direct marketing helps producers make a fairer living without charging a fortune. But ecologically responsible farmers are contributing to the national wealth by the costs they don't impose on the rest of us, and it would be only just to reward them for this – or to charge intensive systems for the damage they do cause. As *Sierra* magazine said in an article which, like this book, called for direct consumer action through better food shopping, 'there is definitely a role for collective action; the archaic policies that keep agribusiness slopping at the public trough won't change without it'.

YOU CAN'T KEEP A GOOD IDEA DOWN

Some forward-looking local councils and health authorities are beginning to recognise the benefits local food links could bring to the communities they serve. As we saw in the last chapter, Devon County Council believes local customers will be an important 'safety net' for Devon farmers. Devon's health authorities have found farmer links equally beneficial to consumers. One Devon farmer, frustrated by the waste of perfectly good but misshapen or uneven-sized produce he was ploughing back in, arranged to supply a health-authority supported Plymouth food co-op with potatoes and other field vegetables. Not only did this mean people who had very poor access to fresh produce near their homes were able to get very fresh, good value vegetables – they were also able to visit the farm and enjoy, and learn about, the countryside.

In Sandwell, the health authority has supported the local food co-ops' efforts to finds sites for food growing because they believe a link to food growing will benefit people in many ways: 'Market gardens, and the opportunity to work on them, will benefit environmental health, enable people to take more exercise, bring social contact and self-esteem which will be good for mental health ... these if anything will be even more beneficial than the fresh vegetables which will be produced!' explains health promotion officer Sue Simpson.

Eric Booth at the Soil Association believes local food links offer the perfect way for local authorities to meet their obligations to promote sustainable development: to enhance neighbourhoods, attract other business and to offer better access to healthy food to local residents. 'Local food links enable local authorities and other interested bodies to meet so many of their objectives at once,' Booth explains. 'All authorities are under an obligation to meet sustainability targets under Agenda 21, and while some authorities are doing almost nothing, others have recognised that connecting consumers with local growers and with the land is a way to meet a wide range of these objectives at once.'

Other political changes should help to boost the supplies of good, local food. Already some tentative brakes are being put on the further intensification of agriculture. Animal welfare and nitrate application regulations have been introduced; pesticide firms are beginning to advise farmers on how to minimise chemical use. There is pressure to reform the EU's Common Agricultural Policy now that set-aside has proved so unsuccessful and so unpopular, and to replace it with a subsidy which delivers social and environmental sustainability.

The government is slowly changing its rhetoric on road building and transport as enraged citizens protest against expensive, traffic-boosting road schemes such as the M11 extension in East London, the Newbury bypass and many others; eventually the European administration will get the same message. And ultimately those who are building their future on air-freighted produce will have to accept that as with roads, so with airports: you cannot just go on building more airports to accommodate projected increases in air traffic or the whole country will go under tarmac. And most famously, the government has directed that out-of-town superstores should not, on the whole, be given planning permission. When local authorities do grant permission, the government calls such a scheme in for public inquiry. In 1994, Sainsbury's lost nine out of 10 such inquiries.

These suspensions, question marks and bans have all arisen because of the unacceptable costs of carrying on as we did before. The pressures for industrial farming and industrial shopping are still there. But we know things can't continue to develop this way for ever. So we need a new future for agriculture and shopping, one which the country and the planet can afford.

Happily, that future has already begun. Not only is it eminently affordable, it's a lot more delicious and healthy too. Although a shop like Pipers Farm, for instance, is very traditional in terms of their way of rearing and selling produce, it is also very much a shop of the future. It sells delicious ready-to-roast dishes with the flavours we have no wish to give up: garlic, coriander; and ready marinaded meat for a healthy and oriental stir-fry. More than that, it is a shop for people who believe that things don't just unfold according to some higher authority (governed by 'the market' or notions of 'progress'), but who believe that individuals can take steps to improve their own lives and the environment around them. And why should good, friendly service ever become unfashionable?

Buying 'traditionally reared' or 'hand-grown organic' food is sometimes dismissed as being hopelessly tweedy, 'fogey' and nostalgic. People who want to eat good, authentic food are sometimes assumed to want to go without hot bathwater, female emancipation, polio vaccination, paid holidays, washing machines and universal literacy in their desire for a 'golden age'. In fact, what is really old-fashioned is to say 'Progress is progress. I don't understand it, I'll just buy the whole package: I'll leave the decisions to government and big business, they know better than me.' This was the attitude promoted by the Church ('Do as you're told, the priest knows best') which sparked the Reformation in the sixteenth century! In these post-'enlightenment' days we are supposed to think for ourselves, and we are entitled to throw out the toxic bathwater of progress while holding on to the baby; because we want electric light it doesn't follow that we must accept veal crates.

Buying food direct from the producer often springs from a desire to eat better, but that step in turn inspires other changes, in behaviour and attitude. Many people buying their food directly do so from an understanding that by doing so they are taking control, they are empowering themselves and exercising their right to make choices: surely a very modern concern.

The fact that people want, and are often prepared to pay for, better agriculture and a better environment, yet they are denied both, could be described as an example of market failure. Hard economic theory tells us that one of the most common causes of such failure is a lack of information. As we have seen, local farmer links are the surest way to get a reliable, meaningful exchange of information between producer and consumer. This works not only at individual household level, but at a community level too. The Pesticides Trust reports that in Munich, Germany, people are able to buy the produce from local farms whose land is the origin for the local drinking water. The water company saw that supporting farmers to go organic would reduce their expenditure on removing agrochemicals from the water supply; they also realised that with local farm links, consumers – tap water consumers – would be able to contribute to this support of farmers by buying organic produce which would protect them twice over. An organic conversion scheme and marketing co-op have been set up, so that Munich householders can buy a litre of organic milk 'which protects 400 litres of Munich drinking water'. The scheme succeeded quickly, attracting around 70 per cent of the eligible farms in the first three years of operation, and seeing reductions of up to 80 per cent in pesticide pollution almost straight away. Only because Munich households were able to buy from surrounding farms was such a scheme possible.

The latest scientific research is also coming up with evidence that we need to do more to protect our health than eat just an apple a day. According to ongoing work by one of the country's top nutritionists, Professor Philip James, in order to gain maximum protection from heart disease, cancer and other degenerative diseases, the intakes of some necessary vitamins probably need to be well above the usually quoted 'recommended daily allowances'. Professor James told a conference on food in 1996 that there is no way the conventional British diet can supply the kinds of levels he believes we need, without a dramatic increase in the amount of fresh fruit and vegetables eaten – and of course, the more vitamin-packed the individual foods are the better. Achieving this level of nutrition means engineering a revolution in our attitude to food – the kind of revolution already being enjoyed by the devotees of many vegetable box schemes.

The partnerships springing up between growers and producers through box schemes, subscription schemes and community farms are not quite like anything there has ever been before. The instinct to tend our little plots, to provide good, fresh food for our families is there in most of us. But, of course, almost no one has both the time and the physical space available to provide everything, and many of us have almost no time, or no space, or none of either. Yet the longing is still there, and the thrill of seeing one's own food growing on a farm where you have a real, friendly involvement with the producer can be tremendously satisfying.

In Japan there is an organisation called, rather solemnly, the Society for Reflecting on the Throwaway Age. Its first initiative was to promote paper recycling, its second to involve consumers directly in the production of their own food, alongside professional growers. The founder, Tsuchida Takashi felt that the petroleum-based civilisation which uses things carelessly and quickly, then throws them away was treating people and land in a similarly thoughtless and exploitative way, and that such thoughtlessness threatens our very survival.

Thoughtfulness is at the centre of what I am trying to communicate in this book. What we put into our bodies, the way we treat the land, the way we care for our families and relate to our community – all these deserve thought, consideration, care. As Harriet Festing says, all the research indicates that people in the UK do care very much about how their food is produced, but time and convenience have been allowed to become more important for many. The biggest lesson we can learn, she says, is exactly what has been sacrificed for this convenience. People who buy direct from local food schemes in the UK and abroad 'take time to value the food they eat, and learn to respect the people who produce it'.

A more gentle, thoughtful, care-full approach to living our daily lives might mean less time in front of the TV or less money to spend on a bigger car. But such an approach brings its own kind of enrichment. Few of us would want to devote the 16 hours a day, for example, that the Youngs of Kite's Nest spend supporting and feeding themselves in the best way they know how, but happily they, and many other excellent, enthusiastic producers like them are prepared to work hard, on a modest scale and for less-than-modest returns, to produce food for us and for our families. We need only take an interest, seek them out, and support them in return.

The production, transportation and processing of the food we eat several times a day has profound effects on our environment, on other people all over the world, and on the well-being, enjoyment and health of our families and ourselves. Several times a day we make decisions about what to eat which have wide ramifications. That means that we have power to exercise – we can indeed choose a better or a worse future for real fields, real people, every time we put something in our mouths. The most exciting thing of all is that, time and again, the choice which is environmentally responsible, socially constructive, nutritionally sound – all those solemn and worthy things – is also far and away the most delicious.

Eat well!

APPENDIX:
HOW TO DO IT:
BUYING LOCAL FOOD,
BUYING FOOD DIRECT

Farm shops, pick-your-own (PYO), roadside stalls, 'farm gate'

Advertised by signs at the roadside, in local papers: PYO advertise when produce is in season, and may also publish prices. Shops on the Soil Association register and some other organic farms appear in the Association's *Directory of Organic Farm Shops and Box Schemes* (see bibliography). Farm shops vary from small and simple to very elaborate; the larger 'farm shops' and 'farm markets' may contain a large proportion of bought-in or even packaged produce. Most, however, are genuinely selling farm produce, and offer freshness and, often, extremely good value. They usually sell potatoes, field veg like carrots and cabbages, and eggs, and may also be a good source of ciders, perrys and fruit juices. Ask your neighbours, use your eyes, ask questions.

'Farm gate' means that the farm does not run a shop but will sell certain things like milk or meat if you ring up to arrange in advance. Locate by roadside signs, word of mouth, or for Soil Association/organic producers, as above.

Local shops (greengrocers, butchers), street markets

All are likely to carry much more local produce than supermarkets; often but not always identified as such in the display. Ask. Shops can give you much more information, as well as better prices (especially for fruit and veg), than supermarkets. There are only a handful of farmers' markets, where farmers sell their own produce, but these are worth visiting.

Bakeries

The easiest way to judge a good loaf (before tasting it) is by its weight: a heavy loaf has not been 'pumped up' industrially with extra gas, and gives you far more food value per slice. It should also smell and taste good, and continue to do so for two or three days. It should become firmer over time, not damp and floppy as wrapped, sliced, industrial loaves do. Many independent bakeries do an organic loaf. Some bakeries bake on premises from flour, others buy in dough – though this may still be from a local firm. Ask.

WI markets

Delicious local treats: duck eggs, honey, vegetables, etc from the smallest-scale, often semi-commercial or amateur producers (not restricted to WI members, though you can usually get their marvellous cakes!). Get there early.

Home deliveries and vegetable box schemes

Find out by word of mouth or through the Soil Association directory (as above). Some farmshop/farm gate operations will deliver, especially to groups of customers who order together. For example, a group can order one animal and divide it between them: this is very handy for farmers who are likely to be helpful with delivery in return.

Vegetable boxes are generally weekly, some for six or eight months of the year, others 12 months. Most boxes offer 'this week's selection' rather than allowing/bothering with individual orders. Some box schemes offer bread, milk and dairy produce, eggs and even meat along with vegetable deliveries. Some boxes come direct from one grower or a small group of growers. Others come via wholesalers, or large grower co-ops.

The very best schemes are often those run by a single producer: they have a commitment to selling direct, they have minimal food miles and so maximum freshness, and service is very personal. Such schemes are often so good they have waiting lists. However, it is almost impossible for a single grower to provide year-round vegetables. Box schemes supplied by a small group of producers or a larger farm can extend the season and/or reduce the amount of bought-in or imported produce, though necessarily the service is less personal. Even with the biggest co-ops, some imported produce is usually added to the range to 'liven up' the choice in the 'hungry gap', and also to provide perennial favourites like bananas and oranges. Schemes are also including local, organically- or ecologically-raised produce such as eggs, bread and sometimes apple juice.

Growers have been persuaded to start up box schemes when enough customers ask them to, and this has worked out well for everyone. To find a grower, look in *Yellow Pages* (market gardeners, fruit and vegetable growers or nurseries) or, for organic, contact one of the organic bodies (see bibliography/resources) for addresses of local growers.

Consumers can also get together and set up consumer groups for buying vegetables – often combining this with a wholefood buying co-op. THIS IS A LOT OF HARD WORK: make sure you guarantee that members share the workload – it can result in good fun and fellowship, as well as terrific food and the benefits of connection with a grower or growers. To find other households in the area who might be interested, try contacting the nearest Friends of the Earth (FoE) group, LETS scheme, or other local environmental group. Several box schemes have been set up though intital contact with FoE local groups. (See Resources)

Subscription farming and community supported agriculture

These are schemes with a closer involvement by consumers in the farm. Customers pay for a season's produce 'up front', and may agree to accept a loss on the vegetables if the harvest is poor, in return for gluts when the harvest is good. You are not just a customer, you are a member/supporter, with the chance to have an active role in planning and administration. There also tends to be a higher level of practical farm work done by members: sometimes this is part of the 'fee' for membership. In the closest consumer-involvement systems, members may even invest capital and become joint owners of the farm.

A detailed account of the different kinds of set-up for box schemes, subscription farming, CSAs etc., is given in the Soil Association booklet *Local Food Links* by Judy Steele (see bibliography/resources). Anyone planning to set up a scheme is urged to talk to others who have already done so: the 'Local Food Links' desk at the Soil Association will help you to find someone.

Co-ops and community food schemes

To find out if there is a food co-op active in your area, or for advice and information on how to set up co-ops, community cafes, cook-and-taste sessions and so on, contact Jacqui Webster at the National Food Alliance (see Resources).

LETS

To find out if there is a scheme in your area ask around, for example local Friends of the Earth group, community development officer of local authority, or contact LETSLink. LETSLink will also give you advice on setting up a scheme. Ask them for contacts in neighbouring schemes, ring round to see who is doing well, and go and see them. LETS groups often form 'reciprocal arrangements' with neighbouring groups so you may be able to continue the contact. LETSLink UK phone: 01985 217871 or write with six first-class stamps to 61 Woodcock Road, Warminster BA12 9DH.

If you are interested in having more food traded on your LETS scheme, contact the LETSEat! project: John Rhodes on 01452 812709, 6 Pullens Road, Painswick GL6 6QZ.

FOOD IN SEASON

When shopping for food it helps to go with an idea of what is in season, so you are automatically drawn to the produce most likely to be local.

Meat

British lamb is available from early summer through to Christmas: at other times it is likely to have been frozen, imported, or both. Mutton should be available all year round, but is much harder to find.

Chicken, duck, beef, pork and bacon are available all year round.

Quality producers of turkey and goose may only raise animals for sale around Christmas and, possibly, Easter – and be sure to order early!

Fish from British waters. For a longer version and advice on selecting fish, see Joanna Blythman, *The Food We Eat* (in bibliography), from which this information is taken.

Cockles	JFMAJJASOND
Cod	JFXXXXXXSOND
Coley	JFXXXXXXSOND
Crab	XXXAMJXXXXXX
Dover Sole	JFXXXJJASOND
Eel	XXXXXXXXXOND
Haddock	JFXXMJJASOND
Herring	JFXXXJJASOND
Huss (dogfish)	JFMXXXXXXOND
John Dory	JFMXXXXXXXXX
Dublin Bay prawn, scampi	JFMAMJJASOND
Lemon sole	JFMAXXXXXXXD
Mackerel	JFMAMJJASOND
Monkfish	JFMAMJJASOND
Mussels	XXMAMXXXSOND
Oysters	JFMAXXXXSOND
Plaice	XXXXXXJASOND
Prawns	XXXXMJJASOXX
Salmon (wild)	XXXAMJJAXXXX
Scallops	JFMXXXXXXXXD
Sea bass/bream	XXXXXJJASOND
Sea trout	XXMAMJJXXXXX
Shrimps	XXMAMJJASOXX
Skate	JFXXXXXXSOND
Sprats	JFMXXXXXXOND
Whiting	JFXXXXXXXXND

Vegetables in season

Root vegetables and pumpkins are traditionally stored through the winter. As roots are storage organs, they do not deteriorate in the way non-root crops (like asparagus or sweetcorn) do in cold storage: indeed in some the flavour even improves.

To extend the growing season of vegetables in Britain, many growers use greenhouses or plastic ('poly' tunnels) in order to bring you salad greens in February, or French beans in June. Because of the capital involved in setting up and maintaining the houses, and the fact that slower winter growth means that land is tied up for longer, prices of these crops may be higher – but then imported equivalents are also likely to be very pricey. Growers for box schemes invest more effort in extended-season growing, to offer variety to their customers, than do growers producing for wholesale or supermarkets. Entries marked with a * means that vegetable may well be available through box schemes in a certain month, but less likely to be available from local producers, ecologically raised (ie without chemicals and artificial heat and lighting), in the shops.

The table gives seasonality for the Midlands/Wales region of the UK. Further north, the season for summer crops is likely to be shorter (depending on how much protected cropping is possible), and all the seasons will be later (winter crops may last longer into the spring). Further south, summer crops may begin earlier and continue later, but winter crops will run to seed earlier in the spring.

Asparagus	XXXAMXXXXXXX
Aubergine	XXXXXXJ*A*S*O*XX
Beetroot	JFMAMJJASOND
Broccoli (green – calabrese)	XXXXXXJASOXX
Broccoli – (purple sprouting	XFMAMXXXXXXX
Broad beans	XXXXMJJAXXXX
Brussels sprouts	JFMXXXXXSOND
Cabbage	JFMAMJJASOND
Cauliflower	JFMAMJJASOND
Carrots	JFMAXJJASOND
Celeriac	JFMAXXXXSOND
Courgettes	XXXXXXJASOXX
Globe artichokes	XXXXXXXASXXX
French beans	XXXXXXJ*ASOXX
Jerusalem artichokes	JFMXXXXXXOND
Kale	JFMAXXJ*A*S*OND
Kohl rabi	XXXXMJJASOND
Leeks, onions	JFMAMXXASOND
Parsnips	JFMXXXXXSOND

Potatoes   JFMAMJJASOND
Peas   XXXXXJJASOXX
Runner beans   XXXXXXJASOXX
Salad greens   JFMAMJJASOND
(includes lettuce, chicory, endive, oriental brassicas and many others)
Spinach   JFMAMJJASOND
Spinach beet, chard, Chinese leaf JFMAMJJASOND
Spring onions   JFMAMJJASOND
Sprouted seeds, beans and grains JFMAMJJASOND
Squash and pumpkin   JFMAXXJASOND
Swede   JFMAXXJASOND
Sweetcorn   XXXXXXXASOXX
Sweet peppers   XXXXXXJ*A*S*O*XX
Tomatoes   XXXXXJJASOXX
(though there are some slow-ripening varieties which used to be grown
    under glass for November and December, so you could always
    suggest your grower tries to find some!)
Turnip   XXXXMJJASOND

As you can see from this, choice of local vegetables is distinctly
thinner in March-May, the so-called 'hungry gap'. Purists do very well
using imaginative cooking and plenty of bean sprouts – others may
find this its the time of year they will accept some imported food.

Fruit

Apples   JFMXXXJASOND
(note, different varieties are available at different times)
Blackberries XXXXXXXASOXX
Blackcurrants XXXXXJJAXXX
Cherries   XXXXXJJAXXXX
Gooseberries XXXXMJJAXXXX
Pears   JFMAXXXASOND
Plums   XXXXXXJASOXX
Raspberries   XXXXXJJASOXX
Redcurrants   XXXXXJJAXXXX
Rhubarb   XFMAMJJXXXXX
Strawberries XXXXXJJASXXX

Resources and Bibliography

Recommended Reading

Joanna Blythman, *The Food We Eat*, Michael Joseph, 1996. Comprehensive account of what is wrong with much of the food that we eat, with detailed guidance on how to find and identify good food. Covers meat, fish, fruit, vegetables, bread and basic groceries.

Henrietta Greene, *Food Lovers' Guide to Britain*, BBC, Second Edition 1996, regularly updated. County-by-county gazetteer of direct and specialist outlets for good basics plus many 'specialities'. Informative accounts of the way the food is produced as well as comments on the taste of the food itself.

Judy Steele, *Local Food Links – new ways of getting organic food from farm to table*, Soil Association, 1995. A 60-page booklet detailing structure of various 'direct buying' systems (mainly vegetables), giving detailed accounts of some schemes. Invaluable to anyone planning to set up a scheme. Available from Soil Association (see resources).

Essay by Wendell Berry, 'Pleasure of Eating', (extracted from *Our Sustainable Table*, edited by Robert Clark, North Point Press, US) in *Resurgence* no 146, May/June 1991. Wonderful article. Back issues available from *Resurgence*, Ford House, Hartland, Bideford, Devon EX39 6EE; tel. 01237 441293

Bibliography

In addition to the list above, the following books and reports made invaluable contributions to the text.

Archbishop's Commission on Rural Areas Faith in the Countryside, ACORA Publishing, 1990.

Martin Birley, *The Health Impact Assessment of Development Projects*, HMSO, 1995.

Tracey Clunies-Ross and Nicholas Hildyard, *The Politics of Industrial Agriculture*, Earthscan, 1992.

Theo Colborn, John Petersen Myers and Diane Dumanoski, *Our Stolen Future*, Little Brown, 1996.

Philip Conford (ed), *A Future for the Countryside: organic practice from a global perspective*, Green Books, 1992.

Gillian Darley, *The Farm*, Crescent, New York, 1985.

Simon Fairlie, *Low Impact Development: planning and people in a sustainable countryside*, John Carpenter Books, 1996.

Peter Goering, Helena Norberg-Hodge and John Page, *From the Ground Up: rethinking industrial agriculture*, Zed/ISEC, 1993.

David Goodman and Michael Redclift, *Refashioning Nature: food, ecology and culture*, Routledge, 1991

Doris Grant, *Your Daily Food*, Faber, 1973.

Jane Grigson, *Good Things*, Penguin, 1975.

Trauger Groli and Steven McFadden, *Farms of Tomorrow: community supported farms, farm supported communities*, Bio-dynamic Literature, USA 1990

Patricia Hewitt, *About Time: the revolution in work and family life*, Rivers Oram, 1993.

Henk Hobbelink, *Biotechnology and the Future of World Agriculture*, Zed, 1991.

Tim Lang and Colin Hines, *The New Protectionism: protecting the future against free trade*, Earthscan, 1993.

Frances Moore Lappé, *Diet for a Small Planet*, Ballantine Books, N.Y., 1982.

Penelope Leach, *Children First*, Michael Joseph, 1994.

Sidney Mintz, *Sweetness and Power*, Viking, 1985.

Cherry Ripe, *Goodbye Culinary Cringe*, Allen and Unwin, Australia 1993.

Cathy Read, *Preventing Breast Cancer*, Pandora, 1994.

Joni Seager, *Earth Follies: feminism, politics and the environment*, Earthscan, 1993.

Vandana Shiva, *Staying Alive*, Zed, 1989.

David Steinman, *Diet for a Poisoned Planet*, Harmony Books, New York 1990.

Martin Teitel, *Rain Forest in Your Kitchen*, Island Press (US), 1992.

David Widgery, *Some Lives*, Simon and Schuster, 1992.

Renée Velvé, *Saving the Seed: genetic diversity and European agriculture*, Earthscan, 1992.

OTHER USEFUL PUBLICATIONS

Directory of Farm Shops and Box Schemes: national list of farm shops and box schemes run by Soil Association registered producers and some registered on other organic schemes, such as biodynamic. Regional *Go Organic* guides: as above, but they also include shops (not supermarkets) selling a good range of organic produce. Available from the Soil Association.

Food Miles, A Feast Too Far, a ground-breaking report and follow-up on the food miles issue, by Angela Paxton; *Farming Foundations*, detailed proposals for reforming the Common Agricultural Policy, by Tracy Clunies Ross and Stuart Turner. Both from the SAFE Alliance.

Growing Greener, a highly informative report on the lack of sustainability of British Agriculture, with many detailed proposals for reform. Available from CPRE and WWF-UK .

Children: Advertisers' Dream, Nutritionists' Nightmare by Sue Dibb, and *Food and Low Income Pack*. Both available from the National Food Alliance.

ADDRESSES

● **Compassion in World Farming**, Charles House, 5A Charles Street, Petersfield, Hampshire GU32 3EH; tel. 01730 264208.

● **Council for the Protection of Rural England**, Warwick House, 25 Buckingham Palace Road, London SW1W 0PP; tel. 0171 976 6433.

● **Farmers' Link**, 38 Exchange St, Norwich; tel. 01603 765670 and

● **Farmers' World Network**, Arthur Rank Centre, NAC, Stoneleigh, Warwickshire CV8 2LZ: Information on fair trade, sustainable farming worldwide, and justice for Third World farmers.

● **Friends of the Earth**, 26-28 Underwood Street, London N1 7JQ; tel. 0171 490 1555: National environmental organisation, and also contacts for local groups.

● **Food Magazine/Food Commission**, 5-11 Worship St, London EC2A 2BH; tel. 0171 628 7774: Consumer food watchdog and magazine.

● **Henry Doubleday Research Association/Heritage Seeds**, Ryton Gardens, Ryton-on-Dunsmore, Coventry CV8 3LG: Organic gardening research and information.

● **International Institute for Environment and Development**

- **(IIED)**, 3 Endsleigh St, London WC1H 0DD; tel. 0171 388 2117.
- **ISEC**, 21 Victoria Square, Bristol BS8 4ES.
- **National Food Alliance**, (NFA), 5-11 Worship St, London EC1 2BH; tel. 0171 628 7261: an umbrella group campaigning for healthier eating, healthier food and more sustainable food production.
- **Panoscope/Panos Institute**, 9 White Lion St, London N1 9DP; tel. 0171 278 1111: Information on environment and social justice in the Third World.
- **Pesticides News/The Pesticides Trust**, Eurolink Business Centre, 49 Effra Road, London SW2 1BZ; tel. 0171 274 8895.
- **SAFE Alliance (Sustainable Agriculture, Food and Environment)**, 38 Ebury St, London SW1W 0LU; tel. 0171 823 5673: umbrella organisation campaigning for sustainable food and agriculture.
- **Soil Association**, 86 Colston St, Bristol BS1 5BB; tel. 0117 929 0661: membership organisation promoting organic farming and gardening, and running one of the approved organic certification schemes. This is also the contact for **British Organic Farmers**, the producer wing (ie the farmers' organisation) within the Soil Association. **Organic Farmers and Growers** is an organic farmers' organisation: it too offers an organic certification scheme, as do the **Scottish Organic Producers' Association, the Organic Food Federation** and **Demeter**, the body which oversees biodynamic farming – all at separate addresses, through the Ministry of Agriculture, London SW1.
- **The Land is Ours**, Box E111, Magdalen Rd, Oxford OX4 1RQ; tel. 01865 722016: group campaigning actively on land access and land rights, and to change planning regulations for low-impact farming and low-impact dwelling.
- **Third World Resurgence/Third World Network**, 228 Macalister Road, 10400 Penang, Malaysia; fax +60 4 229 8106.
- **Worldwide Fund for Nature**, Panda House, Weyside Park, Cattershall Lane, Land, Godalming, Surrey GU7 1XR; tel. 01483 426444.
- **WWOOF: Willing Workers on Organic Farms**, 19 Bradford Rd, Lewes BN7 1RB: Arrange working stays on organic farms (UK and overseas) from a weekend up to several months, in return for keep and campsite or accommodation. Wonderful way to learn about growing and/or animals, to do satisfying work and make good friendships.

WEBSITES

Two excellent sites are:

- **McSpotlight**, (http://www.mcspotlight.org) which pulls together the tremendous range of evidence about junk food, beef farming, animal welfare, employment, food safety and much more collected as evidence in the 'McLibel' trials, as well as jokes and campaign news. The animal welfare entries are compelling – and compulsory for anyone with any doubts about cheap meat.
- **Friends of the Earth**, (http://www.foe.co.uk) a very wide ranging environmental website, including campaign news (chemical releases, rainforests, transport – the lot) recent environmental news through their full directory of press releases, and links to other useful websites.
- Another enjoyable site is the **Canadian Cityfarmer** site (http://www.cityfarmer.org) and the linked **'Seeds of Hope, Harvest of Pride'** site (http://www.bright.net/~gardens) which is based at the University of Ottawa, and contains masses of useful information about cooking and preserving seasonal foods.
- Productive web searches include 'community supported agriculture' which gives a wonderful taste of the very active North American CSA scene; 'pesticides' for hair-raising information about pesticides in the diet and the environment, and 'food' 'health' and 'poverty' in combination for a wide range of insights into food poverty and justice throughout the world.

INDEX